GCSE Design and Technology

Resistant Materials

contents...contents...contents...contents...c

CPL CAUSEWAY PRESS

unit

1 Design ideas

Computers today are smaller than earlier designs.

Identifying a problem

Think about all the products that people use every day. Where do the ideas for these products come from? In industry, customers often present a designer with their ideas. An idea for a product may emerge as a result of experiments and research in a research and development laboratory of a company. It may be research into what customers want. Only occasionally will there be a flash of genius from an inventor.

Most of the time a design idea is a solution to a particular **problem**. It is the problem that is the real starting point when designing and making a product. First, the problem must be identified. For example, fires in living rooms can be a danger to young children. A design to improve safety may solve this problem. Sports people may want to improve their own performances. A design for exercise may help. A school may face high energy costs which could be reduced by better insulation. There may be a problem with space in the garage which could be overcome by storage facilities.

Solving these problems will satisfy people's NEEDS. People have many different needs, from shelter and safety to tools and equipment for work and leisure. Situations may occur that provide OPPORTUNITIES to design new products. For example, a range of products on the market may not cover the needs of all customers. It may be possible to design a new product particularly for young people

Products are designed to be a solution to a problem

- car key - grip easily; illuminate keyhole;
- portable telephone - walk around and talk;
- stepping machine - exercise easily;
- wooden block - store sharp knives safely.

activities

Read the article below.

(a) What products are 'Little Feet'?
(b) What was the problem that was identified which this design was created to solve?
(c) Write a short design brief from the information below.
(d) Suggest TWO other ways in which similar plastic 'grips' could be used.

Source: adapted from The Guardian, 29.6.1995.

Little Feet are 'foot shaped' plastic designs which keep socks together during washing. The idea first came to Andrea Marks, their creator, over dinner when jokes about lost socks came up. One person even said he had to take apart his washing machine to get socks out! There is a gap in some washing machines where socks can get into the outlet pipe and get stuck.

Andrea found that one way of keeping socks together might be to use a device similar to a plastic grip in a kitchen which holds tea towels. She finally decided to do something about it when she lost a £20 silk sock. Little feet are sold in packs of 5. Each is the shape of a foot and packs contain feet of different colours.

or a product that can be used in a different way to existing products. As new products are developed, technological advances may occur which can force modifications to the original design. For example, modern electronic products are much smaller and more complex than earlier designs.

A design brief and specification

Once a problem has been identified and discussed in detail it is then presented as a DESIGN BRIEF. Research and development can then begin. The brief is written as a short statement of intent. Each aspect of the brief can be researched in detail. The purpose of research is to gather as much information about the problem as possible. This might be about other similar products, consumer or expert opinion, the working properties of materials or **ergonomic** requirements (see unit 24).

Information can be collected in a number of ways, including:

- research of similar products;
- letters to/interviews with experts;
- surveys/QUESTIONNAIRES with possible customers;
- investigations of materials or products using models and prototypes;
- photographs/video evidence;
- looking at books, periodicals or journals to find out about past research;
- observation of events.

Figure 1 Possible design briefs.

Glass milk bottles can break easily. They are also heavy to carry around when there is more than one and are sometimes difficult to grip.
People are used to buying milk in one pint (or 568ml) containers. The disposal of used containers can be a problem.

Design and make a milk container from recyclable material, to contain 1 pint of fluid, that is easy to hold and hard to break.

Long hair often needs to be kept tidy. A hair comb or grip that can fasten back hair would be easy and quick to use. It would need to be lightweight and in suitable colours. A mechanism, (perhaps a spring) would be needed so it could open when gripped and closed when let go.

Design and make a lightweight hair grip in a variety of colours, that can be used easily and quickly.

When collected, all this information needs to be analysed. Summaries made of interviews and past research could show opinions. Conclusions may be drawn from scientific investigations. Surveys and questionnaires may reveal the most popular answers. This work can then be represented using graphs, tables and charts, perhaps as a spreadsheet or computer aided graphs. A decision can then be made about whether the problem is worth pursuing to a final solution. Collectively the research should point to exactly what is needed for many of the component parts of the product. This is called the SPECIFICATION. The specification is

activities

(a) What problem might the design below solve?

(b) Use lateral thinking and brainstorming to suggest:
(i) other designs worn for an evening out that could be used to carry cologne or a woman's perfume;
(ii) other items that could be carried in these designs.

Jane and Emma Hauldren design and make unusual jewellery and other products. One of their designs is a pair of spring loaded cufflinks. The cufflinks are able to hold a small amount of cologne. The screw-in top to the cufflinks can be used to dab on the cologne. A man can wear the cufflinks for an evening out or another engagement and refresh his cologne over a period of time.

Source: adapted from The Guardian, 16.3.1995.

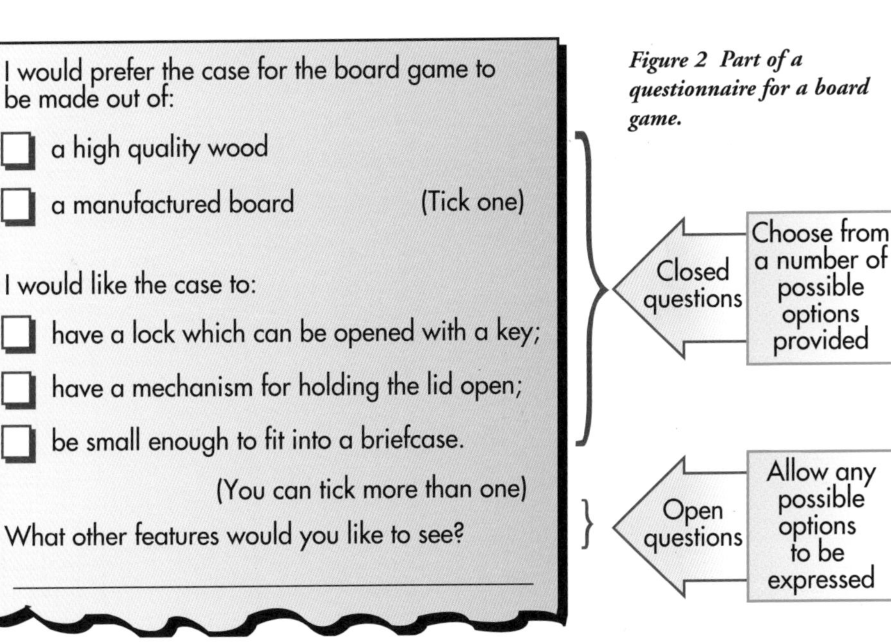
I would prefer the case for the board game to be made out of:

- ☐ a high quality wood
- ☐ a manufactured board (Tick one)

I would like the case to:

- ☐ have a lock which can be opened with a key;
- ☐ have a mechanism for holding the lid open;
- ☐ be small enough to fit into a briefcase.

(You can tick more than one)

What other features would you like to see?

____

Figure 2 Part of a questionnaire for a board game.

likely to show a manufacturer:

- what type(s) of material is(are) preferred;
- the function of the product;
- maximum/minimum dimensions;
- general shape/form of the product;
- special considerations/constraints required by the customer (eg electronic or mechanical requirements);
- ergonomic/anthropometric data;
- likely costs.

Figure 3 Part of a design specification for a recyclable plastic milk container.

Materials	Aluminium foil seal HDPE body Plastic closure
Function	To hold 568ml (1 pint) of half-fat milk To provide easy storage and pouring
Dimensions	Height 138.7mm ±2.0mm; length 88mm ± 1.0mm; width 72.5mm ± 1.0mm
Shape/style	'Cube' shape Clear plastic Handle to allow easy carrying and pouring
Other considerations	Recyclability Anthropometric hand/finger measurements Indentations' to plastic to give greater grip

Generating ideas

Designing can begin on the basis of the above information. Designers come to the table with more than one idea in mind.

activities

Fluid Juice Surfboards is owned by Adrian Phillips who hand shapes every board. He has 18 years experience of making surfboards in England and Australia. He argues that 'surfboard design and shaping is a science. By quantifying and measuring all aspects of each shape you are in full control of the performance of each board. This eliminates the hit or miss results of shaping by eye.' Over 200 dimensions are measured for each board. Boards are tested by test pilots. The company keeps in contact with the latest designs from the pro tour, by visits from foreign 'shapers' and from contacts in Australia, South Africa and the USA.

Source: Fluid Juice Surfboards.

(a) Explain how the company obtains information about:
(i) new designs;
(ii) a board's performance;
(iii) a customer's requirements.

(b) What details about a surfboard may appear on a specification for a customer?

FLUID JUICE SURFBOARDS
The Old Airfield St Merryn Padstow Cornwall PL28 8PU Tel: (01841)520928
VAT reg no: 591-1863-24 Proprietor: A.J.Phillips

CUSTOM ORDER FORM

DATE
NAME
ADDRESS
NUMBER
PHONE: WORK HOME
POSTCODE
HEIGHT WEIGHT FOOT SIZE
EXPERIENCE / ABILITY / PRESENT BOARD DIMENSIONS
WAVE SIZE RANGE / AREA(S)
SPECIAL COMMENTS
SHAPE
LENGTH WIDTH THICKNESS
NOSE WIDTH TAIL WIDTH
NOSE ROCKER TAIL ROCKER
FINS:- FIXED / BOXED *
SHAPER USE ONLY LEASH PLUG:- NATURAL / GOOFY *
GLASSING:- FULL (6 / 6+6) / MEDIUM/STANDARD (6 / 6+4) / MEDIUM/LIGHT (6 / 4+4) / LIGHT (4 / 4+4) *
DECK ARTWORK (IF REQUIRED) BOTTOM
FIN COLOUR
* = DELETE AS APPLICABLE
BASIC PRICE
ARTWORK
OTHER GOODS:-
BOARD DELIVERY / P+P
TOTAL
DEPOSIT
PART / EX.
BALANCE

Most designers are working for clients who want to see a range of ideas. It is important to present different ideas in order to consider as many solutions as possible. A designer may come up with totally new designs or interesting variations or INNOVATIONS on an original design. At this stage design ideas need only be simple sketches or drawings with annotations or labels (see unit 2). There is a number of strategies that can be used to help provide ideas.

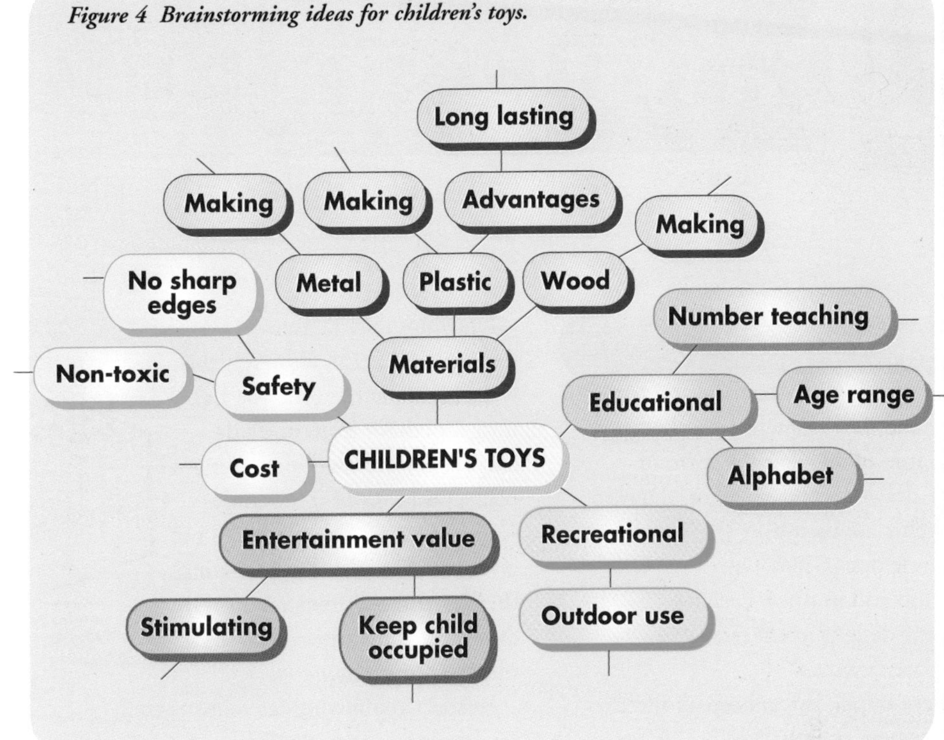

Figure 4 Brainstorming ideas for children's toys.

Considering all features Designs have many different features. Each feature can be identified by making a list or by labelling a sketch. Then one, two or more of the features can be changed. An original design might be altered to suit a variety of different needs. For example, a chair might be changed to suit a disabled person, a young child or an office worker. Changing a design to suit different needs is called **adapting** (see unit 24).

Many products are designed for a particular use. For example, a kettle is used to boil water safely. A plate is used to put food on. However, existing products can have alternative uses. The kettle could be used as a watering can. The plate might be used as a piece of pottery to decorate a room. An existing design like a plastic bottle might be adapted for use as a shovel and scuttle, by simply removing the neck. These alterations could lead to a whole new range of products.

Role play Designs can be generated by putting yourself in different situations. For example, what if there was no electricity for lighting or washing clothes in the house? It may be possible to suggest solutions to this by acting as campers who face such problems.

History/culture By studying how similar design problems were tackled in the past or are dealt with by different cultures, design ideas can be generated. For example, a clockwork radio has been developed in the UK to solve the problem of the lack of batteries in many African countries. This idea could be used to provide environmentally friendly electronic devices in the western cultures.

Lateral thinking To come up with completely original ideas is very difficult. Completely new ideas are called INVENTIONS. It is sometimes possible to prevent others copying an invention by obtaining a **patent** (see unit 25) for a product.

One way of looking for 'new products' is to examine existing problems or products from a different perspective. For example, most items of furniture rest on the floor, but what if they were to hang from the ceiling or be fixed to a wall? This way of looking at things from 'peculiar' angles is called 'lateral thinking' and was developed by an American, Edward De Bono.

Brainstorming Brainstorming, and perhaps producing a spider diagram, allows all ideas and thoughts to be considered. There are no right or wrong answers. It is simply a way of expressing all potential solutions. **Spider diagrams** are usually set out with a key word or title in the central position from which other ideas stem. An example is shown in Figure 4.

Needs - people's requirements and desires.
Opportunities - situations that arise which give chances for new designs.
Design brief - a short statement explaining what is to be designed and made.
Questionnaire - a series of questions asked to a variety of people in order to gain information.
Design specification - a list itemising features of a design with a reason for each.
Innovations - changes made to designs to adapt and improve them.
Inventions - completely new designs that are created after research and study.

unit

2 Drawing and modelling

Drawing

Because products have shape and form, ideas and development work before manufacture often takes the form of pictures, drawings and sketches. Drawings and sketches are used to:

- generate design ideas;
- develop and improve designs;
- present designs to others;
- evaluate designs.

It is very important to keep all sketches no matter how `rough' they are. They are useful for looking back at to see how ideas have developed or for development work at a later stage.

Drawings can be very accurate or they may be just rough sketches so that designers can see their thoughts on paper. Rough sketches are called CONCEPT SKETCHES. DEVELOPMENT DRAWINGS are more accurate drawings.

Drawings may be **two dimensional** (2D), although this will only show the idea as a flat image, perhaps from one side only. They are used for outline plans, positions of items and surface design. Drawings can be given shape or depth by drawing them as **three dimensional** (3D) drawings. This shows ideas in a more realistic way.

Perspective drawings are constructed by drawing lines out from a point. Single point perspectives are good for showing the inside of objects, whereas double point perspective drawings are good for showing the outside of objects. Oblique and isometric drawings

Figure 1 Concept sketches.

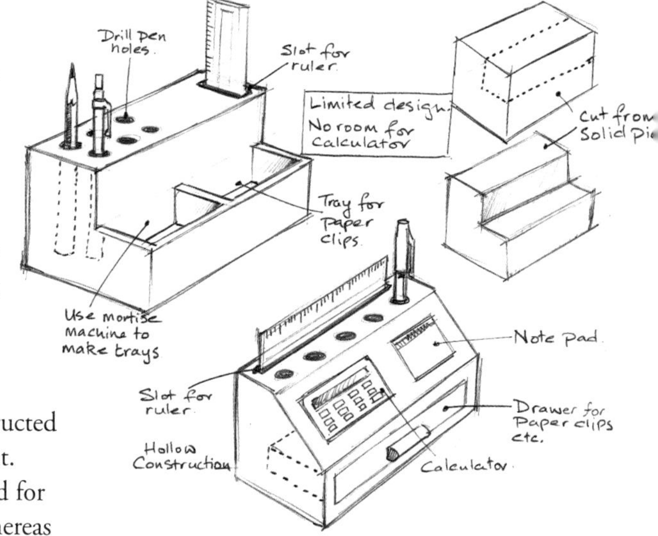

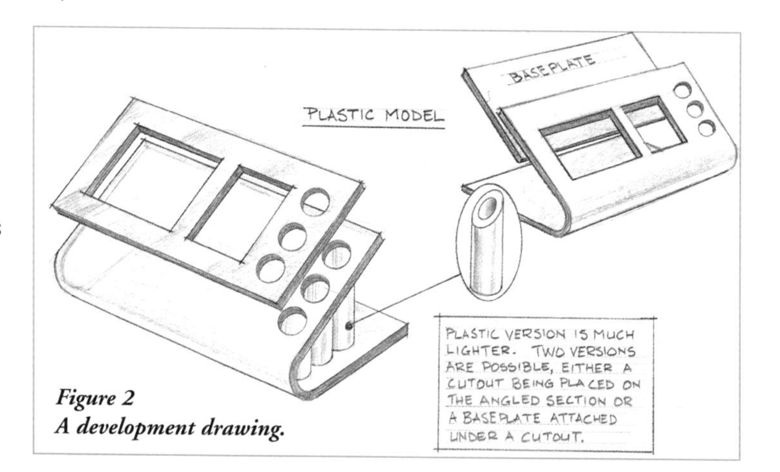

Figure 2
A development drawing.

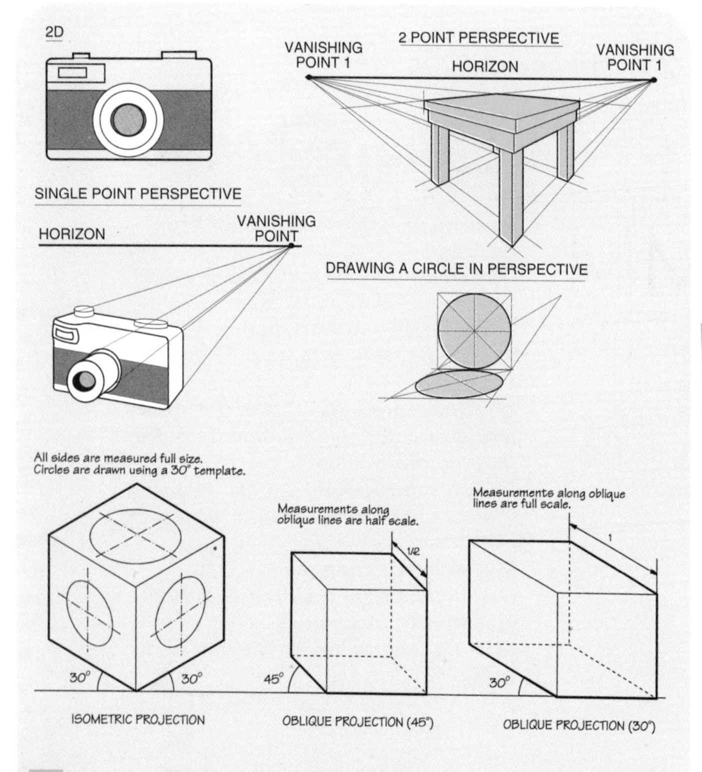

Figure 3 Perspective drawings.

activities

* A plastics manufacturer has been asked by a local authority to produce mugs to promote outdoor activities. It hopes to sell the mugs in seaside resorts, village fetes and sports facilities.
* Disabled people are often uncomfortable in wheelchairs. One solution is to design a chair with a moulded plastic seat, shaped to the contours of the person sitting in it.

(a) What is a concept sketch?
(b) Why might a designer use concept sketches in the initial stages of a design?
(c) Draw concept sketches for ONE of the designs above. Select which of your sketches you feel is most appropriate.

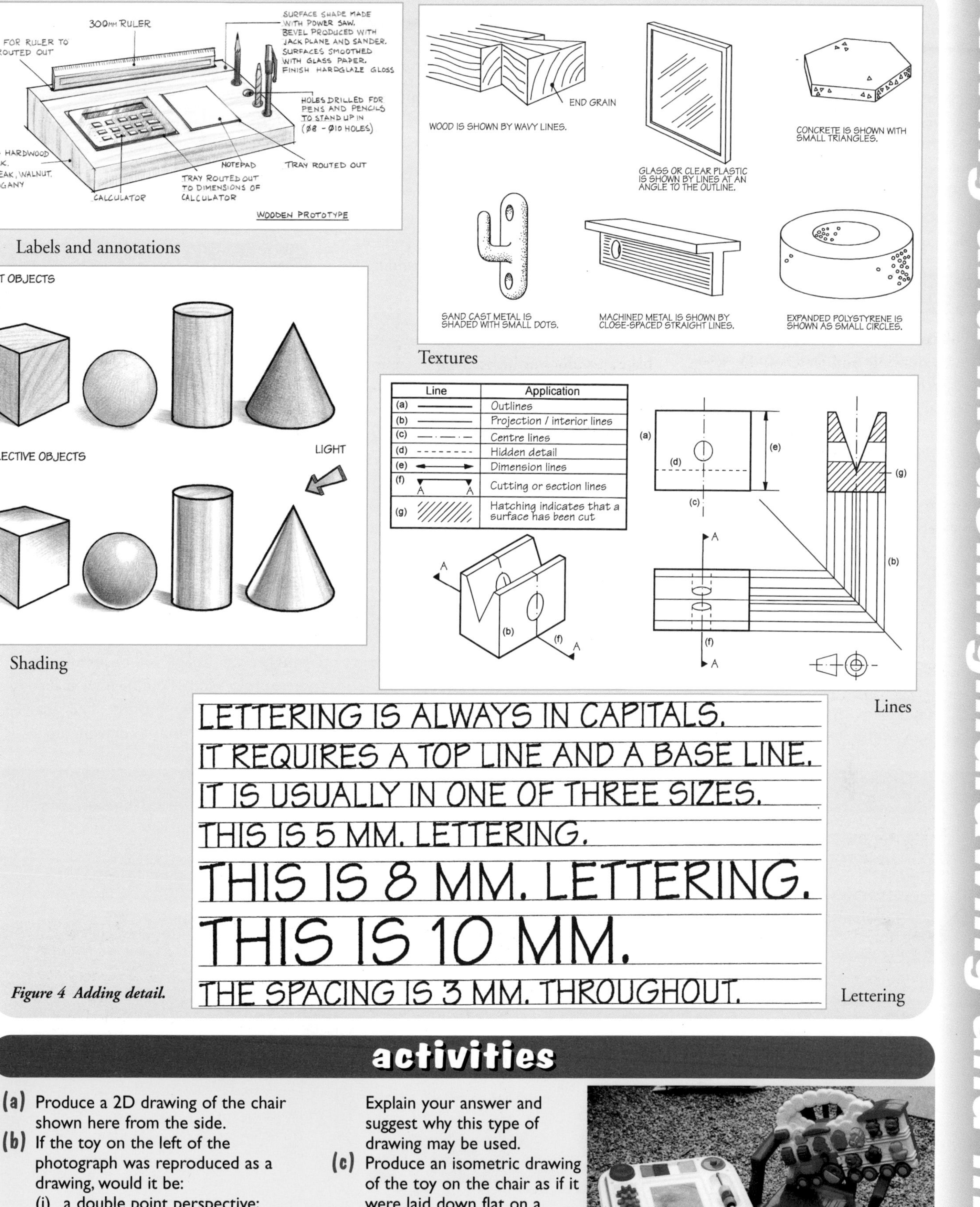

Figure 4 Adding detail.

activities

(a) Produce a 2D drawing of the chair shown here from the side.

(b) If the toy on the left of the photograph was reproduced as a drawing, would it be:
(i) a double point perspective;
(ii) a single point perspective?
Explain your answer and suggest why this type of drawing may be used.

(c) Produce an isometric drawing of the toy on the chair as if it were laid down flat on a table. Only the outline needs to be drawn.

are drawn at 45° and 30° to the horizontal respectively. They do not come to a point at a distance. They are useful for sketching 3D shapes accurately. Cylinders are drawn using 'squashed' circles at the top (circles in perspective) called ellipses. Construction lines need to be drawn faintly at first and then the main body of the item highlighted with a heavier pencil or ink line. The drawing is then called a line drawing.

Adding detail

Having drawn the main edges, a line drawing needs to be given texture. This can be done by **shading**. To do this you have to imagine light falling on one side of the drawing. The other sides will be in shade. Different materials have their own conventions for shading in. Certain parts of a drawing may want to be **emphasised** to make them stand out. This can be done in a number of ways as shown in Figure 4.

Lines In constructional drawings (see later) different types of lines have different meanings.

Rendering This is used to help sketches and other drawings stand out from the page with colour and shading. It is also used to emphasise lettering and writing.

Labels and annotations It is useful to include these with concept and presentation drawings in particular. Labels are simple words to point out what something is. Annotations are short phrases used to describe something in a little more detail. For example, a label may just say 'padding' whereas an annotation may say 'padding to protect the object inside'.

Lettering Exact constructional drawings have a precise way of lettering to conform to British Standards. For concept sketches and presentation drawings, neat hand printed writing or stylish creative lettering is equally acceptable. Most CAD systems (see later) carry lots of lettering styles. These are called fonts. The size and thickness of these fonts can be changed easily. Stencils are another way of providing neat lettering.

Semiology

SEMIOLOGY is the study of signs and symbols. Symbols are a short and simple way of giving information. They enable a designer to give lots of information in a small space. Symbols and signs in design work might include signs for:

- warnings (see unit 15);
- instructions (see unit 15);
- movement (see unit 24);
- recycling/environmental information (see units 4-6);
- circuits (see unit 18);
- materials (see unit 4-6).

Modelling

Having generated a number of possible design ideas for a product, each idea or parts of an idea will have to be examined in detail. This is called PRODUCT DEVELOPMENT. Product development involves testing and trialling to find the optimum (or most suitable) design that will be carried through to manufacture.

Models show designers how a product or parts of a product will look or behave before the product is actually made. Sometimes a 3D sketch looks good but when a 3D model is made the design might need major adjustments. The information gained is essential in deciding whether that design will be useful or successful. Models can be used at many stages in the design process. They may be used in research prior to drawing up a

activities

Read the information across the page.

(a) What materials were used in the production of the model for the Tigra?

(b) State TWO advantages to a designer of producing a model.

(c) Using examples from the article, explain the difference between scale models and life size models.

(d) Suggest how:

(i) a mock up was made;

(ii) a simulation using the Tigra model took place.

Clay modelling helps bring to life sketches of designs. Models give the designer the first chance to see what the product will look like.

The Vauxhall/Opel Tigra had 5 designs approved by Richard Bolz, the studio engineer. These were turned into scale clay models, each taking about 2 days. 2 of the 5 were rejected, for example because the windows would not open as required. The final design chosen gave the Tigra its distinctive look. The models helped to identify designs that did not work or were not feasible. Two full size clay mock ups were made of this design. Under the 35-40mm clay skin was a foam base and a wooden frame. The clay model was painted and looked like an actual car. Measurements were calculated accurately and wind tunnel tests took place.

Source: adapted from The Daily Telegraph, 7.1.1995.

specification, to help develop ideas or as part of presentational work. Rough models that are used in the early stages of designing are called MOCK-UPS. More detailed working models that are used in development work are called PROTOTYPES.

Mock-ups and prototypes can be made to the same size as the actual product. They can also be made to SCALE. If you are designing a large object. Each part is made smaller (scaled down) or larger (scaled up), by the same amount so that all aspects of the design stay in proportion. Examples of scale models might be buildings or vehicles. Once constructed, models can be tested and tried out. A model of a helmet or a bridge might be tested to destruction to see how it reacts to different forces. A model of a boat or garden furniture might be tried out in a variety of different situations to see how it functions. These types of tests using models to gather evidence are called SIMULATIONS. This can also be done on computer (see later).

The material chosen to make a model depends on what information is required from the model. Models are only used when a drawing cannot convey an overall effect or give the information needed. Most modelling is used, therefore, for three dimensional work. It is also used a lot where electronic and mechanical systems have to be constructed.

Modelling materials

The type of material chosen for modelling must:

- be easy to work with and/or assemble;
- give a good impression of the design idea required;
- be able to be tested, examined and/or handled.

For 3D models that have complicated shapes or whose shape needs to be altered frequently (eg hand grips) then clay or plasticine is ideal. Clay and plasticine are also useful for taking pressings and moulds of shapes. For more permanent,

Clay modelling of a car design.

rigid shapes that are solid, expanded foams like EPS and styrofoam are useful. These can be cut using a heated wire cutter (although care needs to be taken with fume extraction) or can be sanded to the required shape. Other materials that might be used include MDF and jelutong (although this hardwood is quite expensive). These materials are used a lot to gauge the ergonomics (see unit 24) of products like telephone receivers, kettles and irons. The model itself might be used as a former for manufacturing in plastic, for example.

For hollow work, where inside detail is needed, card is useful. A framework might be constructed using a net. The edges can then be cut away to suit. The insides of rooms and buildings are usefully modelled in this way. Tabs are used to glue edges together. Card is also useful for making templates. These will give a 2D model of a design.

For structures that are to be made using frames, metal rod, dowel or straw are useful. Tin-plate, hardboard or card might be fixed to the frame if a shell is required. This technique is useful if a vehicle chassis, bridge or linkage is being modelled. Balsa can also be used for this type of modelling (although it is quite expensive). It can be easily shaped and joined using balsa cement. Construction kits can also be used.

Systems can be modelled using construction kits, particularly mechanical systems (see unit 17). There are many electronic modelling kits. Some have components on ready made boards that slot together to make systems (see unit 18). These are good to establish basic ideas. For more detailed electronic modelling, breadboards or soldering onto veroboard are used.

A design proposal

Once all research and development work has been completed a designer will

Figure 5 Orthographic drawings.

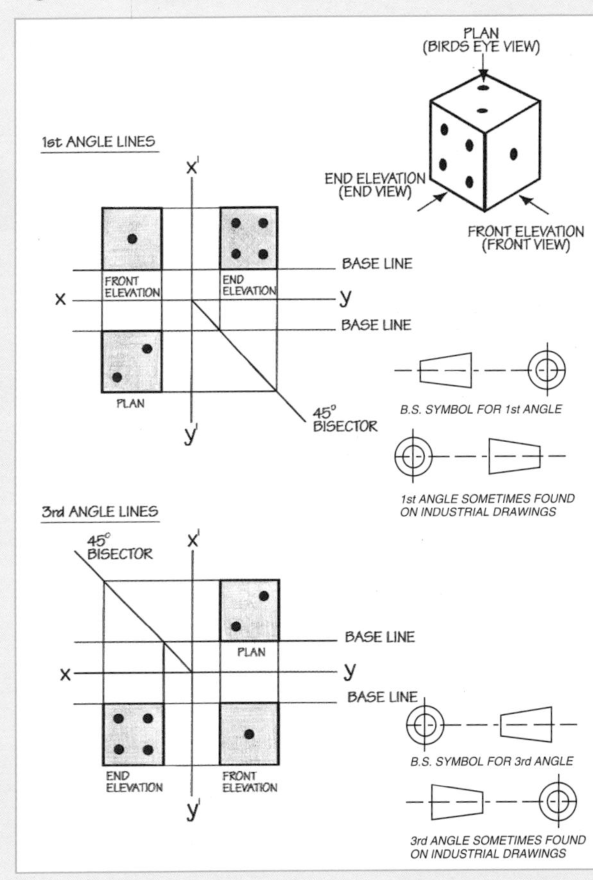

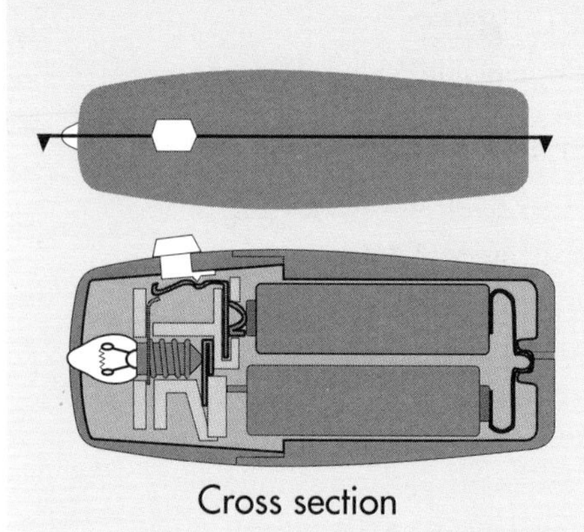

Figure 6 A sectional drawing of a pocket torch.

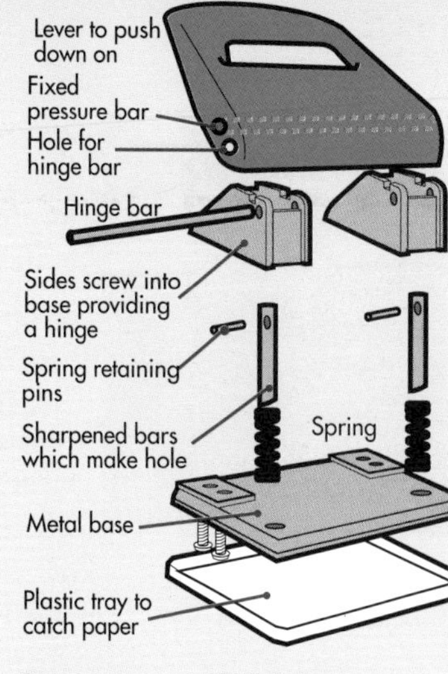

Figure 7 An exploded diagram of a hole punch.

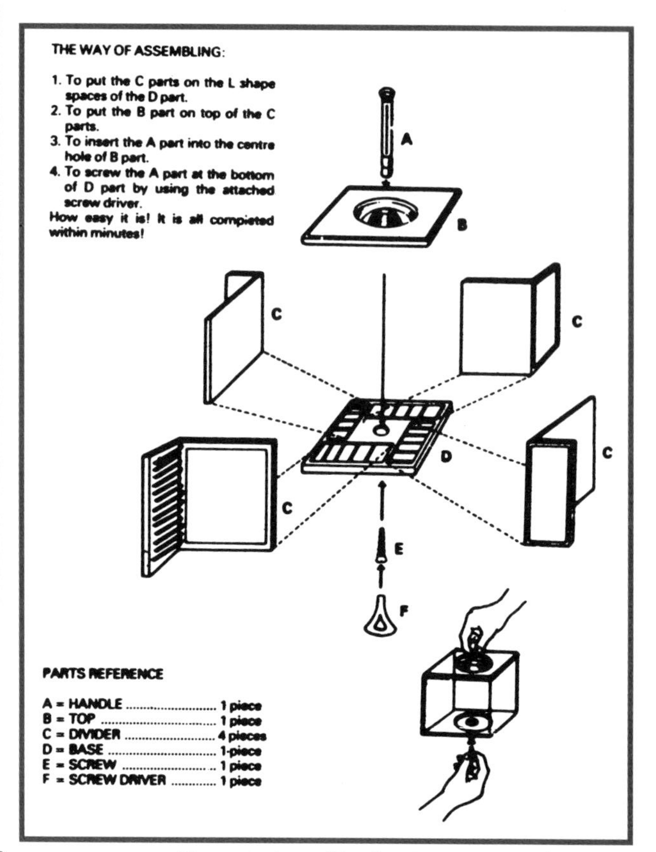

Figure 8 Assembly of a CD storage rack.

put together the successful ideas and discard the unsuccessful ones. Decisions will be made based on the information gained through research and development, compared against the specification. From this a finalised design proposal will be draughted. The design proposal will be drawn in the form of PRESENTATION DRAWINGS. Presentation drawings can be **freehand** or **technical**.

Freehand drawings are artistic impressions using perspective, oblique or isometric techniques. Perspective drawings are often used to give impressions of architecture such as precincts and shopping malls.

Oblique and isometric presentational drawings are generally used for smaller products, such as electrical goods.

Technical drawings tend to show a lot more detail. They are working drawings that contain information like:

- the type of materials;
- sizes or dimensions;
- the number of components;
- assembly.

There are the British and International Standards with which drawings have to conform. Formal ORTHOGRAPHIC drawings allow the designer to show all faces of the design. The top view is called the plan, the front view is the front elevation and the side view the end elevation. Together with any specific information, a materials list and dimensions are often added. The lines on an orthographic drawing must follow the conventions, which conform to British Standards.

The two types of formal orthographic drawings are 1st angle projection and 3rd angle projection. Today 3rd angle projections tend to be used, although some designers mix 1st and 3rd angle projections to give the advantages of the two methods.

activities

The drawing here is an industrial drawing of a plastic milk container.

(a) What type of drawing is being used?

(b) Explain what this type of drawing shows about the product.

(c) Suggest TWO reasons why it might be important to illustrate the product in this way.

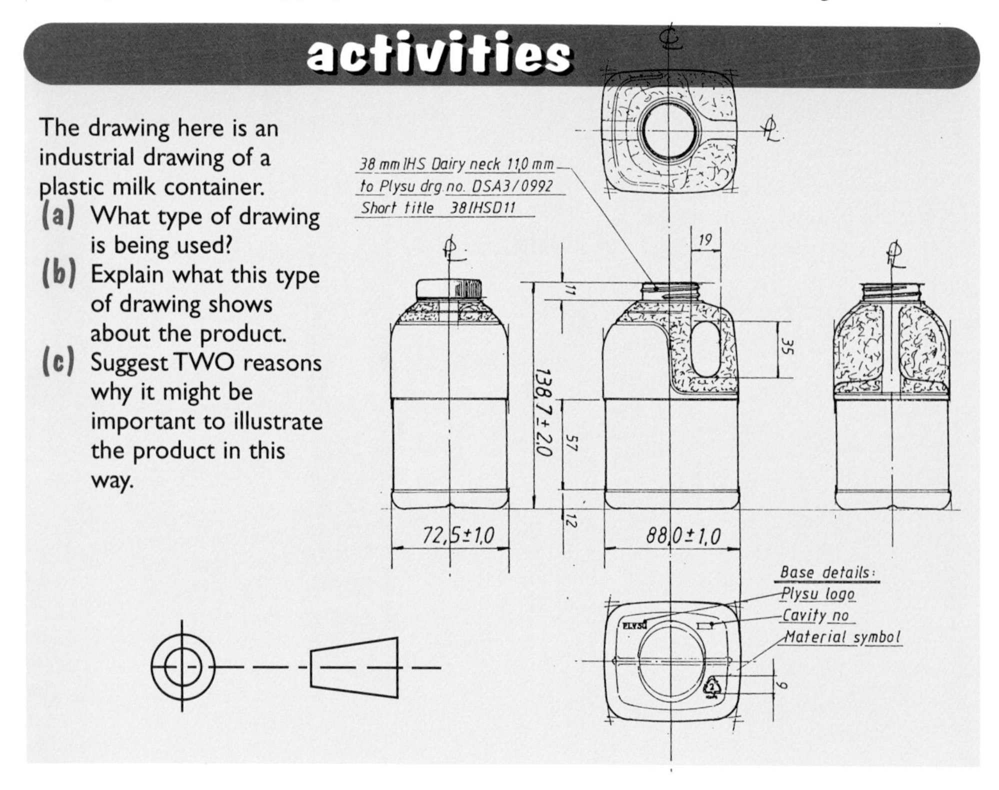

Hidden detail

To show detail inside a product, for example how deep a blind hole or recess is, dotted lines on an orthographic or isometric type of drawing can be used. SECTIONAL and EXPLODED DIAGRAMS may be better as they show more information, in particular how parts are assembled. A sectional drawing has an imaginary line that cuts through a product. Drawings of

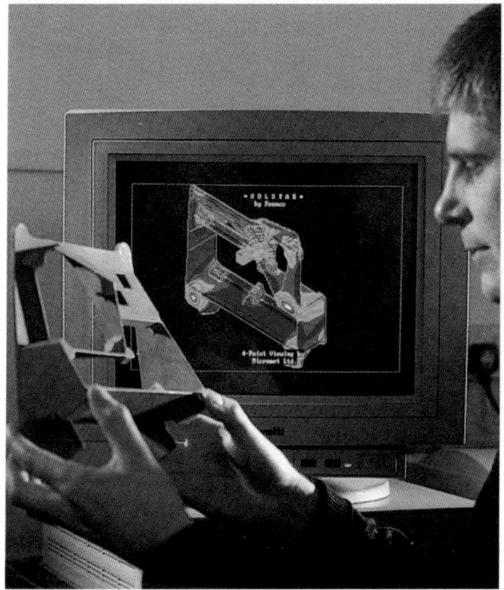

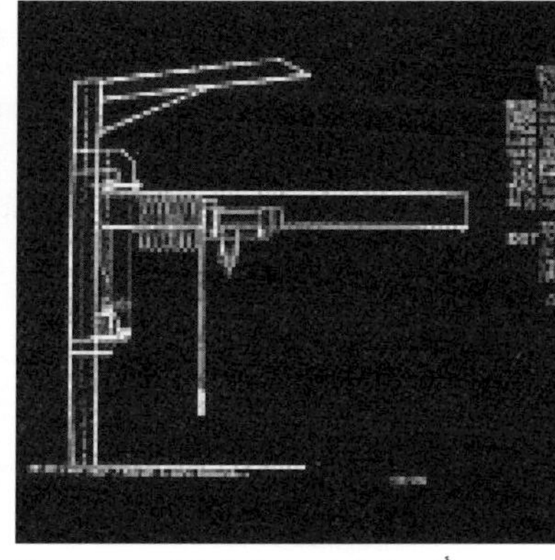

Computer aided design of plastic components and cranes.

Key Terms

Concept sketches - **quick, freehand sketches of ideas.**
Development drawings - **more detailed drawings showing design ideas.**
Semiology - **the study of signs and symbols.**
Product development - **examining the aspects and features of a design.**
Mock-ups - **rough models used in the early stages of development.**
Prototypes - **final working models prior to manufacture.**
Simulation - **tests using models.**
Presentation drawings - **final design proposals using technical or freehand techniques.**
Orthographic drawings - **drawings that show different views of a design in a formal manner to BSI standards.**
Sectional drawings - **a drawing made of a product as if an imaginary line has cut through it.**
Exploded diagrams - **a drawing showing different parts of a product, their positions and how they would fit together.**

laboratory apparatus use this technique. Sectional drawings can be used with formal orthographic drawings to provide more detailed information. Exploded diagrams are used a lot when DIY is purchased. The drawing must show how the parts fit together and in what position they will need to be. The diagram is pulled apart (exploded) but all the pieces are kept close enough to see where they have come from. Dotted lines can be used to show where screws etc will fit to assemble the product.

Maps/plans and layouts can be drawn as 2D diagrams. Again there are set conventions to follow if these are chosen. A key will be necessary to indicate what certain symbols mean and shading might be needed. Circuit diagrams are a particular form of drawing convention used to show the layout in electrical and electronic systems. Similar symbols can be used for mechanical systems like pneumatics, mechanisms and logic systems. Further working drawings might be constructed by drawing printed circuit boards (see unit 18). All these drawings are described as schematic drawings.

Computer aided design

Computers are increasingly being used by designers. Computer aided design (CAD) involves the use of computer software packages in the design of products. Many different packages are available which help design products as varied as signs, baskets, vehicles and their parts, cranes and office buildings. Designers can make changes easily and quickly to designs, draw accurately and rotate designs so that they can be seen from any angle. They also allow a design to be seen and modified before a model has been built, which could save time and reduce costs.

Advanced software modelling packages allow designs to be tested on computer and simulations carried out to test strength and reliability, for example. CAD can be used in the design of one off items, batches or mass produced products (see unit 19).

activities

- Mailbox International Ltd manufacture plastic containers. Customers contact the company with their initial design proposals. CAD is used to turn the proposals into 3D designs on screen. The designs can be tailored to customer's needs, including the incorporation of company names or logos into the containers.

Source: Mailbox International Ltd.

- Philips Business Communications used CAD software to design the Octopus range of business telephones for Deutsche Telekom. The design took around 50 weeks, about half the 'normal' time without CAD. The client provided concept sketches at the start. The telephones were more complex to design than domestic models. When an extension to the main terminal had to be designed it was possible using CAD to transfer existing information and place it in a new housing. This took only around 5 days, but would have taken several weeks without CAD facilities.

Source: adapted from Engineering.

(a) What is meant by CAD?
(b) Suggest THREE functions that may be carried out to a product designed using a CAD program that would be useful to a designer.
(c) What are the possible advantages of using CAD to the businesses mentioned in the article?

unit 3

Planning

Table 1 A cutting list for a coffee table.

Description	No. required	Material	Length (mm)	Width (mm)	Thickness (mm)
LEGS	4	TEAK	300	60	20
RAILS	2	TEAK	350	90	20
RAILS	2	TEAK	750	90	20
TOP	1	BLOCKBOARD	1050	420	16
TOP	FOR SURFACE COVERAGE	TEAK VENEER		TO COVER BLOCKBOARD	
TOP EDGING	2	TEAK VENEER	1100	20	5
TOP EDGING	2	TEAK VENEER	450	20	5
FIXING BLOCKS	4	TEAK VENEER	50	30	15
CSK WOOD SCREWS	4	BRASS OR PROTECTED STEEL	1"	No 8s	
SURFACE FINISH	1 250ML CAN	TEAK OIL			
DOWEL	1 LENGTH	RAMIN	500	Ø19	
(IF DOWEL JOINTS TO BE USED THEN:)					
DOWEL	1 LENGTH	RAMIN	500	Ø9	
(IF TUBE STEEL TO BE USED FOR FRAME AND LEGS:)					
EITHER					
ROUND STEEL	1 LENGTH	MILD STEEL	2000	Ø19	
OR					
SQUARE STEEL TUBE	1 LENGTH	MILD STEEL	2000	19	19

Planning

Once a design has been finalised the manufacture of the product will have to be planned in detail. Forward planning like this should tell the manufacturer:

- whether the design can be realistically made or not;
- how much material is needed;
- how much it will cost and whether it is commercially viable (see unit 25);
- what types of material are needed;
- the number of components required;
- how long it should take to make;
- whether one, a few or many can be made (see unit 19);
- any foreseeable problems.

Cutting lists

Preparing a CUTTING LIST is an important part of planning. This will tell a manufacturer what types of material will be needed and how much of each is required. Materials can be bought in standard sizes (see units 4-6) so there may be some wastage. Cutting lists need to show exact sizes and dimensions, with an allowance for wastage.

It is important to keep wastage to a minimum in order to reduce costs. One way of doing this might be to recycle materials. Another is to use the cheapest available materials. This may involve 'shopping around' to find the cheapest source. It may also mean using a cheaper alternative. However, a manufacturer must be careful not to use materials that are so cheap that they affect the quality of the product.

Many businesses keep a stock of available materials, but some may have to be ordered before or during manufacture. This stock control (see unit 19) will have to be built into any production plan at the start.

Production schedules

Once the types of materials and components have been identified a PRODUCTION SCHEDULE can be devised. This will describe the sequence of tasks needed to make the product. The first step will be to identify each major stage in the schedule. Each stage can then be broken into sub-stages. Most production schedules for the manufacture of products will include:

- measuring and marking the materials;
- cutting the materials to size, drilling etc;
- shaping and/or forming the material;
- assembling and joining the parts;

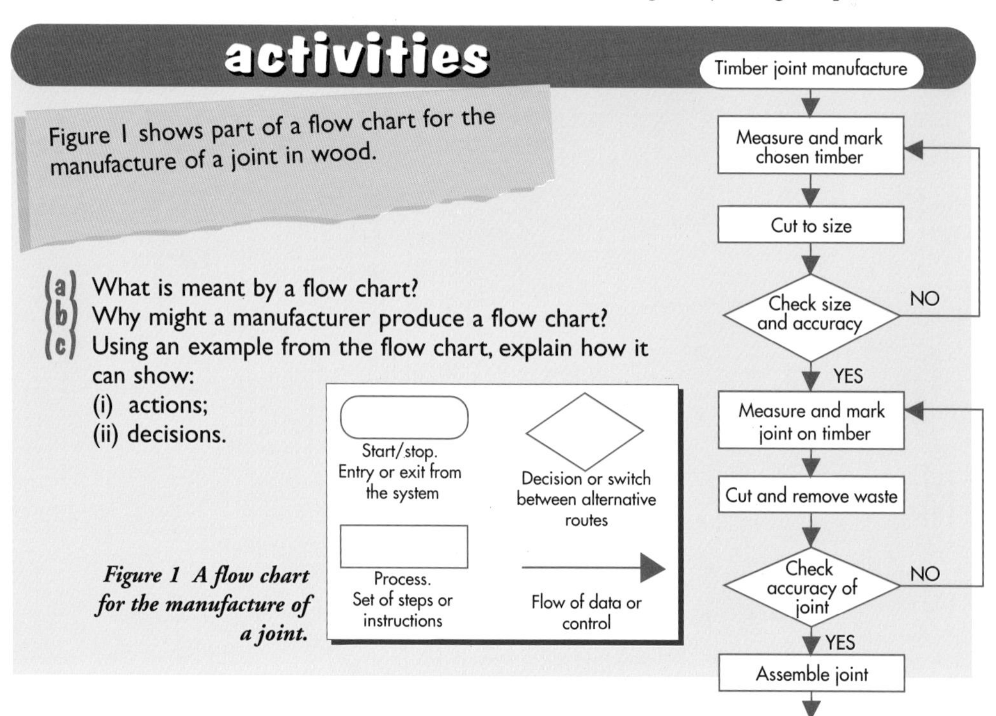

activities

Figure 1 shows part of a flow chart for the manufacture of a joint in wood.

(a) What is meant by a flow chart?
(b) Why might a manufacturer produce a flow chart?
(c) Using an example from the flow chart, explain how it can show:
(i) actions;
(ii) decisions.

Figure 1 A flow chart for the manufacture of a joint.

- finishing the product;
- tidying/clearing away tools, equipment, waste;
- storing the product safely at each stage.

A production schedule can be illustrated in a number of ways. A FLOW CHART shows the order in which tasks are carried out. Each task is a short phrase in a box or circle. They are often used in computer and logic systems to show the sequence of events. A STORYBOARD is a series of sketches, diagrams or photographs that show, for example, how a design has developed, the different stages in its operation or how it is manufactured and assembled.

The tools and equipment for each stage of the production schedule must be identified so that they are available when needed and when maintenance is required. A TICK LIST will be useful for this, as it allows items to be ticked as a record that they have been checked.

BOARD COMPONENTS

ITEM	SIZE (approx) mm	QTY.	REPLACEMENT REQUIRED
End	550 × 400	2	✓✓
Shelf	371 × 399	1	✓
Top	402 × 402	1	✓
Drawer Back	291 × 70	1	✓
Drawer Front	368 × 163	1	✓

ITEM	SIZE (approx) mm	QTY.	REPLACEMENT REQUIRED
Drawer Bottom	367 × 335	1	
Drawer Sides	335 × 70	2	✓✓
Back	BLACK (3mm)	1	
Glass Door	366 × 357 (4mm)	1	

HARDWARE LIST

ITEM	SIZE		QTY.	REPLACEMENT REQUIRED
Carcase Screw	8 × 1¾″		10	
Catch Screw	6 × ½″		2	
Handle Screw	6 × 1″		2	
Small Screw	6 × ¾″ (Bright)		6	
Handle	64mm		1	
Glue Sachet	–		1	
Cover Cap	–		4	
Drawer Runner	–		2	
Dowel	25mm		10	

ITEM	SIZE		QTY.	REPLACEMENT REQUIRED
Wire Record Divider	–		2	
Magnetic Catch	45mm		1	
Glass Door Pivot Hinge	–		2	
Glass Door Handle	–		1	

Source: Eurospace Furniture Packs Ltd.

***Figure 2** A tick list for a record/cassette storage system.*

Time plans

Each stage in a production schedule needs to be given an allotted time. This will build up to give a time plan. A manufacturer is often working to a deadline, the final date or time by which the product or part of a product must be manufactured. It tells the manufacturer how long is allowed for the manufacturing process or parts of the process to take place. The time plan has be organised to meet these deadlines.

Time plans must make allowances for foreseeable problems. For example, there might be plenty of tenon saws, but only a few pillar drills and possibly only one CNC milling machine. This could lead to a bottleneck, holding up production. Where bottlenecks are likely, alternatives might be suggested in order to keep on target to meet the deadlines set. This could involve changing the organisation of production, or using other workers or equipment. It is important to be aware of how any suggested alternative will affect the quality of the product to be made. Unexpected problems must also be allowed for if possible (eg a machine breaking down). Any production schedule should include a slippage section. This will identify tasks that have not been completed in the set time plan and will have to be fitted in at a later stage.

The stages in production and how problems were resolved must be recorded to help solve similar problems in future.

activities

Look at the pictures below.

(a) What type of presentation is being shown here?
(b) Draw a flow chart to explain what is happening at each stage.
(c) Suggest THREE reasons why a time plan for the manufacture and assembly of taxis would be useful.

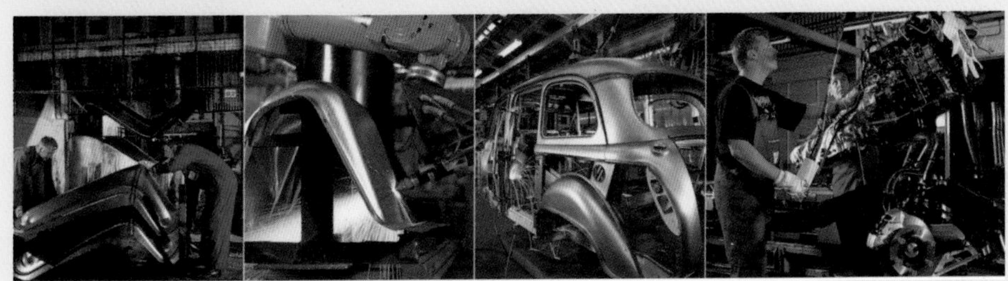

The body panels of the taxi are pressed and cut to size by robot, before assembly and the installation of the Nissan engine.

Cutting list - a record of the materials needed and the lengths required.
Production schedule - a sequence of tasks undertaken to design and make a project.
Flow chart - a sequence of events used to show the order of tasks to be undertaken.
Storyboard - sketches that show how a task is carried out.
Tick list - a record of items or components that can be ticked to check they have been accounted for.

MAGNET'S SHAKER KITCHEN

Magnet's Shaker Kitchens are based on those found in 'shaker' villages. Shakers (or shaking quakers) were people with strong religious beliefs. Their society was started by Anna Lee in Manchester in 1774. She told her followers to 'provide places for all your things so that you may know where to find them at any time, day or night'. Shaker villages and architecture were neat and extremely simple.

The materials used for doors and cabinets are shown here.

Source: Magnet Ltd.

Doors

- 18mm thick MDF coated with 3 layers of polyester lacquer (paint) and individually packaged.

Cabinets

- 15mm thick melamine faced chipboard panels assembled by patented injection moulding method.
- All metal, fully adjustable, 95° opening hinges.
- All plastic, fully adjustable cabinet legs, to stabilise and level floor units.
- Metal and plastic fully adjustable wall hanging brackets for fixing and levelling wall units.
- 3 optional shelf positions with shelf studs locking the shelf in position to prevent movement in transit.
- Beech effect drawer boxes on smooth nylon wheeled drawer runners.
- All doors and cabinets tested to British Standard 6222 and produced in accordance with ISO 9002 quality procedures.

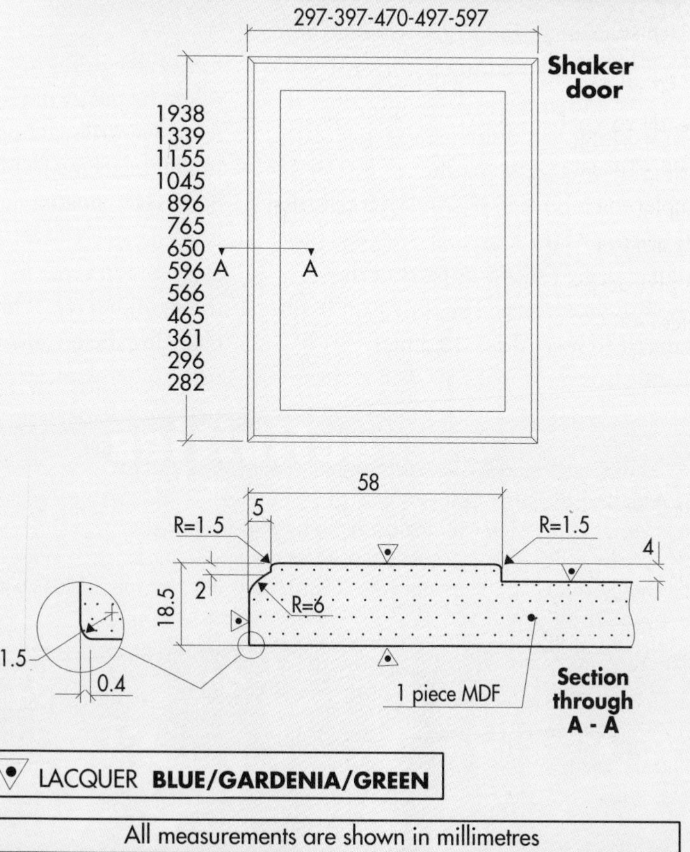

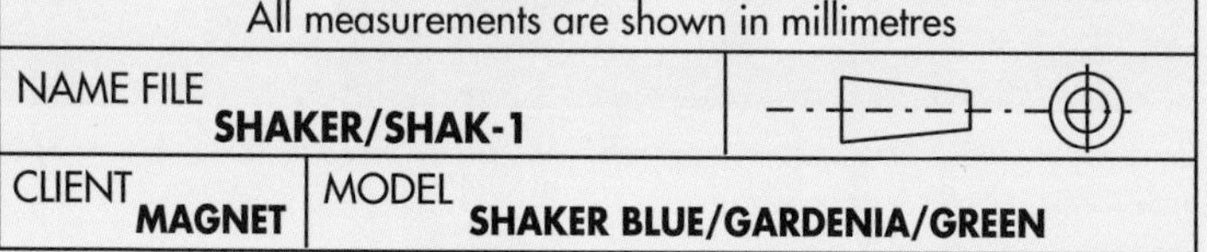

All measurements are shown in millimetres		
NAME FILE SHAKER/SHAK-1		
CLIENT MAGNET	MODEL SHAKER BLUE/GARDENIA/GREEN	

Questions

(a) Where did the idea for the Shaker kitchen come from?

(b) Suggest FIVE pieces of information that might appear in a specification for Shaker cabinets.

(c) Draw concept sketches for:
  (i) a bread bin to match the style of a Shaker kitchen;
  (ii) a bread bin to fit into a kitchen with a 'technological' feel.

(d) What types of drawings are shown of the Shaker cabinet door? What information do these drawings contain?

(e) Make an isometric drawing of a Shaker drawer box to fit inside a cabinet.

(f) Draw an exploded diagram of a simple cabinet. Include a door but not the drawers. Show how the components fit together.

MGA Developments designs car and vehicle bodies, and aerospace structures such as flight simulators. It also offers a modelling and prototyping service for vehicles (eg cars, tanks, transporters and trucks) and aerospace designs (eg the front fuselage of a plane or its undercarriage doors). Another service is the design and production of component manufacturing tools, such as jigs and stretch tools.

MGA provides a comprehensive vehicle engineering facility. Designs are taken from concept ideas to prototype. It has invested heavily in computer aided design and manufacturing (CAD/CAM). CAD design facilities allow designs to be produced in 2D and 3D on screen. These may be vehicle body designs or computer modelling of vehicle surfaces.

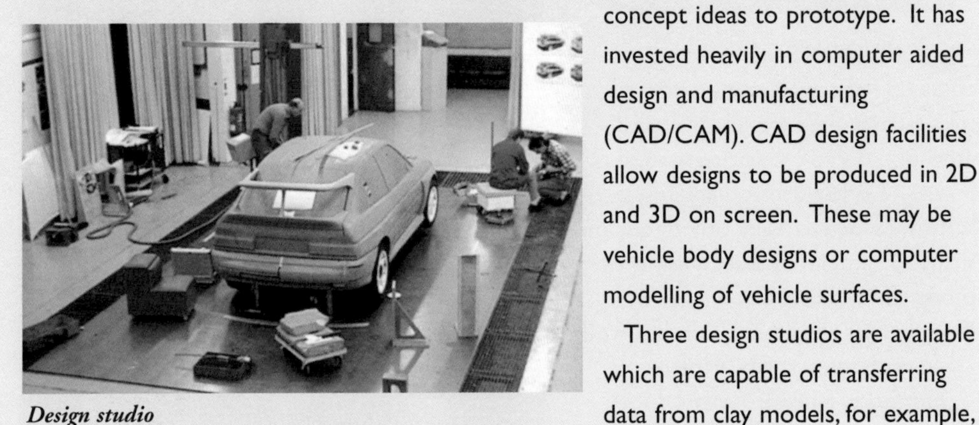

Design studio

Three design studios are available which are capable of transferring data from clay models, for example, directly to CAD facilities. Models can be scale models or life size models.

The company also employs over 20 sheet metal workers to produce prototype panels and complete vehicle bodies as prototypes of vehicles. Body structures are produced from only limited CAD information. This allows prototype vehicles to be produced very early in the prototyping process.

Source: MGA Developments.

Concept design.

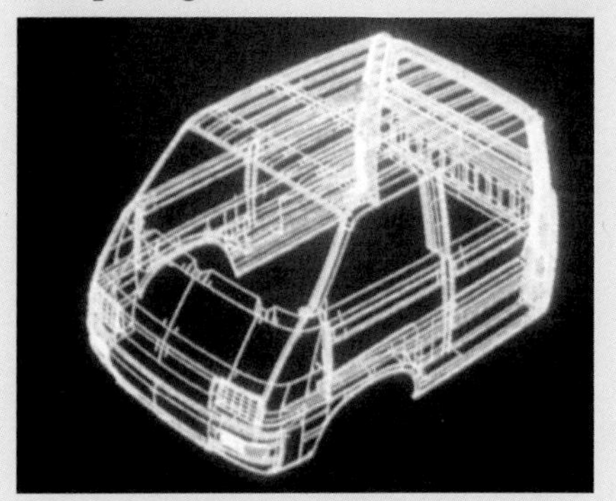

Cab design using CAD.

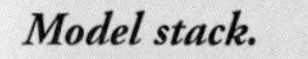

Model stack.

Scale model.

Prototype vehicle.

Questions

(a) Explain the difference between a 2D and a 3D drawing.
(b) What is meant by a scale model?
(c) What modelling material is mentioned in the article? Suggest TWO other modelling materials that might be used to make models.
(d) Suggest TWO benefits of using CAD for a designer.
(e) Explain the sentence 'Designs are taken from concept ideas to prototype'.
(f) Suggest THREE products that might be made as a model or a prototype by the company. How might manufacturing a model or prototype help when designing these products?

unit 4

Wood

Natural wood

WOOD is produced **naturally** as trees grow. Trees grow taller and increase in thickness (girth) each year by adding an annual ring. The bark of a tree is the outer layer which acts as protection as in Figure 1. The cambium layer is where new bast (working cells) and new wood are formed. This new wood is called the **sapwood**. It contains a lot of moisture (sap) as it is the living part of the tree where minerals and fluid pass from root to leaf. Sapwood is too weak and moist to be of much use construction work. Young trees are known as saplings.

As a tree grows the inner cells of the sapwood age and die, becoming harder and more compact. It then becomes the **heartwood**, which provides strength and support to the tree. This is the material that is generally used as a construction material.

Once a tree is felled it is cut into logs, which are then sliced along their length. At this stage the wood is called TIMBER. It cannot be used because it still **green** and contains a lot of sap. The timber needs to dry out until its water content is between 10% and 20%. This is done by **seasoning**. Air seasoning is a natural way to let timber dry out. The timber is stacked in layers, separated by sticks and left in an open sided shed with a sloping roof. Air circulates between the layers reducing the water content to 20%. This process takes 1-2 years depending on the thickness of the timber. The stacking of the timber is important, as badly stacked timber may split or twist as it dries. Kiln seasoning is a quicker process. The timber is stacked and stored in a sealed kiln, where the temperature and humidity is controlled. This process can reduce the water content to around 10% and takes about 10 weeks.

Softwoods and hardwoods

SOFTWOODS are woods obtained from evergreen coniferous trees. These trees are relatively fast growing. Because their heartwood is porous, it is less dense. Therefore softwoods are relatively easy to cut and shape. Examples of softwoods, their properties and uses are:

- **red cedar** - light and soft, but weak (greenhouses, sheds, garden furniture, fences);
- **redwood** - works well with hand tools (frames and joists in building construction, outdoor use);

Figure 1 Wood grows naturally by adding rings. It is then cut into timber which is stored in layers.

activities

Garden Products of Kent produces a range of garden related products. It is considering the manufacture of garden seats. Look at Table 1.

(a) Explain the difference between softwoods and hardwoods.

(b) Name THREE hardwoods and THREE softwoods shown in the table.

(c) What factors might Garden Products if Kent take into account when deciding which material to use for garden seating?

Table 1 The durability of timber for outside use.

Timber	Class	Durability (years)
Teak	Very durable	25+
Afrormosia	Very durable	25+
Western red cedar	Durable	15-25
White oak	Durable	15-25
Pitch pine	Durable	15-25
American walnut	Moderately durable	10-15
Douglas fir	Moderately durable	10-15
Elm	Non-durable	5-10
Pines and spruce	Non-durable	5-10
Ash	Perishable	0-5
Beech	Perishable	0-5

Source: *adapted from Garden Woodworking, April 1996.*

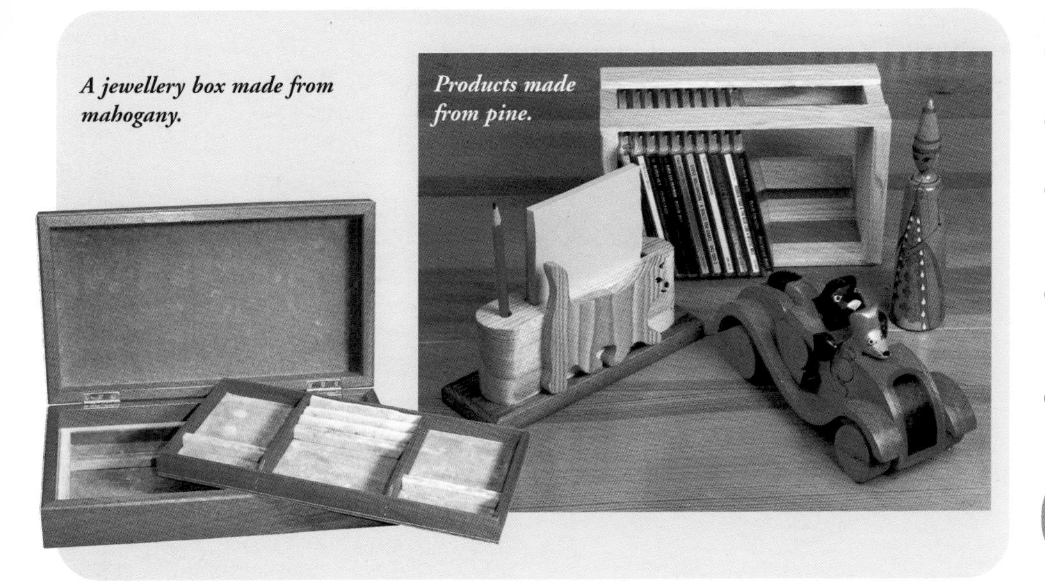
A jewellery box made from mahogany.

Products made from pine.

- **(Norway) spruce** - fairly strong and resists splitting (violin and guitar bellies);
- **douglas fir** - fairly strong, durable and fairly water resistant (outdoor products, gates, ladders, door frames);
- **pitch pine** - durable (heavy gate posts);
- **parana pine** - fairly strong, not very durable (internal joinery such as staircases, furniture and toilet roll holders);
- **yew** - tough, hard and durable (interior and exterior joinery, furniture).

HARDWOODS are generally obtained from broad leaved deciduous trees. These tend to grow more slowly than coniferous trees.

Hardwoods are denser than softwoods. Therefore most hardwoods are more difficult to shape and cut than softwoods.

Examples of hardwoods, their properties and uses are:

- **beech** - hard and strong but can warp (used in indoor and outdoor furniture, mallets and handles);
- **(soft) maple** - fairly hard wearing, used with hand tools, glues well (internal joinery, musical instruments, butchers' blocks);
- **teak** - durable and resists decay but can be hard to glue due to oil in the timber (outdoor furniture, quality indoor furniture and boats);
- **ash** - tough and flexible (handles and sports equipment);
- **oak** - strong, heavy and durable (good quality external furniture, buildings, fittings, handles);
- **elm** - tough and durable, but can warp (garden and indoor furniture);
- **obeche** - soft, light and durable (toys);
- **mahogany** - hard and strong, but can warp (indoor furniture, door panels);
- **jelutong** - soft and can break easily (modelling, industrial patterns);
- **afrormosia** - durable and saws, planes and glues well (interior and exterior joinery and furniture, boat building);
- **American walnut** - tough, strong and moderately durable (furniture and interior joinery);
- **balsa** - soft and light, sands and glues well (model making);

Manufactured timbers

MANUFACTURED TIMBERS have been developed to suit particular needs. Chipboard, for example, was developed in Germany in the 1940s as natural timbers were in short supply. Developments in glue technology allowed such boards to be produced as they were stronger than the natural bonding of wood fibres. Plywood emerged in the late 19th Century. It provided craftsmen with a large panel size which was strong and easy to work with. Today there is a large range of manufactured timbers, which may be classed as laminated boards, particle boards and fibreboards. Manufactured boards are examples of **composites** - boards made from a mixture of materials, such as woods, glue and veneer.

Laminated boards

Laminated boards are made by taking thin sheets of timber (known as VENEERS) and gluing them together under high pressure and temperature. Each layer (or ply) usually has its grain at right angles to the next. This makes the board stronger and resistant to warp.

The most common laminated board is **plywood**. Plywoods have a number of advantages. They can come in different numbers of sheets. They can be moulded to make curved surfaces and can have a decorative veneer glued to their surface to

Read the information below.

(a) What timbers are used to make these two products?

(b) Suggest reasons why these timbers may be used.

Aluminium extension ladders and metal rakes are in common use today, but there are still manufacturers of wooden ladders and rakes made from wood. The tines (the pegs) for wooden rake heads can be made by purchasing dowel of the correct diameter, cutting it to the right length and sharpening with a knife. The best material to cope with the rigours of raking in a rough field is ash. In the past, wooden ladders were made from oak. Today they are made from timbers such as douglas fir and ash.

Source: adapted from The Forgotten Arts, John Seymour, Dorling Kindersley.

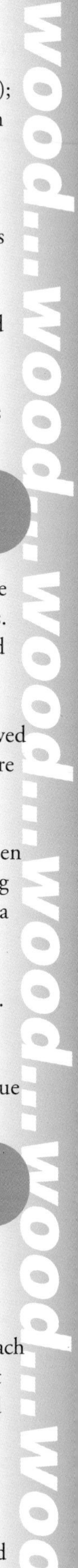

become a veneered laminated shape. A melamine (plastic) surface, for example, can make the board useful as a kitchen worktop.

There are different grades of plywood for different jobs. They differ in the type of adhesive, veneer and finish used. For example, marine grade board is used for boat building as it is water resistant. Birch-faced board is used for interior construction and is likely to be painted, but is not water resistant. Plywoods are used to make everything from lorry bodies to toys, such as jigsaws and brick trolleys, and furniture. They are used in the construction industry because they are cheap to manufacture. Examples are structural, shuttering, one side good and veneered. **Blockboard** and **laminboard** are types of plywood. Instead of having alternate layers of veneer, their centres are made from strips of solid wood, edge butted together.

Particle boards

Particle boards are made from small chips or flakes of wood bonded together by high pressure to make a **reconstituted** board (particles of wood bonded together and compressed). These small chips are taken from off cuts, poor quality or left over wood after timber has been made.

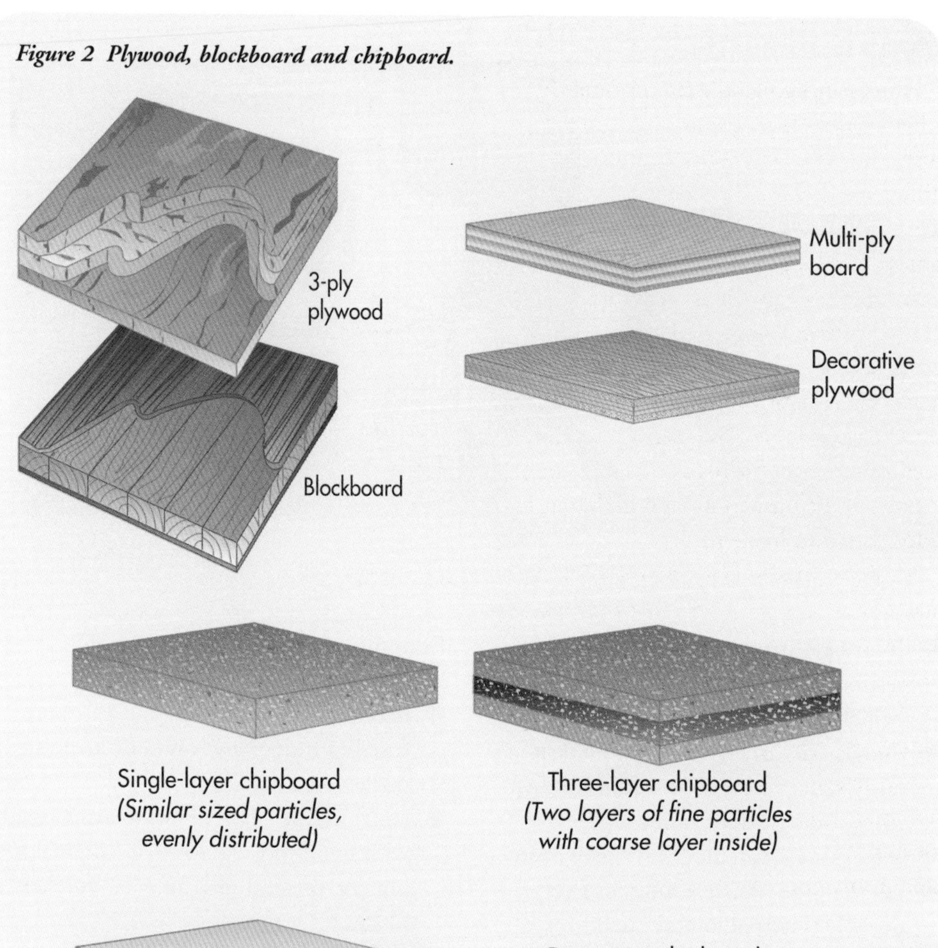

Figure 2 Plywood, blockboard and chipboard.

activities

Read the information below.

(a) Suggest a type of particle board that may be used in the production of a worktop.
(b) Describe the likely production process when manufacturing a particle board for a worktop.
(c) Suggest THREE different 'looks' that could be given to a particle board worktop.
(d) What type of surface finish is: (i) a particle board and (ii) a wood worktop likely to have?

IKEA produces a variety of kitchen work surfaces which are incorporated into its kitchen designs. It considers that durability, heat resistance and practicality are important considerations when choosing a suitable worktop. IKEA's Pragel range of worktops is high pressure laminate in 38mm particle board, in lengths from 60cm to 240cm. Its Pronomen range is for those who want a 'real' wood surface, in lengths from 40cm to 240cm.

PRAGEL RANGE
Anthracite stone
Grey marble
Beech
Grey stone
Cherrywood
White
PRONOMEN Solid beech

Source: adapted from You magazine, The Mail on Sunday, 31.3.1996; IKEA.

Chipboard is perhaps the most common type. Various types are made. They tend to differ in terms of the shape, the size of the particles, the distribution of particles in the board and the type of adhesive used to bond the chips. **Flakeboards** or **waferboards**, for example, use large shavings which are laid horizontally overlapping each other, which improves the tensile strength of the board.

Particle boards are usually made from softwoods. Most are used for internal construction work because they absorb moisture easily. They are quite brittle and have a lower tensile strength than plywoods, although strength can be considerably improved with added veneer. They can also be **laminated** (see unit 14) with a variety of finishes. As with plywood, kitchen surfaces can be made from chipboard with a melamine veneer. If water is absorbed around the sink area, however, it can lead to swelling and rotting.

Fibreboards

Fibreboards are made from timber fibres. These fibres are reassembled to make a stable material. Fibreboards come in different forms. **Hardboard** is a high density fibreboard made by pressing wet fibres at high temperatures. The natural resins in the fibres act as an adhesive, bonding them together. Standard hardboard is often used to make drawer bottoms or cabinet backs. **Medium boards** come in two grades, low density (LM), used to make pinboards as it is soft enough for pins to be pushed in, and high density (HM), used to make panels.

Medium density fibreboard (MDF) is made by adding resin and wax to fibres and drying before pressing takes place. It can be used for modelling and making moulds for the plastics industry because of its smooth surface. It provides a good base for a veneered finish and will machine well and cut cleanly. MDF is often used as a substitute for natural wood, particularly in indoor furniture.

Figure 3 Fibreboards.

Medium boards | **Hardboard**

High density (HM)

Low density (LM)

Medium density fibreboard (MDF)

Standard board

Tempered with resin to give a water resistant board

Board with decorative face

Perforated board

Uses of MDF.

Properties

The mass of plant cells that is compressed as tree material dies to form natural wood is called the **grain**. This is seen as long thin strands running through the wood as in Figure 4. The grain gives wood strength and is also the cause of its

activities

Redwood Ltd is a manufacturer of office equipment. Recently the managing director has decided that, in order to cut costs, the company will no longer have large desks made out of expensive mahogany, but will have to move to desks made of manufactured board. The company is concerned, however, whether desks will retain their strength, durability and appearance.

(a) Explain the difference between: (i) natural wood and manufactured boards; (ii) laminated boards and particle boards; (iii) particle boards and fibreboards.

(b) Suggest a suitable material for the new desks and explain why the material you have chosen could be used.

(c) Suggest ONE other way in which the company might save money on its desk design.

Figure 4 A shelf built from A would have more tensile strength than one built from B, which is more likely to snap holding a heavy weight.

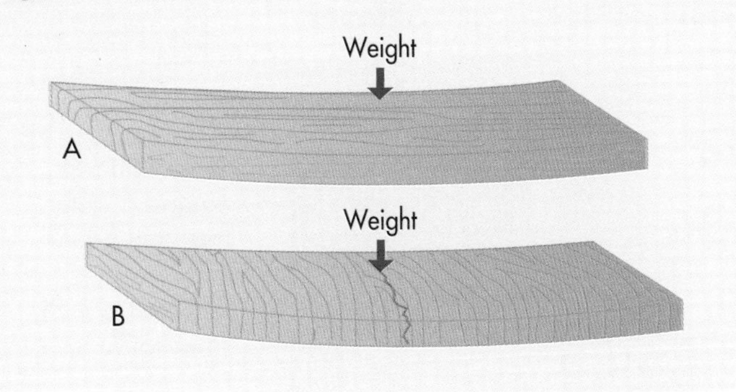

Figure 5 Wood problems.

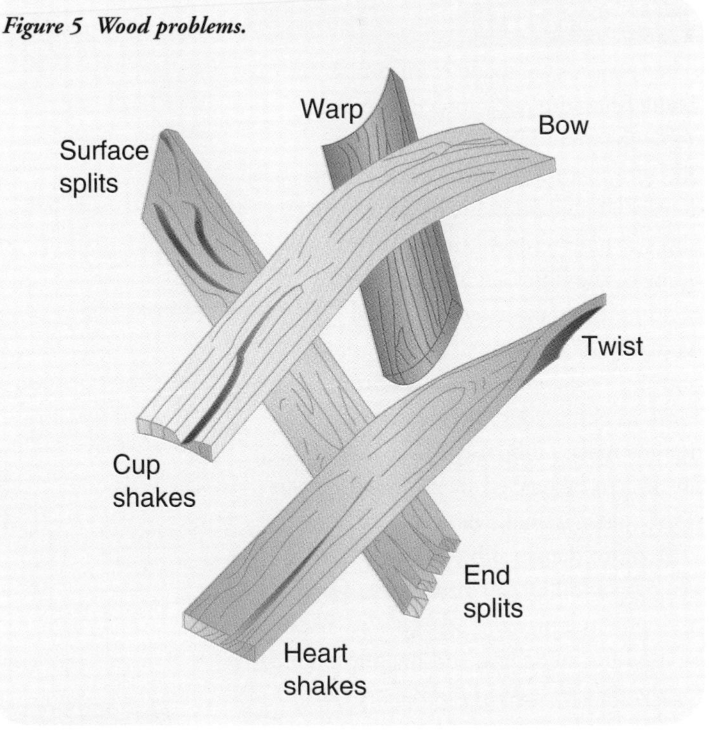

greatest weakness. Wood tends to have a higher tensile strength (see unit 7) along the grain than across the grain. This is important to bear in mind when choosing natural wood for construction.

Plywood layers are aligned with their grains at 90° to each other. This means that plywood is strong in all directions. Plywoods, once layered , are more difficult to cut and shape than natural woods. However, they can be shaped around moulds during the layering process. This is a skill used by cabinet and musical instrument makers (see unit 12). Once set, the plywood will not lose its shape. Particle and fibreboards are more easily cut. Fibreboards, in particular, can be glued and then shaped using sanding techniques which makes them ideal for moulds and formers.

Wood is **hygroscopic**. This means that it absorbs and releases moisture even after seasoning. When it gets damp it swells and when it dries it shrinks, mainly across the fibres of the grain. It is important to chose wood with the correct water content when manufacturing products. Generally speaking, if it is for outside use then a higher water content is required. A piece of wood that swells may not only get bigger but lose its shape - it might bow, twist or warp as in Figure 5. Frequent swelling may cause the wood to split.

Because of the alternative direction of the grain, plywood does not lose its shape or split. Chipboard swells as it absorbs moisture and, once dried, does not return to its original shape. Fibreboards, like most MDF and hardboards are not affected by moisture to the same extent.

activities

(a) What is meant by the grain of wood?
(b) Why might plywood be stronger than solid timber?
(c) Jim Carnforth is a local joiner. He has been asked to build a test tube holder by a client and was given the drawing below to follow. Jim contacted the client to suggest that there may be problems in following the drawing.

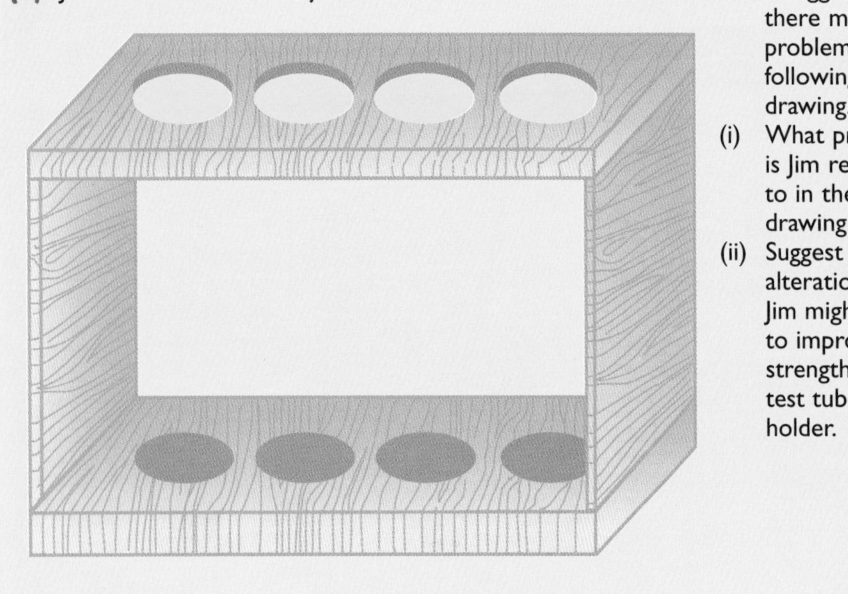

(i) What problems is Jim referring to in the drawing?
(ii) Suggest alterations that Jim might make to improve the strength of the test tube holder.

Commercial stock of materials

Timber can be bought in a number of standard forms and sizes as shown in Figure 6, although others are available. The relative price of one type of wood compared to another will vary depending on:

- quality;
- size;
- the cost of cutting and preparing the timber;

- shape;
- availability.

Recycling

Trees are a **renewable** resource - they can be replaced once cut down. Softwoods tend to grow faster than hardwoods, reaching maturity in about 25 years. In tropical rainforests, where conditions encourage growth, some hardwoods may reach maturity almost as quickly.

The high demand for timber, despite the development of man made materials, places great pressure on forests. Many hardwood forests have already been lost in temperate regions, making timber from oak, for example, expensive because of its scarcity. Tropical rainforests have been cut back in the search for hardwoods. This not only places wood as a resource at risk, but also leads to other environmental problems. Such problems make the efficient management of forests vitally important (see unit 25).

The use of manufactured boards which are made from 'waste' wood may help to reduce the amount of trees that need to be cut down. Another method is to **reuse** or **reclaim** timber. Timber products decay naturally over time as a result of insects feeding on the wood or fungus (dry rot or heat rot). Some decay in less than 5 years while others last over 25 years. If still in good condition timber products can be reused. Offending areas can be stripped of paint or varnish, planed smooth, cut and used to make other products. Broken products may be repaired and used again or reassembled and used in a different way.

Figure 6 Standard sizes and shapes of timber

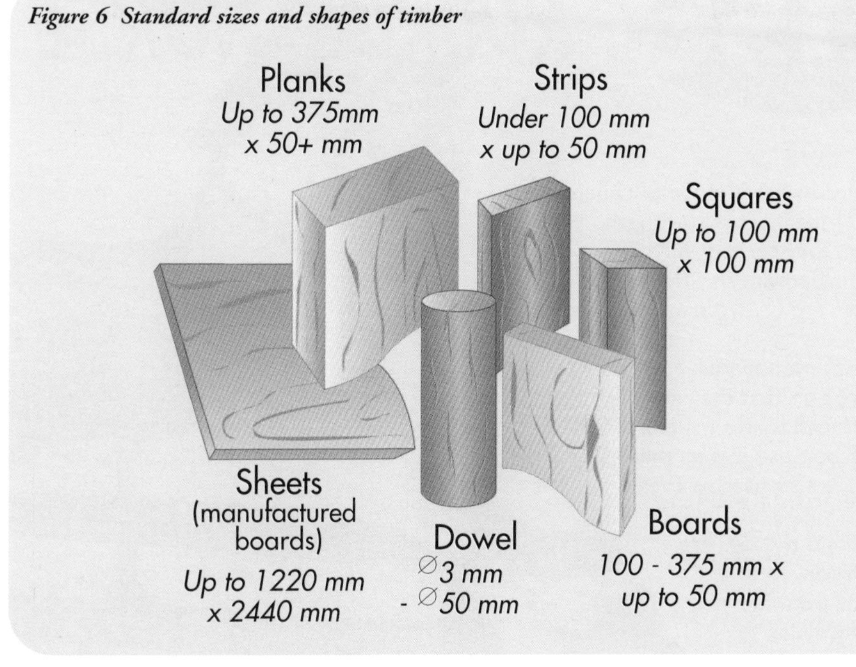

Wood - plant/tree heartwood that is used for timber.
Timber - logs cut to length.
Softwood - timber from evergreen trees.
Hardwood - timber from broad leaved deciduous trees.
Manufactured timber - 'wood' material that has been reprocessed by industrial processes.
Veneers - thin strips used in manufactured boards.

activities

Read the information below.

(a) Suggest TWO benefits of wooden shutters compared to curtains.
(b) What types of finish can be used on shutters?
(c) To what extent is Victorian Pine environmentally friendly?
(d) Do you think pine is a suitable material for shutters? Explain your answer.

Wooden shutters are a simple, sturdy and stylish alternative to curtains or blinds for interior use. Many pre-1920s houses were manufactured in quality seasoned woods, mainly pine. Victorian Pine of Brockley, London, specialises in modifying old shutters. Once shutters were stripped of paint and finished with a coat of varnish or beeswax. Now the inclination is to leave them unstripped to show off the subtle paint shades of earlier times. The security offered by shutters is another incentive to buy.

Other specialist shops provide a variety of different designs, including lattice shapes, plantation and colonial styles, and even carved Indian designs. Pine may be popular, but painted MDF is perhaps a cheaper alternative.

Source: adapted from The Times, 17.6. 1995; Victorian Pine.

ROCKING HORSE MANUFACTURE

NJ Barber makes a range of children's toys, including rocking horses. He makes them for specialist high street shops as well as for individuals. The legs and rocker of the horse are cut from a single sheet of MDF. He uses a template to cut the initial shape for one side of the horse, and then uses a router to cut the second shape so that they are both the same. The head is also made from MDF. 'I use MDF because it is so much cheaper. It is also hard to break and easy to shape.'

The seat and the legs are glued and screwed to a frame made from Norway Spruce. This helps to space the legs and provides support. The seat is made from standard 3 ply and the handle is made from 1 inch (25mm) dowel.

The horses are 1.25 metres long and about 1 metre high. Once constructed they are primed, painted with an undercoat and glossed using a lead free paint. They are customised by using colours requested by people buying them and by adding the horse's name on the back rest.

Source: NJ Barber.

'Traditional' rocking horses have been made for many years. Before the wide availability of MDF some were manufactured with a softwood inside frame and hardwood outer parts joined and glued to the frame. The stand for the horse may have been made from a hardwood such as beech as it is hard and maintains its strength, and is also knot free, which gives a smooth appearance. It may also have been made from a softwood such as pine or spruce.

Hand carving the outer parts using shaping tools would have required time and skill from the manufacturer.

A 'traditional' rocking horse.

Two MDF rocking horses.

Questions

(a) Explain what is meant by:
   (i) hardwoods;
   (ii) softwoods;
   (iii) fibreboards;
   (iv) plywoods;
   and give ONE example of each used in the manufacture of rocking horses.

(b) For each of your examples in (a), suggest why this wood might be used in the manufacture of rocking horses.

(c) Compare the rocking horse manufactured by NJ Barber to a one-off rocking horse manufactured using traditional methods taking into account:
   (i) the materials used;
   (ii) the cost;
   (iii) the time taken;
   (iv) how it might be manufactured.

case study MEDITE OF EUROPE LTD

Medite of Europe Ltd is a specialist manufacturer of medium density fibreboard (MDF). MDF is supplied in panel form and is manufactured from 'residual' wood left over from forest cutting and saw mill processes, such as pine and spruce. MDF is used in a variety of applications. Other advantages are that MDF can often be cheaper than 'natural' wood and that it is a stable board which cuts without splintering, making it ideal for a variety of finishes. It is also 'environmentally friendly', as it is manufactured from material that would normally have been scrapped. The manufacture of MDF takes place in a number of stages once the wood has been turned into wood chips.

Source: Medite of Europe Ltd.

Questions

(a) Explain why MDF is an example of:
(i) a manufactured board; (ii) a fibreboard.

(b) Draw a flow chart to show the manufacture of MDF at Medite of Europe's plant.

(c) State FOUR types of MDF produced by Medite of Europe. Explain how they might be used and why that board is suitable.

(d) A business is considering using MDF in the manufacture of window ledges and partitions in its new building. Explain the advantages of using MDF to the business.

Medite HD
High density MDF for greater strength and more exacting machining characteristics.
Uses: bedroom and office furniture, industrial shelving and flooring systems.

Medite Standard
Awarded the BS1142 Kitemark. It is produced from sustainable supplies of softwoods from managed forests.
Uses: Furniture, children's toys, shop-fitting, Hi-Fi speaker cabinets and doors.

Medite Exterior
The world's first MDF for outdoor use.
Uses: signs, doors, garden furniture, conservatories, shop fronts, exterior mouldings, hoardings and display stands.

Medite FR
Flame retardant MDF for use as required in walls, partitioning, ceilings etc.
Uses: public buildings, shops, hotels, schools, hospitals, cinemas, discos, offices and ships.

Medite 313
Moisture resistant MDF for use in more humid situations.
Uses: kitchen and bathroom furniture, window boards, skirtings and architraves, internal joinery, flooring and staircases.

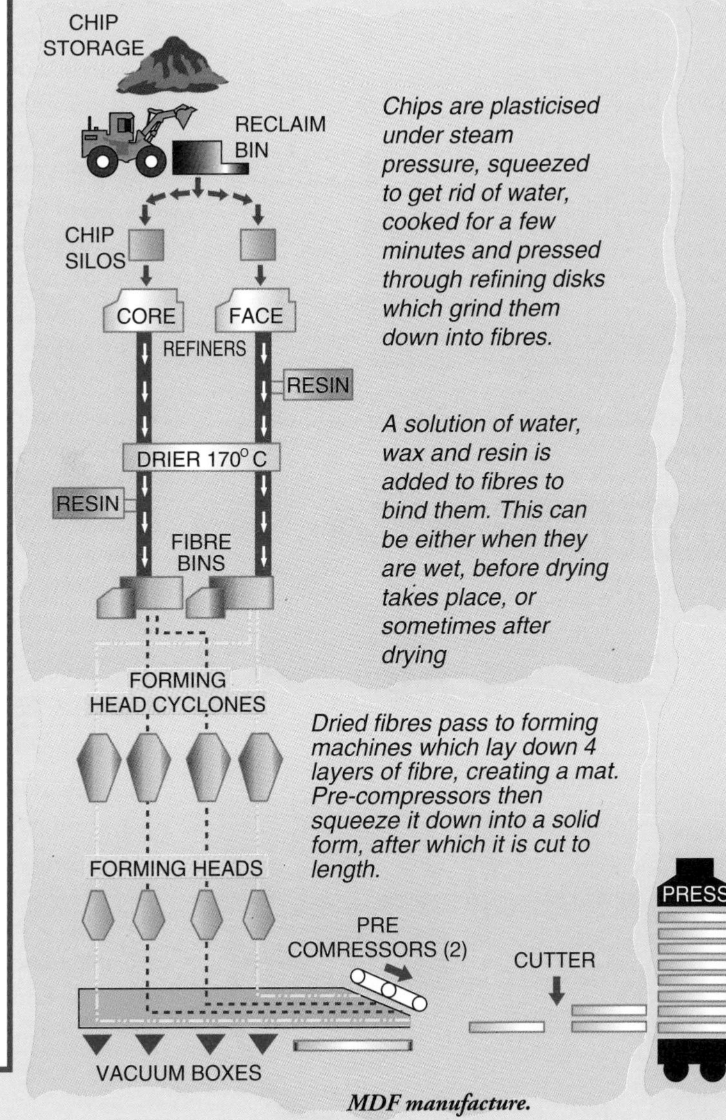

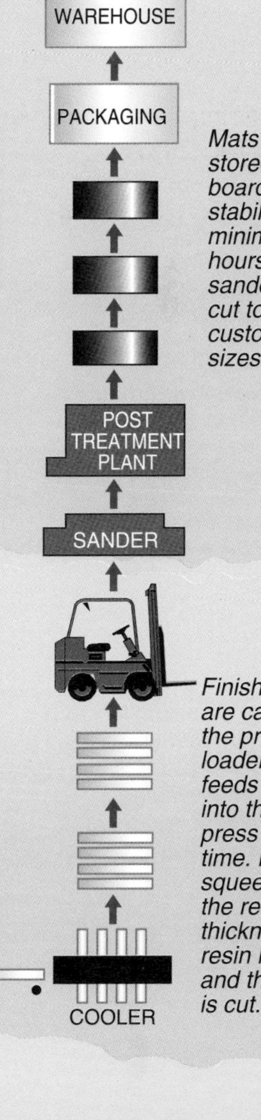

MDF manufacture.

unit 5 Plastics

Piping can be made from thermoplastic HDPE or PVC using extrusion techniques.

Plastics manufacture

Man-made (SYNTHETIC) plastics have replaced woods and metals in the manufacture of a wide range of products. The first synthetic plastic was celluloid (a thermoplastic). It was made from cotton and camphor and was very flammable. It is still used today to make some photographic film and table tennis balls. Before this the only plastics were modified natural substances, such as shellac (used as a varnish) and rubber.

Commercial production of plastics really started in the 1950s after years of experiments. The raw material for modern plastics is either oil or coal. They contain a complex mixture of different chemicals. This mixture is separated into its parts, called fractions, by a process called fractional distillation. Some of the fractions contain chemicals that are small molecules (MONOMERS). The monomers are chemically joined together to make very long molecular 'chains' (POLYMERS). This process is called **polymerisation** as shown in Figure 1. Some fractions are made of larger molecules. They are cracked into smaller molecules before they can be polymerised.

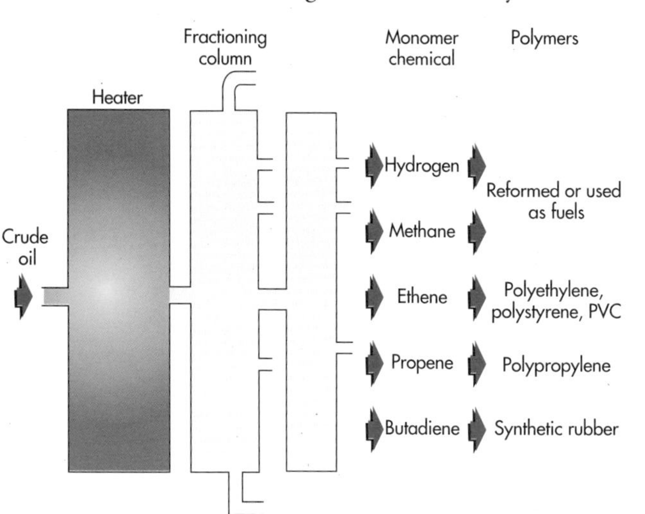

Figure 1 A schematic diagram showing plastics production from crude oil.

Chemicals can be added to the plastic during manufacture. These include:

- **plasticisers** to make the plastic bendy;
- **pigments** to change the colour;
- **antistatics** to reduce static charge;
- **antioxidants** to reduce attack by air;
- **flame retardants** to reduce burning.

Plastic products are made by heating the plastic and using a mould, a former or a cast (see unit 12). Plastic products can be cheaper than similar products made from wood or metal because:

- the raw materials are cheaper (oil extraction is cheaper than metal quarrying);
- transport costs are less;
- less energy is needed to make the products;
- products are easily mass produced (see unit 19).

There are many different types of plastics. They can be placed into three groups: thermoplastics; thermosets; and elastomers.

activities

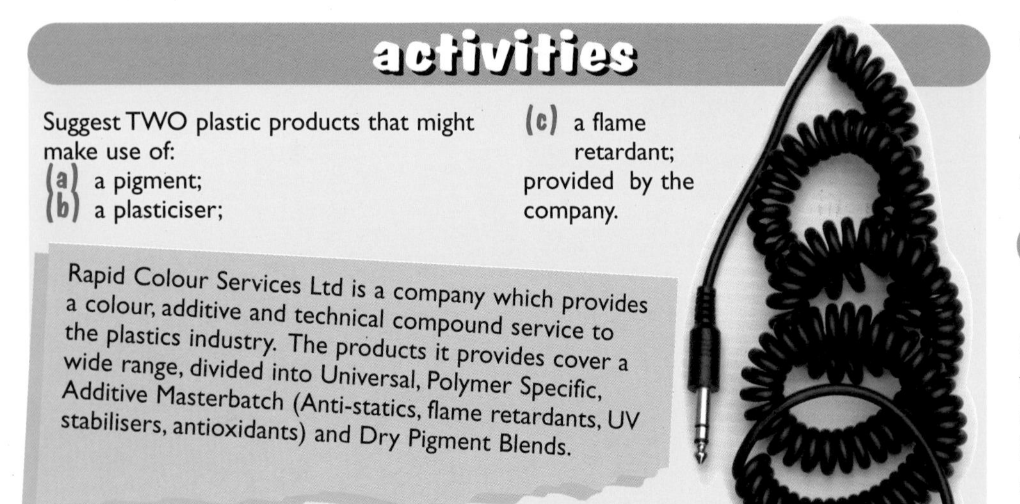

Suggest TWO plastic products that might make use of:
(a) a pigment;
(b) a plasticiser;
(c) a flame retardant;
provided by the company.

Rapid Colour Services Ltd is a company which provides a colour, additive and technical compound service to the plastics industry. The products it provides cover a wide range, divided into Universal, Polymer Specific, Additive Masterbatch (Anti-statics, flame retardants, UV stabilisers, antioxidants) and Dry Pigment Blends.

Source: adapted from NW Business to Business.

Thermoplastics

THERMOPLASTICS are made up from long chain polymers, joined together by weak chemical bonds as in Figure 2. When the plastic is softened by heat the weak bonds break, making the plastic 'semi-fluid' and able to be shaped. As the plastic cools, new weak bonds form across the chains, fixing the shape. Because they do not

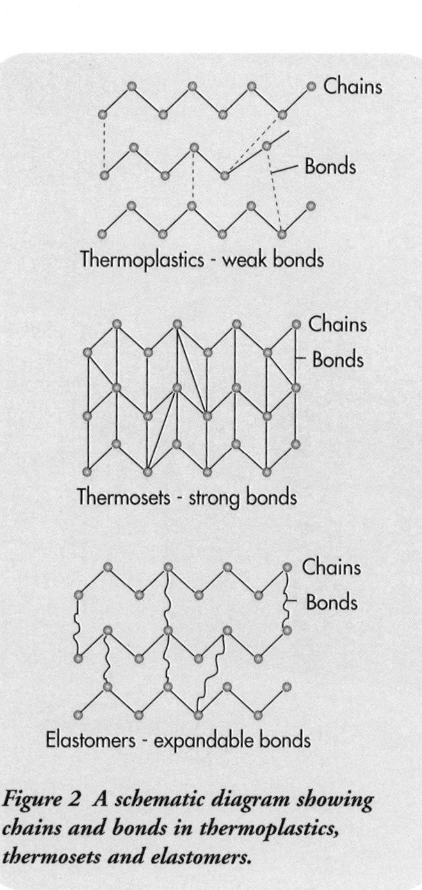

Figure 2 A schematic diagram showing chains and bonds in thermoplastics, thermosets and elastomers.

undergo a chemical reaction when formed this process can be repeated many times, making them recyclable. Excessive heat will permanently damage the chemical structure.

Possible uses for thermoplastics.

There is a wide range of thermoplastics, with different properties and uses.

- **Polyethylene (polythene)**. High density polyethylene (HDPE) is tough and can be blow moulded (bottles for storing household chemicals, eg bleach, shampoo), injection moulded (toys, buckets, bins and crates) and extruded (internal piping). Low density polyethylene (LDPE) is made into thin film (carrier bags, insulation around electrical wiring, squeezy bottles).
- **Acrylonitrile butadiene styrene** (ABS) is a tough, strong, scratch resistant plastic that resists heat and chemicals. It is injection moulded to make toy building blocks. It is also used to make kettles and housings for cameras, telephones and vacuum cleaners.
- **Polychloroethene/ Polyvinyl chloride** (PVC) can be 'plasticised' by different amounts to make a wide range of products (window frames, gutters and drains, 'disposable' pens and razor handles, bottles and credit cards). It is stiff, strong and chemical and weather resistant.
- General purpose solid **polystyrene** (**PS**) is used to make vending cups and model kits. It is light and transparent, but quite brittle. It is vulcanised to make high impact polystyrene (**HIPS**). This is often used in schools when vacuum forming (see unit 12) in thin sheets, which are cheap and easy to work with. Expanded polystyrene (**EPS**) is used as thermal insulation for packaging and food cartons. It is 90 per cent air.
- **Polypropylene** (**PP**) is versatile and flexible without breaking, and can withstand variable temperatures (yoghourt and margarine pots, crisp packets and sweet wrappers, garden furniture and car bumpers).
- **Polyamides** (**nylon**) are hard, tough and resists wear, but are not easy to join (fibres in textile products, combs).
- **Polyesters** are used as fibres in textiles and in cassette and video tape.
- **Polyethylene teryphthalate** (PET) is a clear, tough polyester (fizzy drinks bottles, baby bottles).
- **Polycarbonates** are used to make CD packaging, bus shelters and car lights. They have high strength, are transparent and are good resistors of heat and chemicals.
- **Polyurethane** can be rubbery, rigid or

activities

Children's toys which they can sit in or ride on outdoors can be made of HDPE.

1 **(a)** Make a list of the properties outdoor children's toys would need.
(b) Why might HDPE be a suitable plastic for making these toys?
(c) Suggest ONE other plastic that might be used in such toys. Give reasons for your choice.

Carry-on cabin cases are small enough so that luggage can be taken onto a plane. They fit the dimensions set by airline companies for the maximum in cabin sizes. The Delsey Hemisphere has a shell made out of tough polypropylene and a nylon cover. The Tumi Boarding Bag is made from 'Ballistic' nylon which is said to meet US military specifications and is guaranteed for life.

Source: adapted from The Sunday Times, 5.11..1995

2 **(a)** What materials are used in the manufacture of these carry-on cases?
(b) What properties do they have which make them suitable for case manufacture?

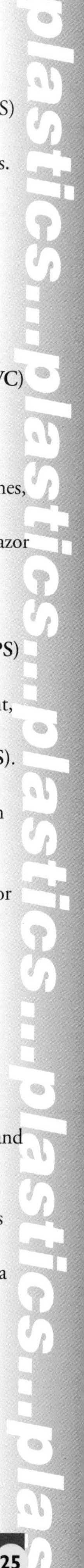

flexible. It is used to make car bumpers, shoes, trainers and furniture.

- **Polymethylmetacrylate (PMMA)** is better known as **acrylic** and often used as a glass substitute. Acrylic is strong and a good insulator, but scratches (street signs, baths and spectacles). It is suitable for vacuum forming, line bending and blow moulding.

Thermosets

THERMOSETS (or thermosetting plastics) are plastics which are converted into their final form by heat. Once set, they cannot be softened by further heating as they undergo a chemical change. They have strong chemical bonds that hold the long chains together. These make the thermosets heat resistant, but not recyclable. It is difficult for thermoset plastics products to be made by extrusion or injection moulding because they harden as soon as they are heated. Manufacturing methods used include compression moulding, laminating or casting. Examples of thermosetting plastics are:

- **urea formaldehyde (bakelite)** which is hard and brittle and a good insulator (electrical plugs, sockets, switches, toilet seats);
- **melamine formaldehyde (formica)** which is scratch, water and stain resistant and is used as a laminate in kitchen work surfaces. When plasticised it is called melamine (children's cups and dishes);
- **epoxy resins** which are mixed with a hardener and left to set. They can be used to make adhesives (eg araldite);
- **phenol** which is used to make saucepan handles.

Figure 3 Some of the properties of plastics.

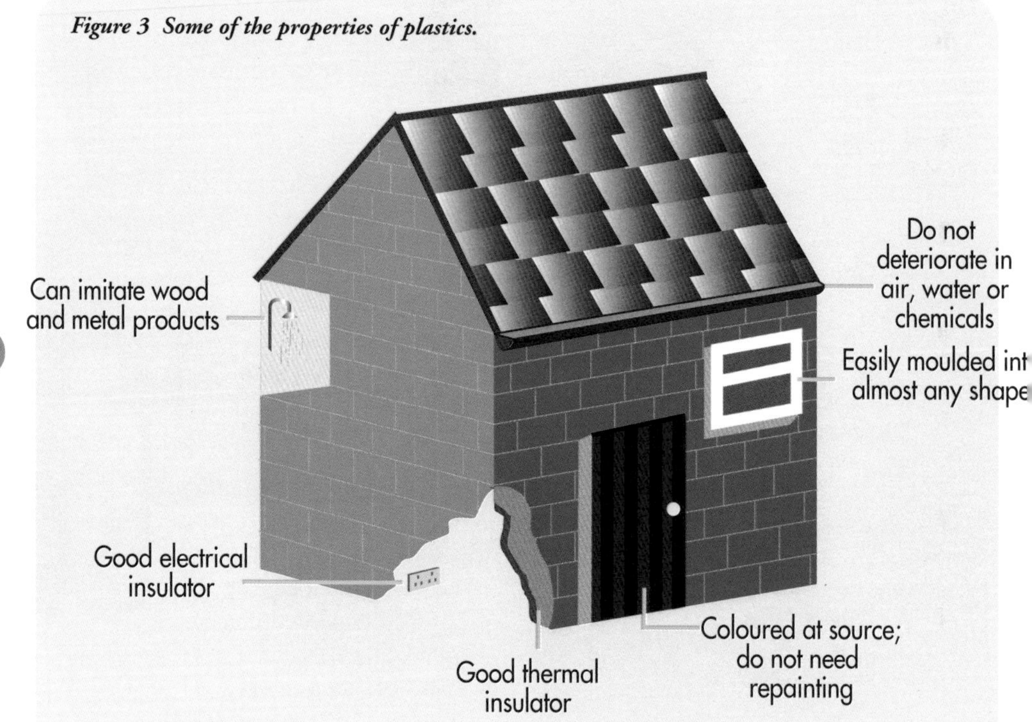

- **Polyester resins** which are combined with fibreglass to produce GRP (see later).

Elastomers

ELASTOMERS are a type of thermoset. The bonds between the chains are 'springy' giving them a rubbery quality. Natural rubber is an example. It can be vulcanised to make it rigid (ebonite). Rubber is useful as a shock absorber in footwear. **Latex** is a stretchy elastomer used to make surgical gloves. **Lycra** is an elastomer used to make stretchy clothing.

activities

Scapa Mouldings Ltd is a producer of expanded polystyrene (EPS). Typical products for which it provides packaging are televisions and their tubes, washing machines, heaters and crockery. EPS is also used in the production of bedding plant trays, insulation panels and child safety seats.

(a) Explain why EPS is a suitable material for: (i) the packaging of crockery; (ii) child safety seats.

(b) Suggest THREE other products that may be packaged in EPS.

Canoes can be made from GRP.

Composites

Glass fibre reinforced plastic (GRP) is an example of a **composite**, where materials are combined so that the composite material has the advantages of each.

The glass fibre provides tensile strength. It is used to re-inforce thermosets and can be obtained as strand, cord, cloth or tape. The resin makes the product waterproof and easy to mould when fluid. The glass fibre is shaped around a mould and a cold casting solution of polyester resin is poured over it to form a plastic 'matrix'.

GRP is used on body mouldings and panels of cars and televisions and on computer housings. It is also used to make fishing rods, canoes and surfboards. GRP reduces weight and is cheaper than metals or wood for these products.

Carbon fibres (graphite) were developed as a filament for lamps. The are made by treating textile fibres and can be wound as threads, ropes or a cloth. Using casting with a thermoset they can be moulded into any shape. They are more costly than glass fibres, but lighter and stronger. As a result they are used increasingly in the manufacture of sports equipment such as cycles, golf clubs and tennis racquets. When mixed with an epoxy resin and wound into a rope they are much lighter than steel cable for the construction industry. **Kevlar** is another fibre which is mixed with a resin and used in a variety of products, from canoes to bullet proof vests.

Properties of plastics

Plastics have a number of properties. These are shown in Figure 3. Their chemical structure gives plastic products a long shelf life. However, it also means that they are difficult to dispose of. Because they do not rot or corrode, they can remain as refuse for many years. If burnt, they produce black choking gases. When molten they are sticky and can cause severe burns.

Thermoplastics can be recycled by melting them down and reforming their shape, but their usefulness can become limited with frequent heating. Plastic production can itself be a pollutant. Oil spillages, coal 'slag heaps' and gaseous emissions from refineries can all cause damage to the environment.

To some people plastics represent the 'cheaper' end of the market as they do not possess the grain or texture of wood or the lustre of metal. However, because they can be coloured at source they offer a wide range of permanent colours. They can also be treated to look like wood or metal. For example, shower coils can be made to look metallic. Cosmetics holders can look as if they are made of chrome, silver or gold but may be made from plastic.

Commercial stock of materials

Plastics are available in many forms. Some are shown in Figure 4 along with an example of a plastic which comes in that form.

The cost of materials must be taken

activities

The following information relates to plastic products. In each case:

(a) explain whether the plastic is a thermoplastic, a thermoset or a composite;

(b) suggest why the plastic mentioned should be suitable for the product.

- Lego manufactures Lego and Duplo toys for children from ABS using injection moulding techniques.
- Plastimo manufactures family canoes that can withstand 'white water punishment' from fibreglass and Kevlar.
- The Mayborn group manufactures melamine plates and bowls as own-label suppliers to Mothercare and Boots.

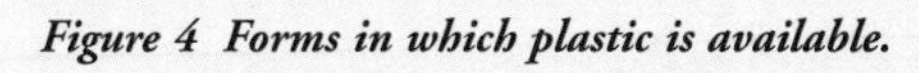

Figure 4 Forms in which plastic is available.

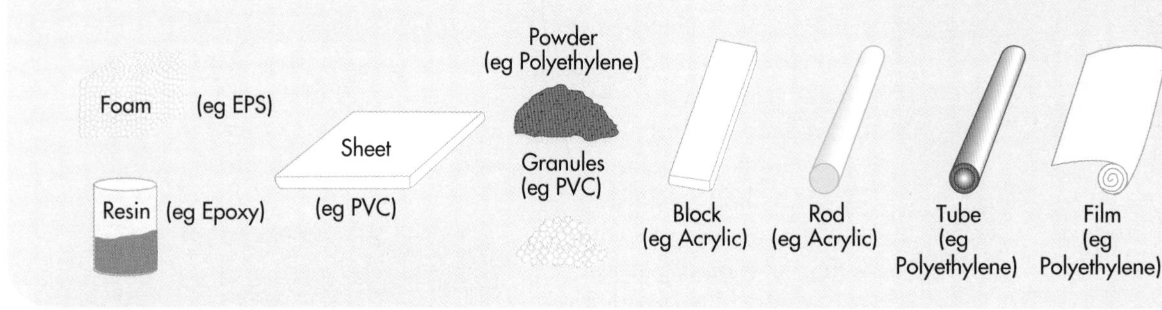

into account when manufacturing products (see unit 25). The relative prices of plastics will change over time in reaction to factors such as the cost of production, quality, size and shape and availability.

Recycling

It is often difficult to distinguish between one type of plastic and another just by looking at them or touching them. This poses a problem when it comes to recycling. A code has been devised to help sort out plastics materials for recycling, as shown in Figure 5.

Figure 5 Classification of plastics for recycling.

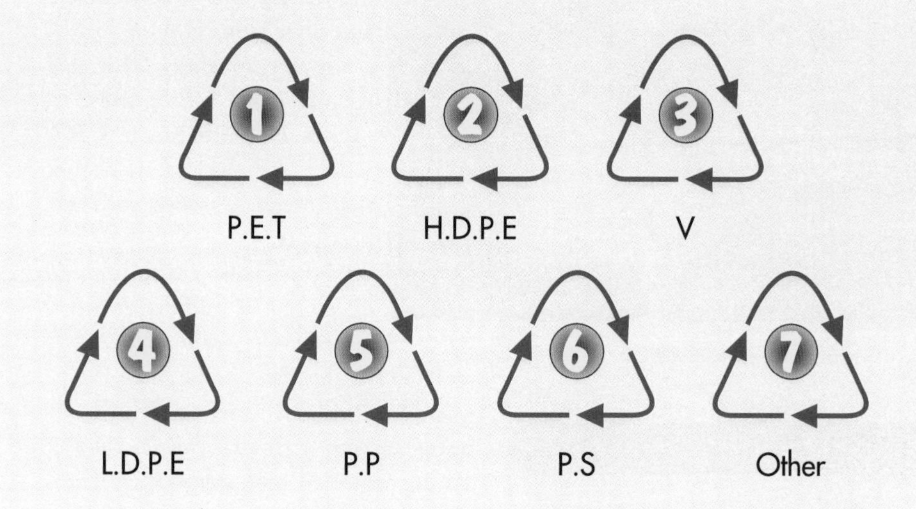

activities

Look at the three plastic products.

(a) List the characteristics of **plastic** that make it a suitable material to use in the manufacture of each product.

(b) Suggest ONE plastic material which may be used to manufacture window frames. Explain why that material is suitable.

Desk tidy.

Swimming pool.

Window frame.

Plastics products are now printed with this code. There are seven numbers - six for the six most common plastics in use and the seventh for all other less common plastics.

A wide range of plastics are currently available and new plastics are likely to be developed in future. Some of these plastics are being designed with the pollution hazard that ordinary plastics carry very much in mind. For example, many new plastics being produced are BIODEGRADABLE, which reduces disposal and environmental problems associated with plastics (see unit 25).

Synthetic plastics - **plastics which are produced artificially (by chemical reaction - synthesis).**
Monomers - **small molecules contained in separated parts of raw materials, such as oil.**
Polymers - **long molecular chains formed from small molecules contained in raw materials.**
Thermoplastics - **plastics which can be softened by heat and reshaped, but harden again when cool; suitable for recycling.**
Thermosets - **plastics which will not soften when reheated.**
Elastomers - **a type of thermoset often used to make stretchy products.**
Biodegradable - **able to 'rot' away into harmless products by the action of living micro-organisms.**

activities

1 Read the information below about ICI plc.
(a) Draw a diagram of the recycling code that will be contained on drinks bottles made from ICI polyester.
(b) Why is this plastic suitable for babies' bottles?
(c) Explain whether you think the benefits of recycled plastic products outweigh the costs for ICI.

ICI (Imperial Chemicals Industries) PLC is a manufacturer of a wide variety of chemicals related products. These include paint, materials and industrial chemicals. The company has an active environmental policy which seeks to 'ensure that (our) products are made - and can be used, stored and disposed of - in a responsible way.' Examples of this policy can be seen:

Products such as soft drinks bottles and containers are made from PET.

- in its production of PET, a polyester used for soft drinks bottles and containers which is 'probably the most recycled plastic in the world'. ICI participates in PET collection schemes;
- in a recovery service, introduced for customers who buy perspex acrylic sheets. Off-cuts of perspex are collected and recycled using ICI's technology to produce new material.

Perspex can be recycled by ICI's unique technology.

Source: ICI.

Car parts are one of the world's largest users of recycled plastic. Plastic bottles are recycled into luggage racks and door padding. Telephone and computer housings become grilles. The bottles or telephone housings are cleaned up, ground down into flakes and reprocessed into pellets. These are then moulded into new shapes. Wheel arches on the Ford Mondeo, for example, are made from recycled polypropylene.

Source: adapted from The Times, 4.3.1995.

2 Read the information above.
(a) Suggest THREE parts of a car that may be made from recycled plastic.
(b) Explain how plastics are recycled.
(c) What type of plastics are recycled? Explain why they are suitable.

CENTURION SAFETY PRODUCTS

Centurion Safety Products is a business which produces safety products. One of its activities is the design and manufacture of cycle helmets. They are manufactured in a variety of sizes, styles and colours. The Sahara range is aimed at children and teenagers. The Vario Pro range is aimed mainly at the teenage and adult markets. The main features of these ranges are shown across the page.

Cycle helmets manufactured by Centurion Safety Products are designed and built to conform to safety standards.

- The ANSI Z790 is a US safety standard which involves a test against a flat and a hemispherical shaped surface.
- Snell tests are carried out by an independent international testing organisation set up after Peter Snell, the motor racer, was killed in an accident. A Snell 90 sticker means that products have passed impact tests carried out on flat and hemispherical surfaces. A Snell 95 sticker, from September 1995, shows that products have also passed a kerbstone test.
- A CE standard shows that a product conforms with safety standards agreed across the European Union. It is intended for trading standards officers rather than a mark of quality for consumers.
- In 1996 a draft European standard was proposed which is likely to replace national standards within 2 years.

Cycle helmets are designed so that in a crash the polystyrene inside a helmet fractures to absorb the shock. People involved in an accident should throw away the helmet and buy a new one even if there are no cracks on the outer shell.

Other features that should be considered when choosing a helmet include the ventilation given by the vents and the internal groove channels, the comfort and fit of the helmet, the helmet's weight, the comfort and fit of the strap and the design, colour and price.

Source: adapted from Centurion Safety Products and Which?, March 1995.

- **Tough expanded polystyrene liner with a hard-wearing PVC outer shell.**
- **Rear reflector for high visibility.**
- **Adult styling to suit children up to their teens.**
- **Available in four colour combinations**

Type: Micro Shell **Colours:** Palm Green, Oasis Blue, Mirage Red, Sunset Purple **Sizes:** XS (480-520mm), S(510-550mm), M (540-580mm) **Weight:** 270g **Standards:** CE, Snell, ANSI

- **"Windrush" ventilation system forces air across your head.**
- **Wild, state of the art graphics.**
- **Lexan® outer shell - this polycarbonate material is bonded to the inner liner for optimum performance.**

Type: Micro Shell **Colours:** Glacier (blue), Volcano (red) **Sizes:** S/M (550-590mm), M/L (580-620mm) **Weight:** 290g **Standards:** CE, Snell, ANSI

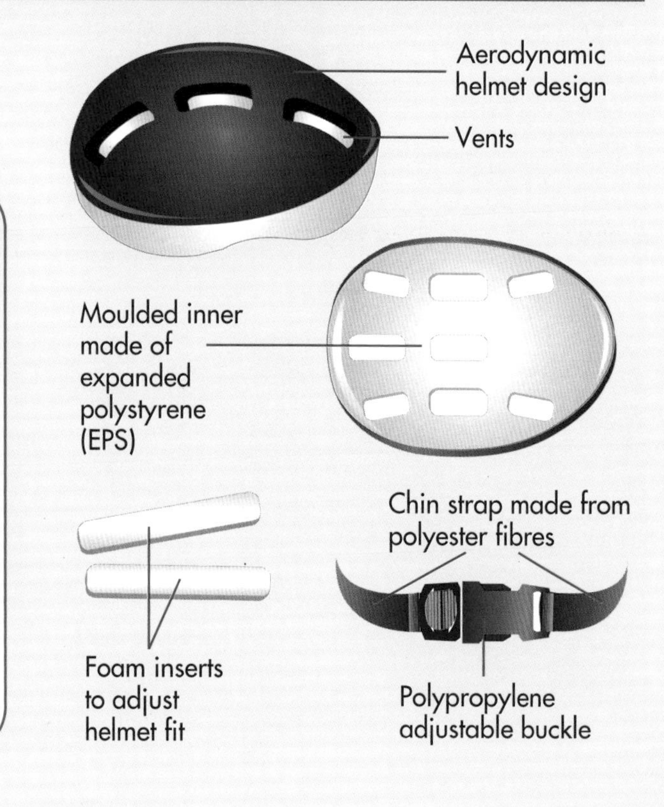

Questions

(a) Identify the plastics used in making cycle helmets.
Classify each plastic as either a thermoplastic, a thermoset or an elastomer.

(b) Explain, in terms of safety, why:
  (i) a helmet shell is made out of PVC or polycarbonate;
  (ii) the inner liner is made from EPS;
  (iii) the strap is made from polyester;
  (iv) the buckle is made from polypropylene.

(c) (i) What tests are carried out to evaluate the safety of helmets?
  (ii) Why might there be a conflict between ventilation and safety features for a helmet manufacturer?

(d) List THREE design features of a cycle helmet. Explain why plastics are suitable materials to use to incorporate such design features in helmets.

(e) Explain THREE differences between the Sahara and Vario Pro designs. What are the advantages of these to a cyclist?

case study MAILBOX INTERNATIONAL LTD

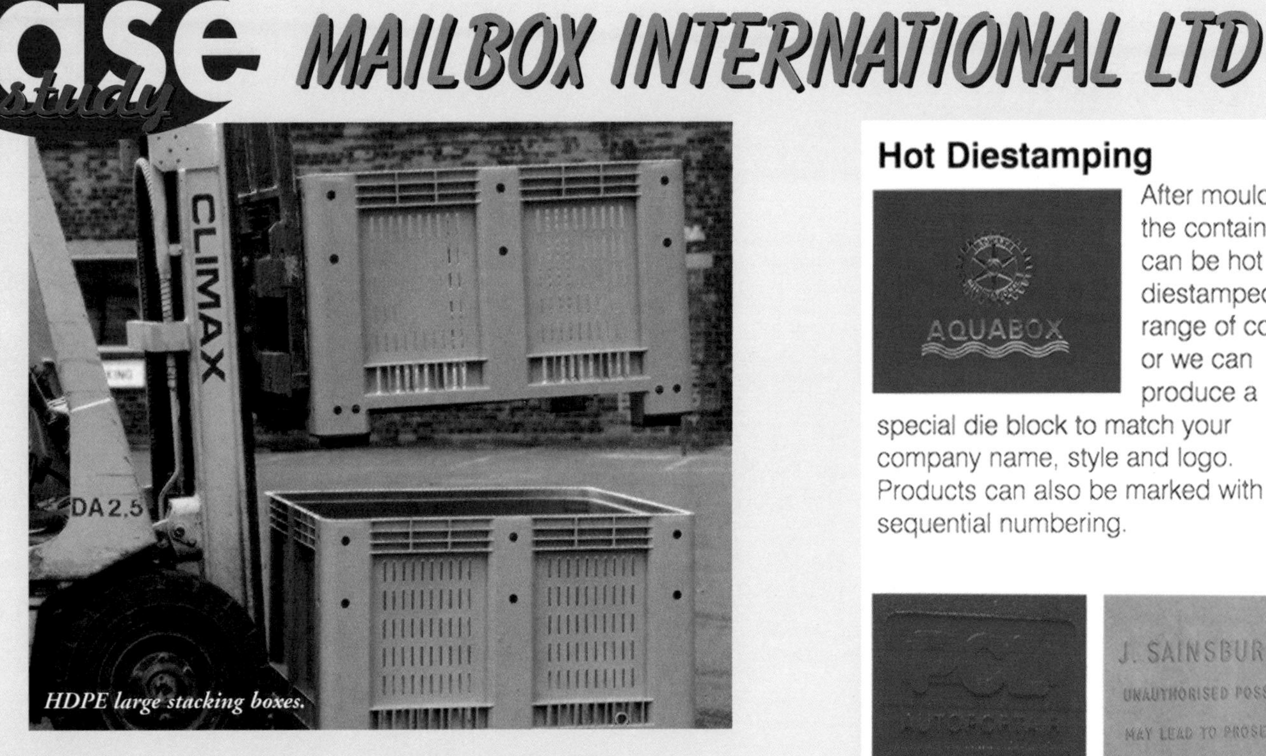

HDPE large stacking boxes.

Mailbox International Ltd specialises in manufacturing plastic, storage, materials handling, logistics, environmental and healthcare products.

Mailbox products are available by mail order from a standard range of over 700 products held in stock and despatched by express delivery. These include storage containers, stack bin nests, logistics boxes, plastic pallets, trucks and airtight bins. The company offers the facilities of hot die stamping or moulded-in information on its products which can contain specialist logos or messages. Another important range of products is the food approved range. The models in this range are suitable for the handling of fish, poultry, dairy products, confectionery and fresh baked items.

Where customers have a storage or handling problem, technical sales staff are able to carry out a site survey. The company can then offer the most effective solution, tailor made to suit the needs of the customer, by making use of its CAD research and development facilities. Products are then manufactured using injection moulding processes.

Other industries which use its plastic products are hospitals, pharmaceuticals, cosmetics, automobile manufacturers, chemical companies and service industries.

Polypropylene ingredient scoops.

Source: Mailbox International Limited.

Hot Diestamping

After moulding, the containers can be hot diestamped in a range of colours, or we can produce a special die block to match your company name, style and logo. Products can also be marked with sequential numbering.

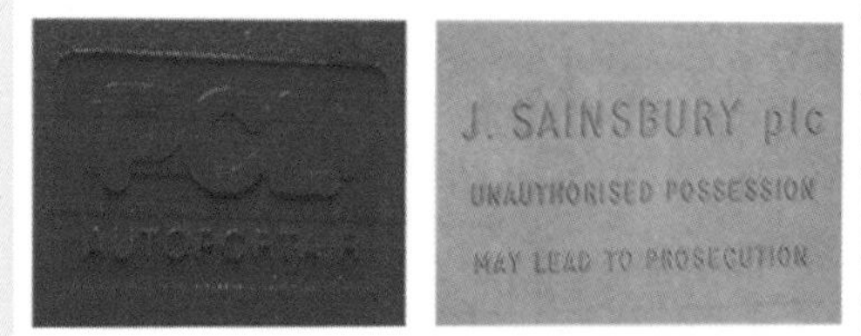

Moulded in Information

On many large orders for injection and rotational mouldings, at the manufacturing stage an engraved steel plate can be fitted into the moulding tool. The name, logo or message is permanently moulded in and is therefore the same colour as the product.

Moulding in Graphics

Logos and names can be moulded into our rotational moulded product range, at the manufacturing stage, in various colours. This method of identification is extremely durable and hardwearing.

Questions

(a) Identify TWO possible uses for each of the three plastic products shown here.

(b) What production process is used to manufacture buckets and crates?

(c) What properties might plastic products have which make them suitable for:
- (i) express delivery;
- (ii) the food industry;
- (iii) hospitals?

(d) Suggest reasons why HDPE, polypropylene and PVC are used to make the products shown here.

(e) Why might plastic be suitable for tailoring products to customers' needs? Suggest THREE ways in which Mailbox International Ltd might do this.

PVC floor matting.

unit

6 Metal

Metals manufacture

Perhaps more than any other material, metals have shaped our history. Stone age people used flint for weapon heads and for tools. The discovery of copper led to stronger weapons and the manufacture of armour. Mixing copper with tin produced bronze alloy weapons. Around 1500 BC, smelting techniques were developed to extract iron. Iron weapons and tools were stronger than those made from either copper or bronze. The discovery of electricity in the early 19th Century allowed metals such as aluminium and zinc to be extracted.

Metal-bearing rocks are called ORES. These are mined or quarried from the earth's surface. Ores contain metal compounds such as oxides and sulphides. In the past, rocks were placed around wooden fires to keep the embers in place. This created an environment of high temperatures, charcoal as the wood burnt and oxygen, which caused metal compounds to undergo chemical reactions, releasing the metal as a molten liquid.

Metals are obtained in much the same way today. The process is called SMELTING. The raw ore is mixed with charcoal and other chemicals, and air is blown into a furnace (to provide oxygen). The molten metal trickles from the foot of the furnace and can be cast or extruded (see unit 12) into shapes. The more reactive the metal the higher the temperature needed to extract it from its ore. Copper needs around 1100°C but iron requires around 1 500°C. A metal like aluminium cannot be extracted by smelting in a charcoal furnace. It is dissolved in a 'cryolite solution' and electrolysed (electricity is passed through) at a temperature of around 650°C. A few metals can be mined from the earth as pure metals. These include gold and some small amounts of copper and silver.

Figure 1 Common products made from metal.

activities

(a) Which of the products here are likely to be made from: (i) high (carbon) steel; (ii) mild steel; (iii) stainless steel; (iv) wrought iron?

(b) Suggest why each product is made from that metal.

(c) Suggest TWO other products that might be made from each. Explain why the metal is suitable for these products.

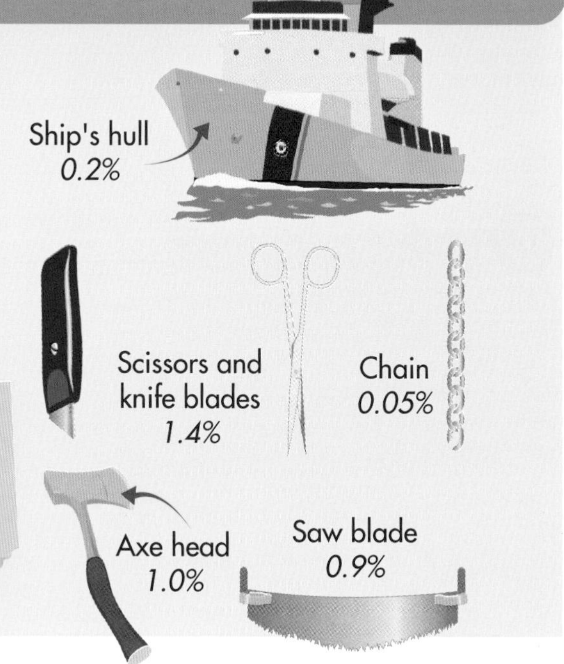

The drawings show metal products. The figures show the percentages of carbon in each metal.

Source: adapted from Metals in the Service of Man, A. Street and W. Alexander, Penguin.

Ferrous metals

FERROUS METALS are those which are iron based. They contain iron and carbon in varying amounts. As iron is extracted from its ore in a furnace it contains a relatively high amount of carbon, which makes the iron very hard, but very brittle. This iron is called **cast iron**. It resists compression but may break if dropped, hit or stretched. It is used to make car brake drums, grids and manhole covers. Cast iron has 4% carbon content.

Further heating of iron while blowing oxygen over it at high pressure reduces the carbon content. This is how **steel** is made. There are many different grades of steel depending on the carbon content.

- **High carbon steel** (tool steel) contains 0.6-1.5% carbon. It is very hard and is used to make tools such as metalwork files, saw blades and lathe tools.
- **Medium carbon steel** contains 0.4-0.6% carbon.
- **Mild steel** is very tough, can be bent or twisted and can resist strong impacts without breaking. It is easy to weld (see unit 13). Mild steel is used to make bodies of washing machines, construction girders, tubing and nuts, bolts and nails. It contains between 0.15% and 0.35% carbon.
- **Stainless steel** contains around 1% carbon. It also contains other metals, mainly chromium. There are over 200 types of stainless steel. They contain a minimum of 11% chromium and must also contain nickel. Manganese is another metal often included. Stainless steel is often used to make medical equipment, kitchen surfaces and pots and pans as it resists scratching, corrosion and biofouling (see unit 9).

Stainless steel is used for industrial kitchen surfaces.

Wrought iron is the most pure iron, containing few imperfections. It is difficult to cast (see unit 12), although it makes excellent material for forge work because it is tough. It has less than 0.1% carbon. It is used for gates or railings.

Non-ferrous metals and alloys

NON-FERROUS METALS do not contain iron. There are many different metals that fall into this group.

Copper Copper is strong and resists wear and shock. It is ductile and malleable (see unit 7) and can be joined easily by hard or soft soldering or welding. It is an excellent conductor of heat and can be used to make the underside of pots and pans to help disperse heat quickly. Copper suspended in a liquid is used in metallic paint. Over half of all copper produced is used in the electrical industry. It is used extensively in electrical wiring, although it is being replaced by multi-fibre optics in telecommunications systems. Copper wire is wound to make transformers, motors and dynamos. Copper is also used to carry water and gas. It resists corrosion well and can be easily shaped to make pipes. It also resists 'biofouling', so that bacteria finds it difficult to grow. In many situations copper is being replaced by cheaper plastic piping.

Brass and aluminium products.

Brass Brass is an ALLOY of copper. Alloys are materials composed of a mixture of metals or a metal and a non-metal intermixed. Metal alloys have certain advantages. The alloy may contain the properties of two metals or other elements. For example, brass is made of copper (which is malleable, resists corrosion and is a good conductor of electricity) and zinc (which is hard but brittle).

General purpose brass contains 60% copper and 40% zinc. However, there are many different 'brasses' depending on the ratio of the two in the mixture. Brasses with more than 36% zinc are less workable than their counterparts at room temperature, but they become 'plastic' when heated (see unit 7). They can be

activities

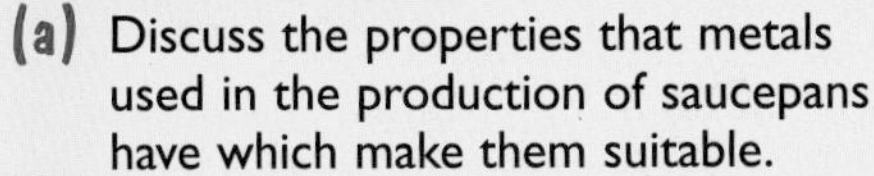

(a) Discuss the properties that metals used in the production of saucepans have which make them suitable.

(b) Suggest THREE other products that might make use of copper to carry out the same function as in a saucepan.

Saucepans can be made from stainless steel with a copper bottom.

shaped by hot rolling, extruding, hot stamping and casting (see unit 12). Because they are strong and resist corrosion, brasses are used to make outside door parts like letter boxes. They are also used to make electrical components (plugs, sockets etc.). Other alloys of copper include bronze (copper and tin), gunmetal (copper, tin and zinc and phosphor bronze (copper, tin and phosphorous).

Aluminium Pure aluminium is malleable and ductile, but has a low tensile strength, (eg aluminium foil). To improve its strength it is usually alloyed with copper or magnesium. Because it resists corrosion it is used extensively outdoors, in satellite dishes and window frames for example.

Aluminium is a very light metal. It has a density of only 2.7 kg/m^3 which is a third that of steel or copper. It is a good conductor of electricity and being lighter and cheaper than copper it is used to make overhead cables once it is reinforced with steel. This means fewer pylons are needed for support.

Aluminium alloys are easy to work. They can be rolled, machined, cast, welded, drawn, pressed and extruded (see unit 12). Aluminium is one of only a few metals that can be extruded, allowing it to be made into a variety of intricate shapes, such as door frames and carpet treads.

Aluminium alloys are used in the manufacture of commercial aircraft. The body of the aircraft is made up from honeycombed aluminium pads, as are boats, racing cars, skis and other sports products.

Aluminium alloys are used for a variety of parts on motor cars including wheels, bumpers and cylinder heads as well as braking and transmission systems. They have helped to reduce fuel consumption dramatically. Aluminium alloys are also used in the manufacture of ships and buildings because they are both lightweight and durable. They place less stress on structures such as walkways, bridges and helicopter decks than other metals. Much of the structure of oil rigs is now made from aluminium alloys.

Figure 1 Standard sizes and shapes.

Round rod or bar From 3mm
Square From 5mm
Flat From 6mm From 1.6mm
Hexagon From 6mm
Sheet From 0.6mm
Round Tube From 5mm
Square tube From 12mm
Retangular tube From 25 x 12mm
Angle
Corrugated sheet
Perforated sheet

activities

1 (a) Explain why aluminium alloy might be a suitable material for the production of mountaineering poles.

(b) Suggest THREE other products that may be made from aluminium alloy for outside use.

Aluminium alloy poles weighing less than 13 ounces on a 16 mile walk can reduce stress on the knees, ankles and hips by almost 375 tonnes. The poles are made in three sections of tough aluminium, which telescope for convenience. They extend to ski-stick length and have wrist straps. It is suggested that two poles are used when walking to prevent a 'droop' developing.

Source: adapted from The Times, 2.9.1995.

2 (a) Explain how (i) the metals used and (ii) the production processes of a car would change if the Maxx was built.

(b) Suggest why aluminium is suited to the new car.

(c) Is the new car likely to be mass produced? Explain your answer.

At the March 1995 Geneva Motor Show General Motors exhibited a car that could change with its owner's lifestyle. The concept model, called the Maxx, has a rigid cage made of extruded aluminium sections welded together. Aluminium sections can then be clipped or bolted to the cage. This enables the car to be changed easily from a hatchback to a saloon to an open air buggy. The new process would replace the use of pressed steel panels and allow the car to be tailored to the customer's wishes as a variety of different shapes to the body and the car parts.

Source: adapted from the Sunday Times, 23.4.1995.

About 150,000 million aluminium cans are produced each year. They weigh less than their steel counterparts and also less than glass bottles. The material used in each can is around 0.3mm thick.

Lead Lead is a metal that was once in common use for plumbing, roof flashing and car batteries. It has been replaced by copper, alloys and plastics in many cases, although it is still used in car batteries. Lead is a soft, malleable metal. It is an accumulative poison.

Tin Tin was used in the past to make brass. Today it is used mainly as an addition to alloys to increase their strength and improve their resistance to corrosion, as well as changing their appearance. Tinplate is not tin but steel coated with a thin protective layer of tin. Other alloys that contain tin are pewter (tin, copper and antimony), which was once used to make cups and plates, and soft solder (tin and lead) which is used to join electrical components.

Zinc Zinc is usually used to coat steel because of its resistance to corrosion. Steel coated with zinc is said to be galvanised. Zinc is also used in the manufacture of protective paints.

Commercial stock of metals

Manufacturers of metal products can purchase materials in a number of **standard** shapes and sizes, although larger sizes can be made. Figure 1 shows some of the most common shapes. Being able to select from standard sizes and shapes will save a manufacturer time and also guarantees that products will be of uniform size. It also helps when designing products as many parts conform to standard sizes.

The relative prices of one metal compared to another will depend on:

- production costs;
- quality;
- size;
- shape;
- availability.

Metal treatment in an annealing furnace.

Properties of metals

All metals have a crystalline structure. This means that they are made up of crystals. A metal's surface appears smooth and many are shiny and highly polished. However, when looked at under a strong microscope the surface has a grain which occurs because of the layering of the metal crystals. The size of the grain depends upon:

- the speed at which the metal has been solidified (the faster the cooling, the smaller the grain);
- the composition of the metal (eg the impurities, the alloys);
- any working or further heat treatment given to the metal.

Changing the properties of metals

If a metal is cold worked (see unit 12), by hammering or rolling, its grain structure becomes deformed and stresses develop along the grain. This makes the metal hard and less ductile. This process is called WORK HARDENING. If the metal is over-worked it will crack. To make sure this does not happen a metal can be ANNEALED. The metal is

activities

(a) Suggest the most suitable form in which the metal might be purchased for the manufacture of a stand. Explain your answer.

(b) What metals might be used in its manufacture? Explain your answer.

Top Stone is a business that manufactures portable, self-assembly display stands. The stands can be made to the required size of the customer, for example 5 foot and 6 foot lengths. The construction has a metal frame and plastic or wooden boards are placed on the stand to provide display space for books or magazines. It is assembled by fitting the circular ends of its component parts into each other. The tension of the structure and the weight of the books provides stability.

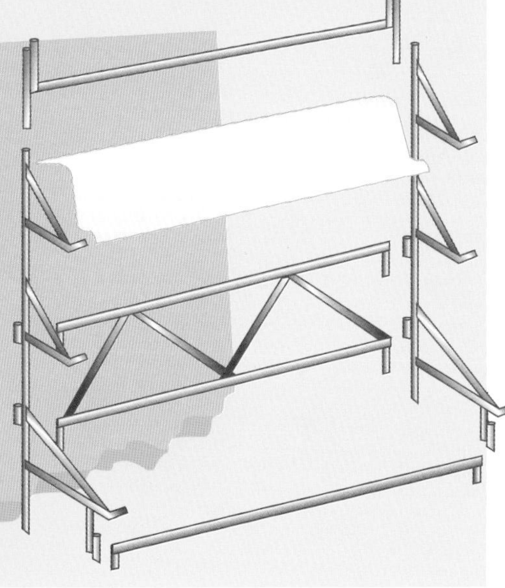

Table 1 Annealing.

Metal	Copper	Aluminium	Brass	Steel
Change in colour when heated	Cherry red	No change in colour	Dull red	Bright red
Process	Heated and then quenched in water	• Coat in soap • Heat slowly • When soap blackens correct annealing temperature reached	Heated then left to cool naturally	Heated and left to soak in heat for a few minutes

heated to a particular annealing temperature (each metal has its own annealing temperature). It is then allowed to cool very slowly, which removes the stresses in the grain. Different metals are annealed in different ways, as in Table 1. **Normalising** is a type of annealing, where a metal is heated to just below its softest state. This refines the grain better than annealing.

If carbon steel is heated to above 750°C and cooled rapidly in cold water or oil (**quenching**), the metal becomes hard but very brittle. This is called HARDENING. TEMPERING is used to make an already hardened but brittle piece of steel tougher. The steel is heated gently until it reaches between 230-300°C. Lower temperatures produce a hard steel that is not very shock resistant. Higher temperatures make the steel less hard, but more resistant to shock as shown in Figure 2. Once the correct temperature has been reached the steel is quenched. It is usually steels that are hardened and tempered and the two processes are carried out sequentially.

Figure 2 Tempering.

Colour	Temperature and uses
Blue	295°C Springs, screwdrivers, spanners, sawblades, needles
Purple	270°C Chisels, scissors, axe head
Red/ Brown	260°C Drill bits, hammer heads
Dark Yellow	245°C Taps and dies, milling cutters
Light Yellow	230°C Scribers, lathe tools

A complete piece of metal can be hardened and tempered or just parts of it.

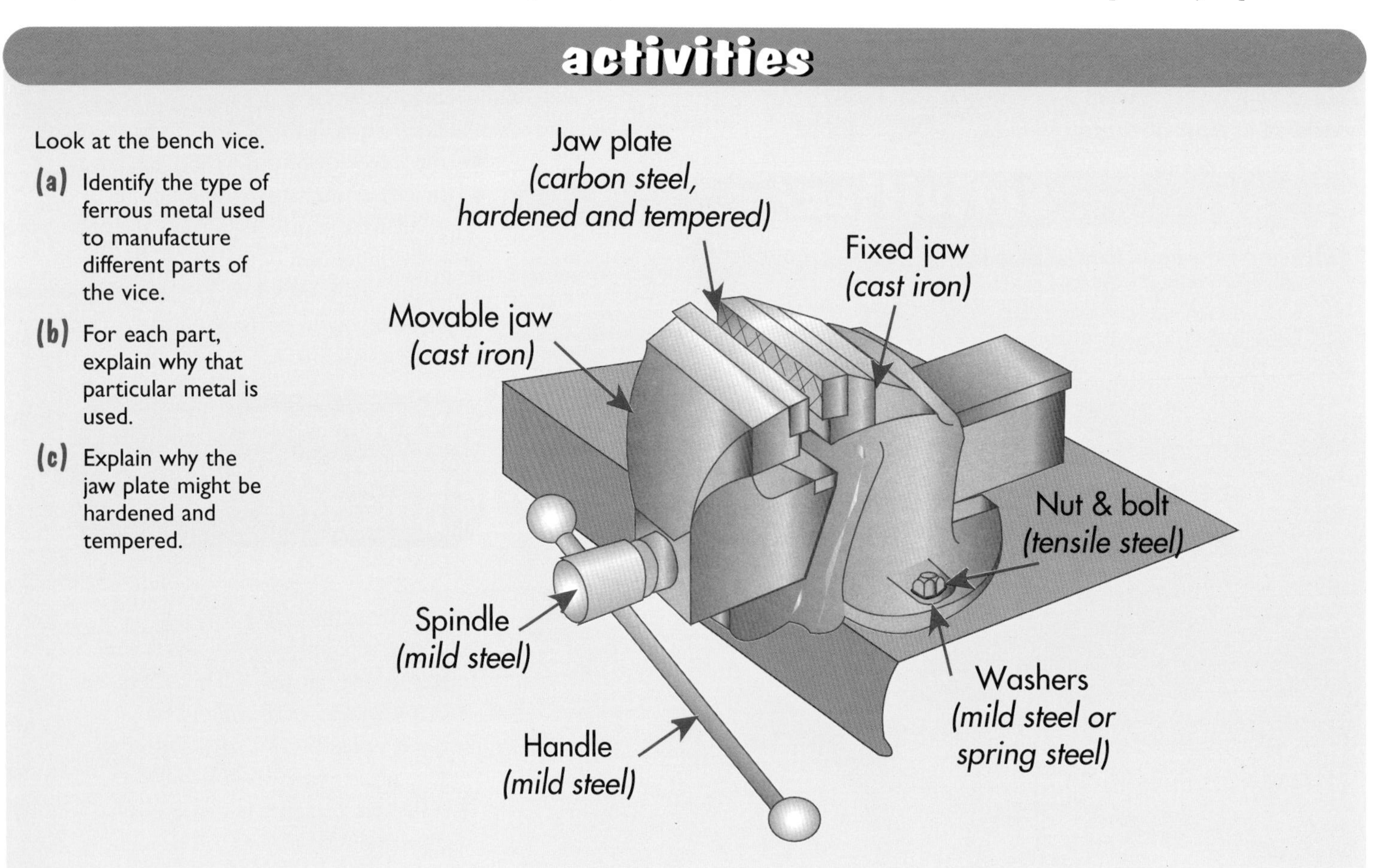

Look at the bench vice.

(a) Identify the type of ferrous metal used to manufacture different parts of the vice.

(b) For each part, explain why that particular metal is used.

(c) Explain why the jaw plate might be hardened and tempered.

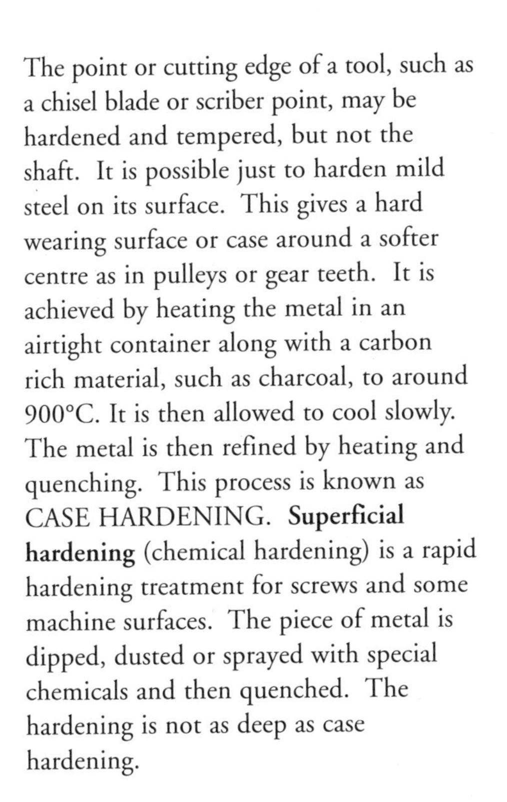

The point or cutting edge of a tool, such as a chisel blade or scriber point, may be hardened and tempered, but not the shaft. It is possible just to harden mild steel on its surface. This gives a hard wearing surface or case around a softer centre as in pulleys or gear teeth. It is achieved by heating the metal in an airtight container along with a carbon rich material, such as charcoal, to around 900°C. It is then allowed to cool slowly. The metal is then refined by heating and quenching. This process is known as CASE HARDENING. **Superficial hardening** (chemical hardening) is a rapid hardening treatment for screws and some machine surfaces. The piece of metal is dipped, dusted or sprayed with special chemicals and then quenched. The hardening is not as deep as case hardening.

Ore - **Raw rock from which metal is obtained.**
Smelting - **combination of heat, oxygen and a reducing agent (carbon) to extract ore.**
Ferrous metals - **metals that contain iron.**
Non-ferrous metals - **metals that contain no iron.**
Alloys - **a mixture of two or more metals.**
Work hardening - **the toughening of metal as it is worked, eg hammering and bending.**
Annealing - **heating of metals to a required temperature, holding the temperature and then slow cooling.**
Hardening - **heating carbon steel to just below its melting point and cooling rapidly.**
Tempering - **using heat at the correct temperature to make already hardened steel tougher.**
Case hardening - **hardening just the surface of mild steel.**

Recycling

Metal ores are mined either by blasting underground or quarrying near to the surface, which can lead to environmental problems. Iron extraction from blast furnaces and other metal extraction processes also demand a lot of energy, a great deal of which is lost as heat to the surroundings (see unit 25).

These problems and the high cost of extracting metals mean that recycling is becoming increasingly important. Today the 'scrap metal industry' has a vital role to play in the provision of metals for the future. Automated disassembly lines for recycling of metal parts for cars are coming ever closer.

At present vehicles are collected, sorted and shredded, and then materials are collected from them.

It takes 95% less energy to recycle aluminium cans than it does to produce new cans from aluminium ore. It is possible that future cans will be made from recycled material. Collection points at supermarkets, for example, have a vital part to play in this process. Stainless steel can be made up from as much as 70% recycled material. Recycled copper can be refined to be as pure as new. Copper and its alloys have a high 'scrap' value as they are relatively easy to recycle.

activities

a) What metals are used to make aerosol cans?
b) Why are aerosol cans becoming more environmentally friendly?
c) What advantages of recycling are suggested by the article?

Manufacturers constantly work to make spray cans more environmentally friendly. All aerosol cans can be recycled. Cans are made from tinplate or aluminium. A quarter of every tinplate can is made from recycled steel and some 100 million steel aerosol cans are recovered for recycling each year. Around 150 million aerosol products come in aluminium cans, but recycling can be tricky as they do not stick to magnets used in the recycling process.

In 1994 the 6 main aluminium producers in the EU, the US, Russia, Australia, Canada and Norway signed an agreement to reduce production of aluminium over the next 2 years, which pushed up prices.

Source: adapted from The Times, 12.9.1995; The Observer, 11.6.1995.

BENDER FORREST LIMITED

Bender Forrest Limited is a manufacturer of components from stainless steel. Stainless steel is a relatively 'new' material, first invented in the 1950s, which is now replacing older materials. It is five times more expensive than mild carbon steel. There are 2 grades of stainless steel - 304 used mainly for cutlery (knives, forks etc.) and 316 used for construction. The company uses 316 to manufacture pipes, tanks and fabrications (doors, valves) for:

- swimming pools;
- swimming pool water guns and jets;
- sewerage works;
- the paper industry;
- most industries using chemicals;
- products in photographic laboratories.

Materials that come into contact with the stainless steel products include clean and dirty water, starch and paper pulp. Stainless steel is used because it:

- is corrosion resistant;
- has a life expectancy between 20 years and 500 years;
- is possible to make thinner and lighter products from stainless steel than from ductile iron which was previously used for these products. This makes large engineering jobs far easier and reduces the amount of heavy equipment required, saving on costs.

Material is bought in a number of forms. These include:

- flat sheet which can be rolled to form a circular tank or used for the sides of tanks and doors;
- tube which is used for pipes or small tanks;
- flat bar and angle bar which are used for stiffening of sheets and for making frames and brackets;
- channels and rods, also used for reinforcement.

Source: Peter Downes, Peter Howcroft - Bender Forrest Limited.

Sizes of metal used by Bender Forrest Limited

Bar
Smallest 25 mm x 6 mm x 4 metres length
Largest 150 mm x 40 mm x 4 metres length

Angle
Smallest 25 mm x 25 mm x 3 or 4 mm thick x 6 metres length
Largest 100mm x 100 mm x 10 mm thick x 6 metres length

Sheet
Smallest 1.5 mm thick x 4 metres x 2 metres
Largest 12 mm thick x 8 metres x 2 metres

Tube
Smallest 25 mm bore x 1.5 mm thickness x 6 metres length
Largest 800 mm bore x 4 mm thick x 6 metres length

Cutting stainless steel sheets.

Drilling stainless steel tubes.

Welding sheets to make tanks and doors.

Finished tubes for joining pipes.

Questions

(a) What are the two different types of stainless steel?

(b) Suggest THREE products that are made from each type.

(c) In what forms is stainless steel produced?

(d) What products might Bender Forrest Limited manufacture from stainless steel: (i) sheet; (ii) tube?

(e) If stainless steel is 5 times more expensive than mild carbon steel, explain why it might be preferred for use in a photographic laboratory or a swimming pool. State as many reasons as possible.

Euroquipment is a supplier of factory and warehouse equipment. Transport and lifting equipment sold by the company includes:

- pallet trucks with pump action for carrying heavy goods in warehouses and factories;
- stackers for loading packaging onto shelves;
- trolleys for carrying parcels over steps.

The company also supplies a variety of ladders and steps. These include:

- industrial telescopic, sectional, extending and platform ladders;
- mobile and stationary safety steps.

Three of the company's products are shown here.

Source: Euroquipment.

Electronic hydraulic stackers. 1 000kg lifting capacity. Suitable for moving products on pallets. Manufactured throughout from high strength steel.

Medium duty steps. Easy to move and lock for extra safety. Highly visible colour for identification in factories. Platform height from 0.69m to 3.45m. Steel frame construction.

Platform steps fitted with hinge locking stays. Size varies from 0.75m to 3.9m. Made from extruded aluminium.

Questions

(a) Suggest suitable forms in which metal might be purchased for the manufacture of each product.

(b) Identify ONE type of metal that might be used to make each of the products above.

(c) Suggest reasons why these metals might be used in each case.

(d) Compare the medium duty steps with the platform steps under the following headings:

- (i) possible uses;
- (ii) metals used in production;
- (iii) possible shape of metal used;
- (iv) safety;
- (v) cost.

unit

7 Effects of forces

Static forces affect a computer stand and moving forces affect a baseball bat.

Properties of materials

It is important to choose the most suitable material to make a product. It may be timber, plastic or metal, although each has a wide array of different types. You might choose a hardwood to make a shelving unit because it is strong. However, you might use mild steel or acrylic plastic for the same reason.

What a material can do, how it performs under certain conditions, how it looks and what it feels like are called its **properties**. A choice is usually made by considering a range of properties. Properties can fall into one of four categories: effects of forces; environmental effects (see unit 9); energy transfer (see unit 8); aesthetics (see unit 22).

Forces

A force is something that will:

- change the direction of a moving object;
- make something move faster (or slower);
- move a stationary object;
- alter the shape of a material.

It is important to know about all these effects when designing a product, although forces that affect the shape of a material are perhaps the most significant. Resistant materials may be affected by **static** forces (not moving), eg a television on a stand or the force on a door lintel. They can also affected by **movement**, eg a wheel spinning on an axle. At any time there is likely to be more than one force acting on a material. For example, the pivot (see unit 17) on a swing has a pulling force because of the weight of the person sitting on the swing and a frictional force as the joint rubs.

Once a force is applied to a material, it will create an opposing force in a different direction. For example, if a child sits on a swing the links in the chains holding the seat will tighten, losing their slackness as they pull against the weight of the child. In effect the chain gets longer. This is called STRAIN. It can be seen when a shopping bag is filled or a balloon is blown up.

Perhaps less visible are the STRESSES created inside the material that make up the links. When the links only have to support the seat there is little force across the thickness of the link, so stress on the metal is low. When the child sits on the seat the force across the link increases, creating much more stress inside the metal. If stress becomes too much the link will snap. The stress caused by stretching is called tensile stress. Twisting causes **shear** stress and squashing causes **bulk** or compressive stress. Stress could be reduced by using thicker links.

Many products are subjected to continuous stresses and strains. Examples might be an engine spinning around for hours or a structure like a steel tube holding a television aerial in place. Eventually the material may show signs of fatigue and start to buckle, split, crumble or crack. For example, a kitchen drawer on plastic runners might find the bottom of the

activities

Sight For Sore Eyes is a manufacturer of spectacle cases. It has produced cases in the shape of the actual glasses that are contained within. The idea is aimed to attract younger glasses wearers, who it hopes will see glasses cases as a fashion accessory.

(a) Explain any possible static or moving forces that the case might need to resist.
(b) What are compression forces? Why is it important for the case to resist compression forces?
(c) Suggest a suitable type of material that may be used to manufacture the body of the case.
(d) Explain THREE properties that you think the material will need to be suitable as a glasses case.

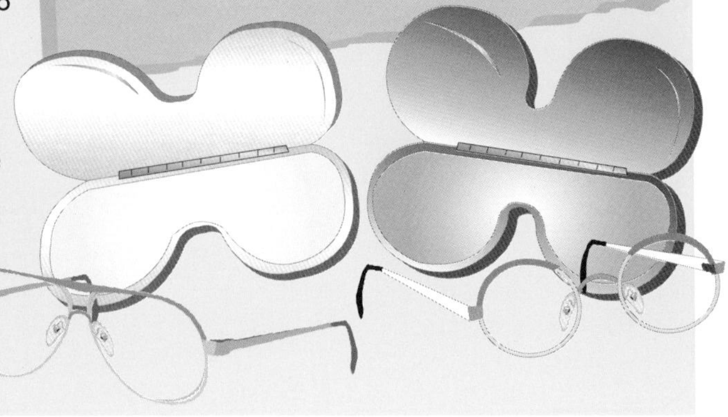

drawer bows and the runners crack or break.

Elasticity

All materials are 'elastic' to some extent. This means that if a force is applied they will stretch or change to oppose the force. Once the force is removed, the material will return to its original size and shape. The bigger the outside force, the greater the stress being placed on the material. The greater the strain on the material, the greater the change in shape.

Every material has an elastic limit. This is the point at which if any more force is applied it will cause the material to alter its shape permanently. Force beyond this point on a material puts it into the 'plastic range'. This happens when metals are work hardened by hammering (see unit 6). Acrylic will break before it gets into the plastic region, but polythene has a large 'plastic' region.

Toughness

Forces on a material beyond the plastic range will result in it 'failing'. It may snap, splinter, break or deform. For example, a piece of wooden shelving will have a permanent bend in it if books are left on the shelf for a long time. This is known as **creep**. How much force a material can absorb before it fails is called its

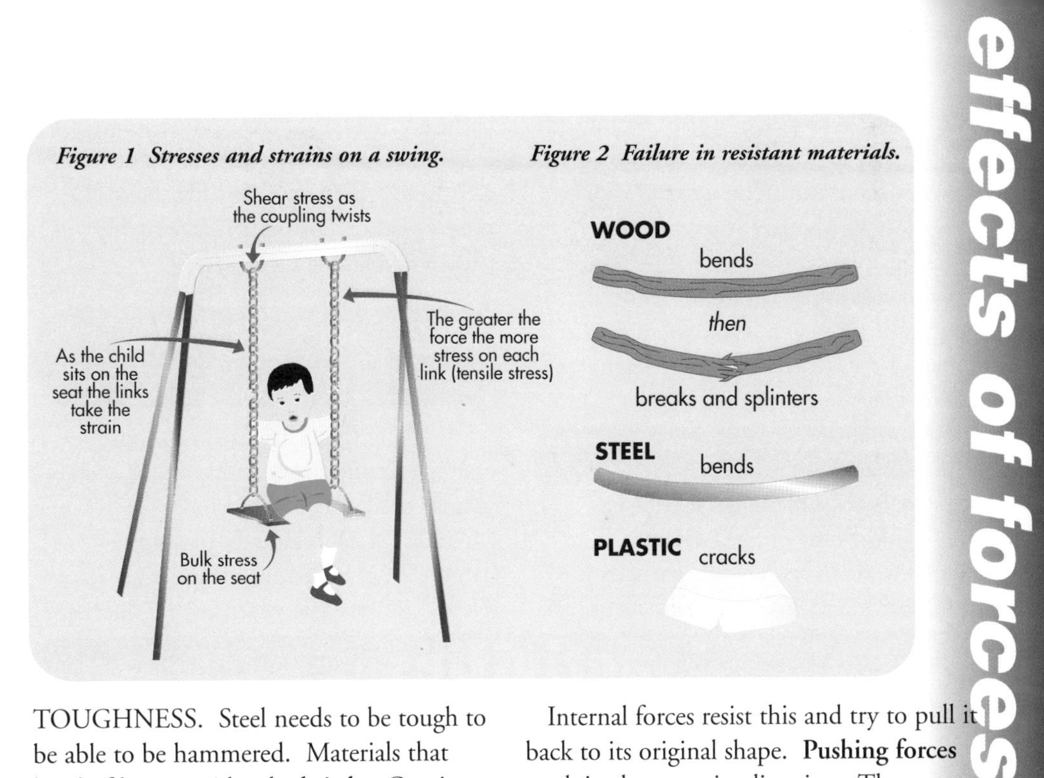

Figure 1 Stresses and strains on a swing.

Figure 2 Failure in resistant materials.

TOUGHNESS. Steel needs to be tough to be able to be hammered. Materials that break if hit are said to be **brittle**. Cast iron is hard but brittle because it can crack if hit.

Tensile forces and compression

Many forces that affect materials in products involve pushes and pulls as shown in Figure 3.

Pulling forces try to stretch a material, for example the strings on a squash racquet. These forces are called TENSILE forces. Internal forces resist this and try to pull it back to its original shape. **Pushing forces** work in the opposite direction. They try to squash the material. These are COMPRESSION forces. Internal forces try to push it back to its original shape.

If external forces are greater than internal forces, materials will buckle, bend or break. Materials that have a high resistance to tensile and compression forces are said to be STRONG.

The weight of one material on another or a material itself will create compression forces. Large structures like buildings or oil rigs and large vessels like ships have to

activities

First Technology designs, manufactures and supplies safety testing products. Crash test dummies are designed to test the impact of car crashes on passengers. Dummies are made from metal and plastic in 'human' shape and tests are carried out to simulate crash conditions. The company manufactures a range of frontal and side impact dummies as well as Child Restraint Air Bag Interaction (CRABI) dummies and full scale dummies. The results of the tests allow manufacturers of vehicles to produce safety devices such as airbags.

Source: First Technology plc.

(a) What types of dummy are manufactured by First Technology?
(b) What properties of metal and plastic make them useful in the manufacture of crash test dummies? Explain your answer.
(c) Suggest THREE other products that might need to be tested for the impacts of forces and explain why testing is important.

withstand a lot of weight caused by the material they are made from. This may lead to great stress on the structure or make it move more slowly than is required. Choosing a lighter material reduces the stress. For example, carbon fibres or aluminium alloys as a replacement for steel in many large structures reduce weight yet maintain levels of strength.

Density

Materials are sometimes described as being light or heavy. The heaviness of a material depends on how the particles it is made from are packed and the mass of each particle (the DENSITY). For example, EPS is light because the particles of polystyrene are spread apart and have a low mass. Lead is heavy because its particles are tightly packed and have a high mass.

Flexibility and rigidity

Stretching forces are used to shape material during production. Some metals, such as mild steel are said to be MALLEABLE because they can be hammered or rolled into thinner sheets. This is not possible with timber. Metals

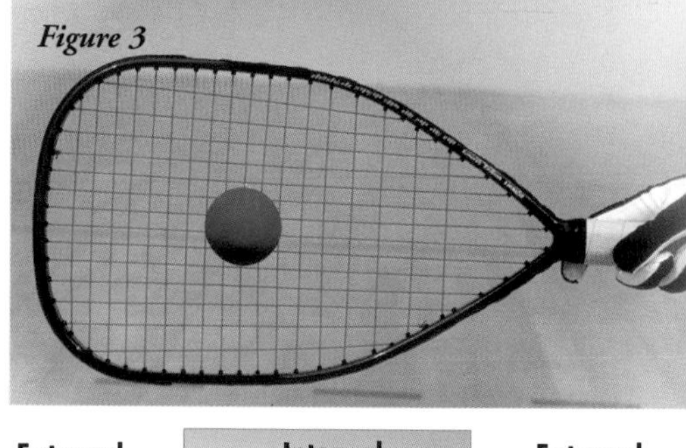

Pulling forces. Materials that resist tensile forces are said to have tensile strength. If external forces are greater than internal forces the product may break.

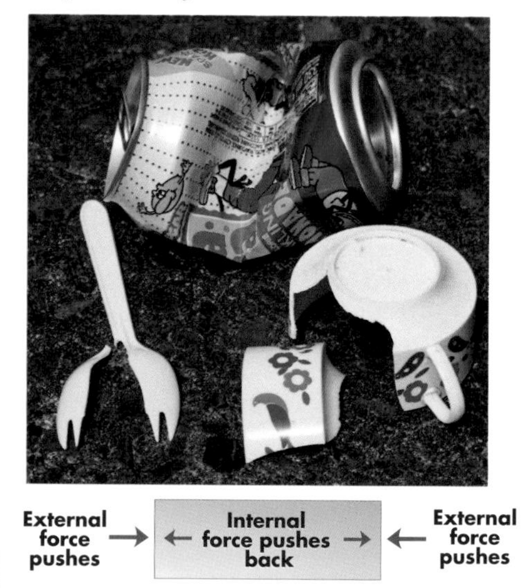

External force pushes → ← Internal force pushes back → ← External force pushes

Pushing forces. Materials that resist compression forces are said to be strong. If external forces are greater than internal forces the product may break.

like copper can also be drawn (pulled) to make rods or wire. This is described as being DUCTILE. Plastics can also be ductile, but may be broken if pulled too far.

Some materials are said to be FLEXIBLE. They can be bent but when the pressure is released they spring back to their original shape. A diving board is an example of a product made from flexible material. Timber is quite flexible, as are some plastics. Acrylic, however, will break if any attempt is made to bend it beyond a certain distance. It is said to be RIGID. Plasticisers (see unit 5) are added to some plastics to make them more flexible and less rigid. PVC comes in many forms, often linked to how much plasticiser is added (eg PVC clothing has plasticisers added to make it more flexible).

activities

1 Look at the photograph of rowing equipment.

Explain why:
(a) flexibility; and
(b) weight are important properties for materials used to make these designs.

2 **(a)** Which material shown in Table 1:
(i) has the highest density;
(ii) is least stiff;
(iii) fractures or yields most easily?
(b) Which 3 materials have similar specific measures of stiffness?
(c) Suggest TWO designs where stiffness is important and where these materials could be used.

Table 1 shows information about different materials. The density is shown in the first column. The second column shows the yield or fracture stress - the stress needed to cause permanent deformation. The specific figure shows the actual figure ÷ density. The third column shows stiffness. Note that although actual figures differ, three materials have similar specific measures of stiffness, so any could be used in designs where stiffness is important.

Table 1 Material properties.

Material	Density $kg\ m^{-3}$	Yield/fracture* stress $MPa\ m^3\ kg^{-1}$ Actual	$(x10^3)$ Specific	Stiffness $GPa\ m^3\ kg^{-1}$ Actual	$(x10^{-3})$ Specific
Mild Steel	7800	230	29	207	26.5
6061 aluminium alloy tube	2690	240	89	70	26.0
Polycarbonate sheet	1200	65	54	2.6	2.2
Advanced carbon fibre composite sheet	1600	2130	1330	134	83.8
Timber, typical	500	7	14	13	26.0

**Yield stress for metals, fracture stress for non-metals.*
Source: adapted from Which Materials?, The Institute of Materials.

Hardness

A material is hard if it resists indentation forces (and soft if it does not). These forces may be punching (eg trying to hit a nail through it) or cutting, for example, using a knife. Beech wood benches are used in workshops as it is not hard. In reverse, cutting tools need to be made from 'hard' materials so that they can cut or puncture other materials. Some drill bits and saw blades are tipped with very hard metals like tungsten carbide to make their cutting edges very hard.

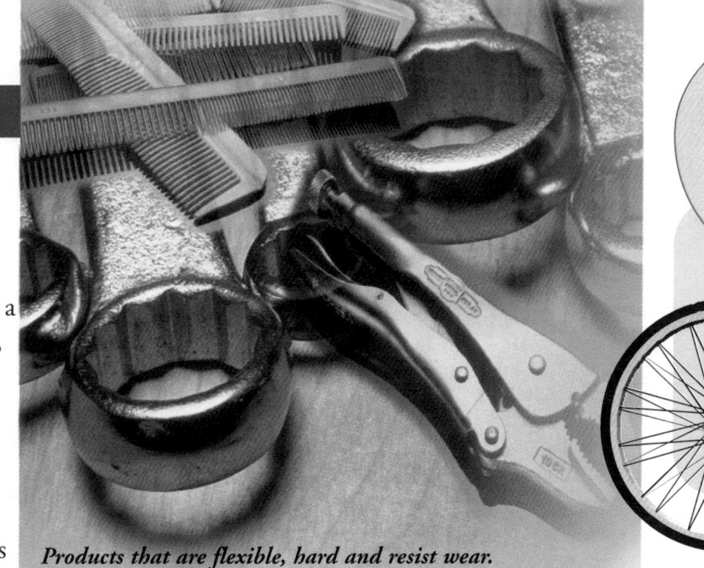

Products that are flexible, hard and resist wear.

Wear, shear and torque

Some materials are described as hard wearing. 'Wear' occurs as a result of frictional forces. FRICTION is a force that works in the opposite direction of movement. As a tyre turns in the direction a vehicle travels its tread grips the road with force in the opposite direction. Over time, the rubber 'wears down' as the road surface and the tread rub against each other. The road surface is harder wearing than rubber tyres. Friction can cause materials to heat up. Concord, travelling through the air, causes friction and its nose cone heats up.

Wear can be a problem when materials rub together. A steel piston rod moving inside a cylinder would soon wear as metals harden when they rub (see unit 6). This may lead to splinters of metal that would cause the rod to jam if a lubricant was not used. Lubricants create a thin film between two materials' surfaces, in order to reduce friction and reduce wear. Most lubricants are oil based, although water can sometimes be used. Oils tend to stick to surfaces better than water. Grease is also used for similar reasons. Ball bearings are sometimes used instead of a lubricant. The circular shape of the bearing means that at any one time there is only a small area in contact with another material, thus reducing wear.

Tearing occurs when two forces pull across a material in opposite directions. These are called **shear** forces. Cutting tools like scissors use a shearing action to cut through materials. Turning forces are forces which move around an axis. The amount of force needed to turn or twist something is called **torque**.

Some metals are malleable and ductile.

Ball bearings
Inner Race
Outer Race

Figure 4 Ball bearings are used in a bicycle pedal mechanism.

Key Terms

Strain - degree by which material is changed.
Stress - force acting over an area of a material.
Toughness - resistance of a material to being hit.
Tensile (forces) - forces that stretch or pull.
Compression (forces) - forces that squash or push.
Density - the mass of materials and how closely they are packed.
Strength - resistance to pushing and pulling forces.
Malleable - ability of a material to be shaped by hammering or rolling.
Ductile - ability of a material to be pulled into wires.
Flexible - ability of a material to bend without breaking.
Rigid - ability of a material to resist bending.
Friction - interaction of materials as their surfaces move.

activities

(a) Suggest FOUR places where these designs might be used.

(b) What properties do the materials in these designs have that make them suitable for the uses you have identified?

Stacking chairs
Frames in 19mm diameter mild steel tube with plastic coated finish. Moulded seats in polypropylene with anti-static additive. Available in five colours.

Workshop wooden chair
Hard wearing laminated wooden chair with adjustable backrest and footrest with a gas lift seat adjustment.

unit 8

Energy transfer

***Figure 1** Conduction in a soldering iron. When metal is heated atoms in the metal vibrate, causing heat to be transferred along the material.*

Energy transfer

There are many different types of energy. One type of energy can be converted into another. For example, electrical energy is changed into kinetic energy in an electric drill. Materials are used to transfer energy from one place to another. Electrical energy travels along copper wire. Heat energy travels through a stainless steel pan. Light energy travels through clear perspex.

Conduction

Heat energy travels through resistant materials (solids) by CONDUCTION. Solid materials, particularly metals, are said to be good CONDUCTORS of heat. This is because the atoms (small particles) that make up metals are closely packed together. When metal is heated the atoms vibrate and heat energy is transferred. Materials that are good conductors are used to make heating utensils, like pots and pans, or radiators for heating systems. They take heat quickly to where it is needed.

Non-metal materials like timber and the plastics are poor conductors of heat They are called INSULATORS. They are used to block conduction, either to protect (eg pan handles) or to keep heat from escaping (eg plastic thermos flasks). Insulating materials can be improved if they contain 'trapped' air or gases, which are poor conductors of heat. Glass fibres and expanded polystyrene are examples of materials that can be used to trap air and improve insulation. Insulators prevent heat loss and save energy.

Continuous heating of timber or plastic (depending on the intensity of the heat) may cause the material to char or blister and eventually to be set alight. To reduce the risk of a material catching fire it may be coated with a flame retardant chemical (eg Borax). Plastics can have flame retardants added when they are made (see unit 5).

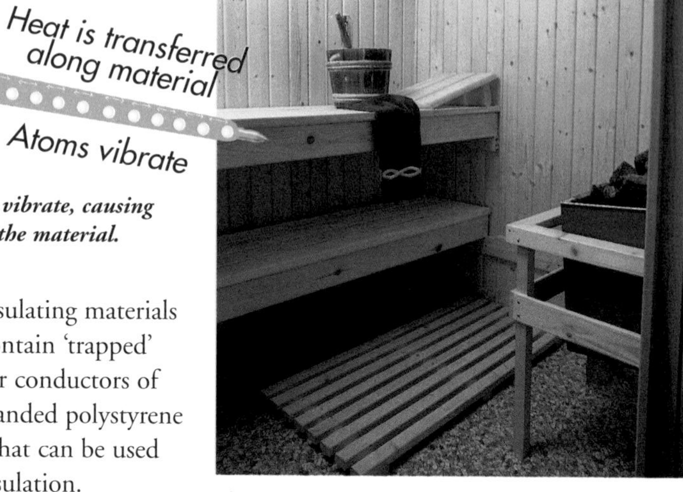

Saunas are made using wood as it insulates well.

Radiation

Heat travels through liquids and gases by convection. Energy can also travel by RADIATION. It can travel across space or through areas where no particles exist (eg a vacuum). Resistant materials can be designed to **absorb** (soak in), **radiate** (release) or **reflect** radiation.

A highly polished, silver coloured surface can be used to reflect radiated energy (usually heat or light). Silver surfaces like stainless steel make good reflectors. This can be found in heating or lighting design, where a shiny metallic surface behind the element reflects the heat/light energy forward. Proper mirrored surfaces are usually made from glass with a coating of silver painted onto them. A silvered finish on normally dull, matt materials will also reflect. CDs can be made from aluminium and plastic which reflect a laser light to make the CD work.

Radiators are made from metal as it conducts heat well.

activities

(a) What is meant by;
(i) a conductor of heat; (ii) an insulator?

(b) Explain which materials are good conductors and good insulators.

(c) Suggest THREE products used in cooking that might make use of materials which are good conductors and THREE which make use of materials which are good insulators.

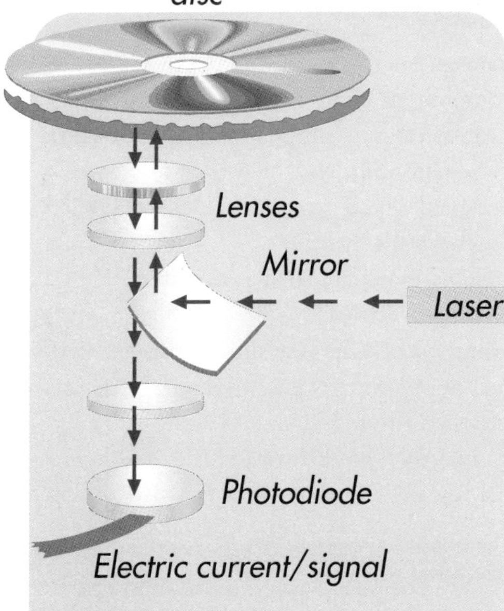

Figure 2 Compact discs. A laser beam is reflected from the disc onto a diode which produces a sound signal.

CD packaging is made from transparent material to see the details inside.

Materials painted white are the next best reflectors. Some microwave ovens have white coloured walls to reflect radiation. A white vehicle will reflect heat and keep the inside cooler than one painted black.

Dull matt, black surfaces are poor reflectors of heat and light energy. They are good **absorbers**. This might be useful in a photographic 'dark room', where reflected light may cause problems. A room painted white may reduce the need for lighting.

Materials and light

Materials affect light in different ways. Materials that let light through are either **transparent** or **translucent**. You can see clearly through transparent materials, but translucent materials 'diffuse' the light, making it difficult to see through clearly.

Polystyrene used for vending cups and plastic beer glasses is transparent, as is polycarbonate used for CD packaging. Some acrylics are translucent. They might be used as bus shelter fronts.

Materials that are **opaque** do not let light through. You cannot see through them at all. All metals and timbers are opaque, as are most coloured plastics.

Light energy, in particular ultra-violet light, can cause fading in materials. PVC frames and doors can begin to 'yellow' with age. Wood stains may pale if left in strong sunlight for any length of time. To counter this, surface coatings need to be repeated (eg painting, stain and varnishing). In plastics, where colours are added before the product is formed, UV absorbers are added which slow down the fading process.

Sound energy transfer

Sound is made when a material vibrates. Resistant materials whose particles are tightly packed (particularly metals) vibrate more than softer materials that are less tightly packed (eg rubber, EPS). A wide variety of materials is used to make musical instruments. The choice of the material depends on the type of sound needed. Metals tend to give a 'ringing' sound - they are sonorous. Instruments such as bells, chimes, gongs, saxophones and trumpets tend to be made from metal. Some guitar strings are made from 'wound' metal. Wood and plastic are also used to make instruments. Recorders and 'bodies' of acoustic guitars, violins and pianos are made from wood. Guitar strings can be made from nylon. Some woodwind instruments are now made from ebonite (vulcanised rubber).

Materials can be shaped to amplify sound. Guitars have hollow bodies. Pipes, drums and wind instruments are also

activities

1 Look at the information below.

(a) Suggest FOUR types of building that might be made mainly from wood.
(b) What properties does wood have that makes it suitable for these buildings?
(c) What are the possible advantages of using wood in buildings?

Hampshire County Council, through its County architect's department, has pursued a policy of constructing buildings from timber. Its Head, Professor Sir Colin Stansfield Smith, argues that 'Timber scores in ... energy comparisons with other commercial building materials'. Many schools and libraries are built mainly from wood.

A study was carried out by the department, the Timber Trade Federation and Forests Forever of Stakes Hill Infants school in Waterlooville. Its classrooms have shingle roofs made of cedar (a shingle is a small thin strip of building material for laying in overlapping rows as a cover for a roof). Results seem to indicate that timber buildings are quick to warm and slow to cool - ideal for workshops, halls and schools all of which are not occupied all the time. This suggests that wooden buildings should be cheap to run and should save on energy consumption.

Source: adapted from The Times, 16.3.1995.

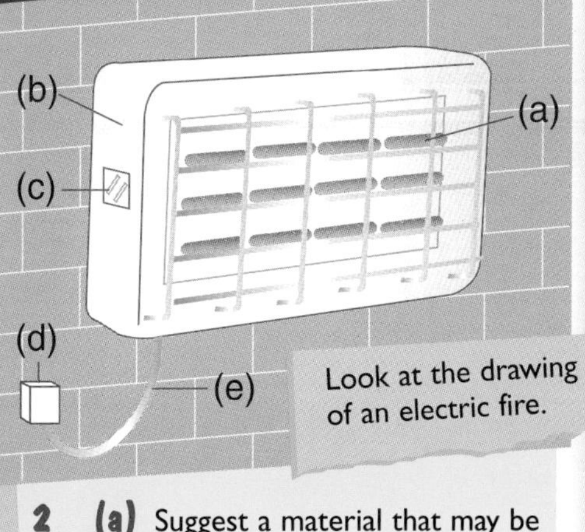

Look at the drawing of an electric fire.

2 **(a)** Suggest a material that may be used for each part of the fire.
(b) Explain why the material you have chosen might be used for each part.

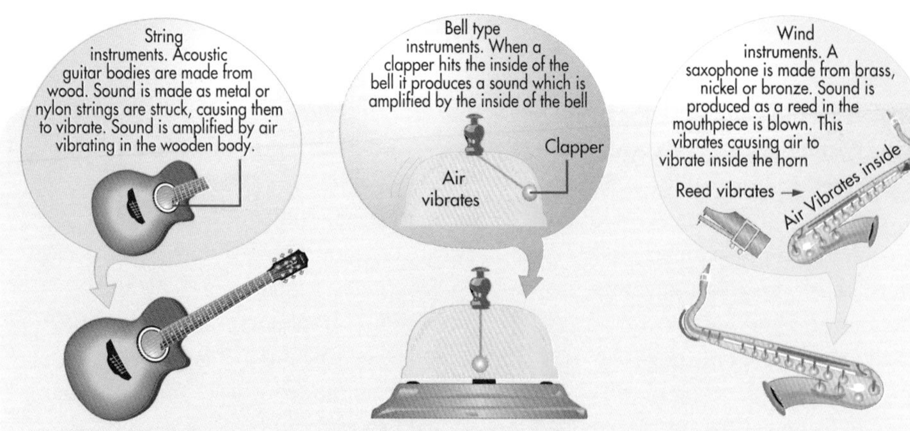

Figure 3 Using resistant materials to produce sound.

hollow. A plucked guitar string will not make much sound on its own. As it is struck, however, it causes air in the hollow body of the guitar to RESONATE at (nearly) the same frequency as the string. This amplifies the sound (makes it louder).

Sound can be a menace, particularly if you live near to a busy road or an airport. Similarly, vibrations in a car or when using a drill which lead to noise can be a nuisance. It is possible to dampen vibrations by using 'spongy' materials like rubber or springs, which absorb sound 'shocks'.

Electrical energy

Electrical energy is used to operate many items, from lighting to heating to moving machinery. In each case the electrical energy is changed to another type after it has been transferred along wires and cables. For example, an electric fan changes electrical energy into movement.

Materials that let electricity pass through are called **electrical conductors**. Metals are good electrical conductors. Graphite is not a metal, but will still conduct electricity. There is a range of materials called **semi-conductors**. Under the right conditions they will allow electricity to pass through. Silicon is perhaps the most common and is used to make a lot of electronic and micro-electronic components such as transistors and integrated circuits (see unit 18). Electrical wiring, cables and electrical junctions like plugs are made from metals like copper, brass and aluminium alloys. Generators of electricity and dynamos are made from wound copper wire.

Timber and plastics are poor conductors of electricity. They are described as **electrical insulators**. They will be used to house electrical wiring and cables, to prevent leakage of electricity and to protect people who handle or use electrical equipment from injury by electrical shock. This is why houses have PVC insulation around cables and plugs and sockets made from urea formaldehyde, for example. TVs and stereos are housed in moulded plastic units. Lamp shade stands may be made from hollowed out timber. Some plastics can build up 'static' electrical charges (eg polythene bags, nylon combs) which can damage micro-electric and electronic components. This is why plastics used to store electronic components are made with anti-static additives. New plastics are being designed which do conduct electricity, such as electronic 'paint'.

Some materials, such as tungsten, conduct electricity, and have a high melting point. When they are thin and have a high melting point they get hot if a large current is passed through them. Heating ELEMENTS in kettles and fires and light FILAMENTS make use of this.

Magnetism

Few materials are MAGNETIC, but many products contain magnets (eg TVs, microwaves and calculators). Ferrous metals (see unit 6) are magnetic, along with certain

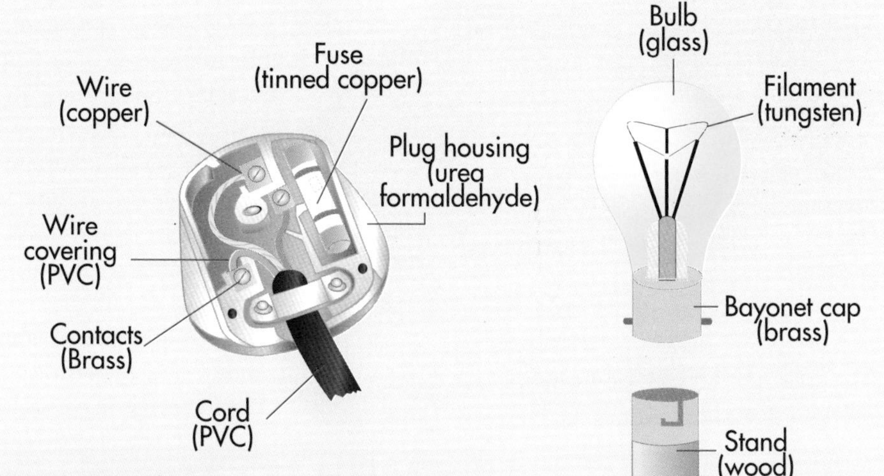

Figure 4 Materials can be used as electrical conductors (metals) or electrical insulators (wood and plastic).

activities

An electric bell makes use of an electromagnet as the diagram shows.

(a) What is meant by the term magnetic?

(b) Why is an electromagnet a temporary magnet?

(c) Draw a flow diagram to show the operations that take place for an electric bell to ring.

Source: adapted from The Way Things Work, D. Macaulay, Dorling Kindersley.

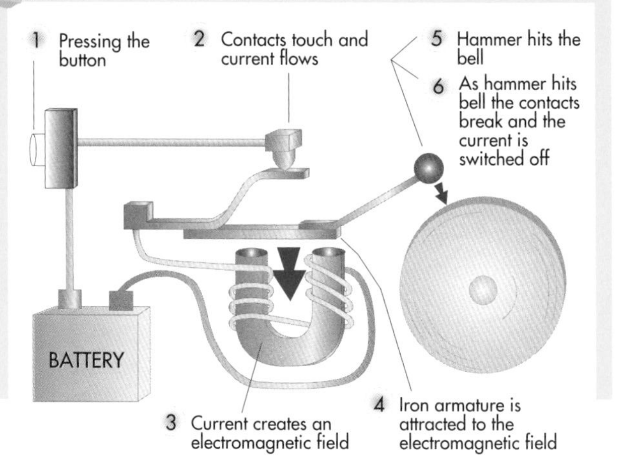

Products incorporating magnets can 'stick' to certain metals.

non-ferrous metals such as nickel and cobalt.

Permanent magnets retain their magnetism. They can be found in the back of microwaves and on fridge 'stickers' and plastic toy letters. Permanent magnets use metallic alloys or are a mix of iron oxide and barium oxide. They can be made by stroking with a magnetised material or placing the material in a solenoid and passing a DC current briefly through the coil. Magnetic strips can be bought which contain magnetic material impregnated in plastic. Video and cassette tape use magnetic strips.

Temporary magnets are only magnetic for a short time. Electromagnets are the most common. They are made by winding a piece of insulated copper wire around a soft iron core. The electric current passing through the coil 'induces' it to become magnetic. Once the current stops the magnetism is lost. They form the basis of electrical motors, dynamos and generators and are more versatile than permanent magnets.

Conduction - heat travelling through solids.
Conductors - materials that let heat through quickly.
Insulator - materials that don't let heat through quickly.
Radiation - energy travel without the aid of matter.
Resonate - to create a greater vibration from a smaller vibration at (nearly) the same frequency.
Element/Filament - coils that give a high resistance making them heat up and glow.
Magnet - a metal that has an artificially created magnetic field and is able to attract ferrous metals.

Expansion and contraction

When resistant materials are heated, their particles vibrate and move further apart. The result of this is that the material grows larger in size. This is called **expansion**. Materials expand in all directions. Metals tend to expand a lot more than plastics or timber. When a material cools its size becomes less. This is called **contraction**.

When working with resistant materials it is important to allow for movement of the material as it expands and contracts due to changes in weather or other conditions (eg oven design, engines). Where this occurs a lot, expansion joints are used. These give the product space to expand and contract to prevent damage. Some bridges are on rollers with gaps at joints. Elongated holes cut in steel material allow it to slide back and forth to prevent buckling, even though it may be fixed with a nut and bolt or screw.

Thermostats using bimetallic strips use expansion in order to operate. The brass (or copper) expands more than the iron, causing the strip to bend in one direction when heated. These metals also conduct electricity so as the strip bends it can make (or break) an electrical circuit. A control dial may set the gap between the contacts. This type of thermostat is used in central heating units, electric irons, ovens, toasters, kettles etc.

Some products are made by 'shrink fitting', such as wheels. A product is cooled until a wheel fits around it. It is then allowed to warm up to normal size, giving a tight fit.

Control
The circuit is incomplete and the product is switched 'off'
When heated the strip bends and contacts do not touch
Iron
Copper/brass

Figure 5 How a thermostat works.

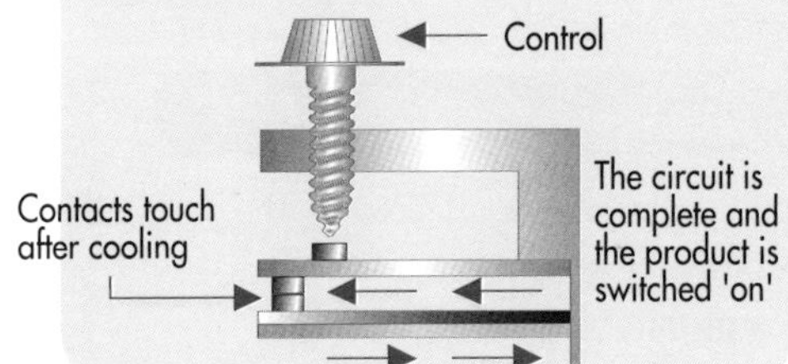

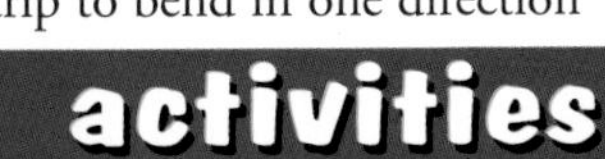

Read the information below.

(a) Why are elements and bimetallic strips made from metal in a kettle?

(b) Explain how a thermostat works in a kettle. Use the terms:
(i) expansion; (ii) bimetallic strip; and
(iii) contacts in your explanation.

(c) Suggest TWO other products that may make use of a thermostat and explain why it is useful for these products.

Automatic kettles have a heating element in the base of the kettle which heats water. They also have a steam thermostat and an on/off switch in the handle. Power wires are connected to the switch, where a pair of contacts can be open (to switch power off) or closed (to switch power on). A spring holds the switch in place.

As the kettle boils, steam enters the thermostat and heats up a bimetallic strip made of two metals, such as brass and iron. When the strip is heated the brass expands more than the iron, causing the strip to bend. This forces a plastic pushrod to push the switch into an off position. There are two safety devices in the kettle to prevent fire if the kettle is switched on with no water in it.

- Another bimetallic strip is attached to the element. The strip has two contacts which touch, so that current remains on when used normally. If the element overheats (as it has no water to boil) the strip bends, which opens two contacts. This switches the power off.
- A thermal fuse is kept 'on' by a soft plastic rod. If the kettle overheats the rod melts and the two contacts separate.

unit

9 Environmental effects

Weathering

Resistant materials are affected by the environment around them. If left outside, a product made from resistant materials will be subjected to all sorts of weather conditions. These 'physical' attacks are collectively called WEATHERING. The material may expand when the sun shines or contract when it is cold. Winds may whip up dust and other small particles which hit the surface of the material, scratching it and spoiling its LUSTRE. All these effects can leave little crevices where water can lodge. As water freezes it expands, which widens these cracks further still.

Waterproof and absorbent materials.

Absorbent and waterproof materials

Some resistant materials are naturally absorbent. They contain spaces where moisture can settle. As they absorb moisture they may swell; as they dry out they may shrink again. Some timbers and manufactured boards, particularly chipboards and fibreboards, are absorbent. Coating with melamine (see unit 4) can prevent absorption at the top. Edging sealants may stop water at the edges although over time these may degrade and water can get in.

Solid plastics and metals are water resistant or WATERPROOF. They create a barrier to water, preventing it passing through.

Products designed for outdoor use usually need to be waterproof or water resistant, eg plastic garden furniture or window frames. Some timbers are better for outdoor use than others. These are usually hardwoods because of the natural 'oiliness' of the timber or the chemicals stored in their cells. It is possible to make timber more water resistant for outside use, however, by painting it or treating it with a preservative

activities

(a) Suggest products in a bathroom that may be made of: (i) plastic; (ii) metal; (iii) wood.

(b) Select THREE products and explain why the materials they are made from are suitable for the bathroom.

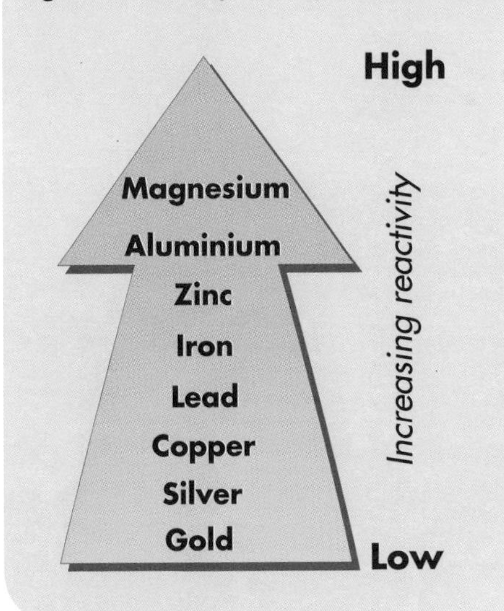

Figure 1 Reactivity series of resistant metals.

(see unit 14). Inside, the problem is less obvious but may still exist. Kitchen and bathroom taps around a sink or basin may drip or leak for example, causing doors to swell and kitchen laminates to become swollen and uneven.

Corrosion

The water that settles in the spaces created by weathering may dissolve some of the gases in the air. These may be oxygen and carbon dioxide, or pollutants like sulphur dioxide from fossil fuel driven power stations and nitrogen oxides from vehicle emissions. Gases dissolve in water to form **acids**, eg carbon dioxide forms carbonic acid.

These acids can attack resistant materials, usually metals. They change materials into new substances. This is called CORROSION. Salt water speeds up corrosion. Ferrous metals corrode to form rust (iron oxide). Other metals can react with oxygen in the air (OXIDATION) to form **oxides**. Some metals will react with different chemicals to form sulphides or nitrates. These might be seen as a discolouration (TARNISH) on the metal, which will lose its lustre. Silver tarnishes as deposits of black silver sulphide appear on its surface. Copper and bronze tend to go green as deposits of **verdigris** (copper carbonate) appear. Figure 1 shows how some metals react to oxidation and attack by water and acid.

Tarnished metal.

Tarnishing and corrosion can be prevented by covering the surface of the metal. Oil and grease may be used but have to be applied frequently. Painting or electroplating (see unit 14) with an unreactive metal like gold or nickel is more

activities

Read the information below.

(a) What materials are used to make picnic products?
(b) What environmental conditions are likely to affect these products?
(c) Suggest THREE properties that materials used in the products may have that make them useful for picnics.

Families gearing up for the summer period often consider restocking on 'picnic paraphernalia'. Families with small children may chose melamine or acrylic plates, mugs and glasses to minimise breakage.

Large family picnics may require a coolbox, a thermos flask and perhaps even portable plastic chairs. To keep the sun away, a collapsible parasol with separating metal extension parts is another useful addition.

Source: adapted from The Times, 10.6.1995.

permanent, but is not useful for moving parts. Galvanising (coating with zinc), electroplating and anodising (coating with aluminium oxide) are other useful methods. Dyes can be added during anodising to give a coloured finish (see unit 14).

Metals can also be protected by alloying with an unreactive metal. Stainless steel is alloyed with chromium and manganese. Bronze contains copper and tin which are relatively unreactive.

Most plastics tend to resist corrosion by 'inorganic' chemicals. Plastics, however, face attack by organic solvents. Over time some plastics may be affected by oxygen and other airborne chemicals. To prevent or reduce the risk of degrading, anti-oxidants are added to the plastic before manufacture (see unit 5). Acids may discolour timber, but are unlikely to cause decay. Painting and varnishing will help to prevent acid attack.

Corrosion can play an important part in the fatigue of a resistant material Where a product has undergone stresses (see unit 7), cracks may appear and corrosion sets in, accelerating the point of failure. Alternatively, corrosion can take place and when stresses occur the material may fail at that place. A rusty chassis or bodywork on a car will offer much less resistance to impact in an accident or to the force involved in an emergency stop. Some steel tubes rust from the inside to out due to manufacturing conditions.

Rotting wood.

Rust.

activities

(a) What is corrosion?
(b) How might corrosion affect resistant materials, such as metal?
(c) What led to corrosion according to Lloyds of London?
(d) Suggest THREE parts of a building that may be affected by corrosion.
(e) Choose a metal product. Explain how it may be possible to restrict or prevent the corrosion of metal used to manufacture the product.

In 1995, Lloyds of London Insurance Market found rust eating away the external piping of its award winning offices. The repair cost was likely to be high.

Severe corrosion was found in the piping that lies behind the insulation and the building's external stainless steel cladding. The worst rust was found in the hot water pipes, although the cold water and air conditioning pipes were also found to have rust. Lloyds commented that the problem arose because of penetration of water under the vapour barrier designed to protect the pipes.

Source: adapted from The Times, 6.10.1995.

Bio-attack

Some resistant materials are affected by 'living' organisms. These may be **micro-organisms** like bacteria or fungi, or more complicated organisms like **insects** or **other animals**.

Micro-organisms

Materials that are used for piping will have recesses where bacteria and fungi may grow. These micro-organisms can produce highly corrosive chemicals, like sulphides and organic acids, which can start corrosion. Other types of 'bio-fouling' may include deposits of plants or animals becoming attached to a material. For example, at sea, barnacles may cling to a ship's hull, or on land lichen or moss may grow in cracks or crevices.

Copper is a useful metal in countering bio-fouling of this type. It is toxic to marine organisms. This is why fish farm cages are made from copper alloys. Copper pipes are less susceptible to bacterial attack for the same reason. In places where it is important to have a sterile environment (eg in hospital operating theatres), plastics can be treated with bio-cides to reduce bacterial growth. This is important because many plastics can become serrated (they have little cuts or are scored), leaving surfaces open to bacterial growth in the slots or cavities that have been made.

Being a natural material, timber is attacked more easily by living organisms than metals or plastics. Like corrosion in metals, the conditions have to be correct before attack will take place. Fungi tend to attack timber with a moisture content above 20%. They also require oxygen using the sugars and starch in the timber as a source of food for reproduction and growth. Softwood is more easily attacked than hardwood because of its higher water content.

Dry rot is the most damaging of the fungi. It can penetrate plaster and even brick to get at fresh timber. It moistens the timber itself. The fungus is white in colour with grey strands. It turns the rotted timber brown and has cracks running both with grain and across the grain. The timber becomes dry and powdery.

Wet rot only attacks wet timber. It is found in areas where ventilation is poor. It is yellow in colour, and turns the timber dark brown, making it brittle with long cracks that run with the grain. There are other types of fungal attack. Once prevalent there is little to do but remove the affected area. Treatment with fungicides, however, is best before installation. Covering with paints or varnishes helps to reduce the problem, although these need replacing over time.

Insects

There is a range of insects that attack timber. Generally these are beetles that lay eggs in the timber. Their larvae live off the sugars and starches in the timber, perhaps for years. Once fully grown they bore their way forwards to the surface, then once the beetle is formed it bores its way out of the timber. This problem is called **woodworm**. This can be prevented by treatment with special chemicals, although affected timber will have to be cut away or replaced totally.

Biodegrading

The action of micro-organisms as they rot resistant materials is called BIODEGRADING. During a material's useful life it is important to resist such degradation. However, once the product is consigned to the 'rubbish' bin the material from which it is made needs to be able to decay otherwise it becomes a 'pollutant'.

Materials are now being designed so that they can biodegrade, particularly plastics which tend to be resistant to natural decay. Aiding such decay helps to reduce the burden of pollution.

Weathering - attack of natural elements such as wind, rain, heat or cold.
Lustre - The natural shine of a metal.
Waterproof - resistance to absorption of water.
Corrosion - chemical attack by acids.
Tarnishing - discolouration due to oxidation.
Oxidation - reaction of a metal to form its oxide or other compound.
Biodegrading - natural attack by micro-organisms to break down a material.

activities

(a) What environmental effects are described in the article below?
(b) What materials are most likely to suffer from these effects?
(c) Suggest areas of a house that may suffer from these problems.
(d) Choose TWO problems and explain how they may be prevented to some extent.

A full structural survey on houses for sale or a Home Buyers' Survey by a building society often reveals structural problems for potential home buyers. Such defects include warped roofs, bulging walls, wet rot, dry rot, rising damp and rampant woodworm. These may not show up on a simple valuation survey.

A full survey is advised for older properties. This can involve lifting fitted carpets or floorboards if wet rot or dry rot is suspected. It could also involve looking at the roof from both the outside and the inside.

Source: adapted from The Times, 28.1.1995.

CHRIS BOARDMAN'S CYCLES

In 1995 Chris Boardman, the Olympic time trial gold medalist, competed in the Tour de France. He continued to use his carbon fibre Lotus built cycle for time trials, but used three cycles built by former winner Eddie Merckx in the Tour.

Although the Tour cycles look like those available in high street shops, they are lighter and more comfortable. Getting the geometry of the frame right is crucial and each cycle is tailor made to fit the rider's requirements. The set up is also important. Having experimented, it was found that the more laid back the forks and the head tube were (the stem with the handle bars and front forks) the more comfortable was the rider and the more stable the steering.

Another difference is that the wheels are thinner and flat 'knife like' spokes are designed to cut through the air, compared to round ones on conventional cycles. Other differences include more sophisticated gears, switches on the handle bars (compared to a knee high lever) and a tiny computer dial on the handle bars measuring speed and distance.

Because the race contains so many hill climbs, saving weight is vital. The cycles weigh only 8.1kg compared to Boardman's 67.7 kg. Bike manufacturers picked up on the weight saving potential of titanium. It has nearly the same tensile strength as steel, but only half the weight. Steel or aluminium only are usually used in high street bikes. The frame weighs only 0.9 kg and other weight savings are made in the titanium and aluminium handle bars and the axles, pedals and wheels made of steel, titanium and aluminium.

Source: adapted from The Guardian, 1.7.1995.

Questions

(a) What materials mentioned in the article are used to make Chris Boardman's:
  (i) Tour de France cycles;
  (ii) time trial cycles?

(b) Suggest ONE static and ONE moving force that a cycle might be affected by.

(c) Suggest TWO parts of a cycle that may be affected by friction. How will friction affect the materials used in the manufacture of the cycle?

(d) Using a cycle chain as an example, explain what is meant by: (i) strain; and (ii) stress.

(e) Suggest THREE properties that materials used in racing cycles might need and explain why they are important.

(f) State THREE differences between these racing cycles and cycles available from high street retailers and explain how they make the cycle more efficient.

Chris Boardman's time trial cycle.

Case study: MADE OF WASTE

Made of Waste is a company that produces multi-coloured sheet material from recycled HDPE plastic bottles, which can then be made into designs such as furniture. It was formed by Jane Atfield (a Master of Arts graduate in Furniture Design) and Colin Williamson (Chair of the British Plastics Federation's recycling council) after Jane had initially made some tables and chairs from recycled plastic imported from America.

Now the company manufactures sheets from the 60 million plastic bottles disposed of in the UK every year in bottle banks. Recycling has, in the past, tended to be confined to the production of 'basic' products, such as bin liners made from recycled plastic dyed black. The company is expanding into more imaginative areas.

Brightly coloured bottles, which previously held shampoo and detergents, are washed, crushed, heated and pressed to produce plastic sheets or slabs sized 3050mm x 1220mm. The colours of the original plastics are combined into a whole variety of patterns, from a natural mix using milk bottles to 'psychedelic' patterns.

The new material can be used in many ways, including worktops, tables, chairs and splash resistant tiles. It has been used for studio sets on television and for canteen tables. The Science Museum's children's centre in London has desks and benches made from the material. It is tough, robust, long lasting, does not scratch easily or show the dirt, is safe for children and it can't be set on fire. It is increasingly being used in homes, particularly for kitchen worktops, and for floors, basin stands, mirror frames and shower screens.

The slabs can be drilled, screwed and cut in the way MDF might be. However, unlike manufactured boards it does not need to be treated or coated. It will also resist boiling water and is easy to clean. These advantages tend to outweigh the extra cost of the material compared to a cheaper manufactured board such as MDF, for example.

Source: Jane Atfield, Made of Waste.

Questions

(a) Suggest FIVE interior designs that may be made from recycled plastic.
(b) What **type** of plastic would be used for recycling? Explain your answer.
(c) Suggest THREE advantages of using plastic for children's products.
(d) (i) Explain why plastic might be suitable for products used outside?
(ii) Suggest FIVE outdoor products that it might be used for.
(e) Suggest TWO similarities and TWO differences between the use of recycled plastic and MDF.

Recycled plastic sheets.

unit 10

Measuring and marking

Measuring

It is important to measure accurately when marking out a piece of material to be cut. Plans should show measurements in millimetres or metres.

The standard instrument for measuring length is a **ruler** which can be made from wood, metal or plastic. Ruler lengths vary, but the most common found in a workshop are the 150mm and the 300mm. The most often used is the 300mm steel ruler. It has a 'zero end gauge' setting to allow accurate measurement from corners. Because it is flat it can be used as a straight edge and its edges can test if surfaces are level. Steel rulers are essential for marking out work when using craft knives or scribers as they keep a blade 'on line'. Plastic or wooden rulers may be cut, making them unusable as a straight edge in future. Steel rulers of 500mm, 600mm and 1 metre are also found in some workshops. Above these lengths a flexible ruler is generally used.

CALIPERS measure diameters and awkward shapes, such as tubing, or take 'inside' measurements. They can be set to fit various distances and then the distance between the contacts can be measured against a ruler. Calipers can also be used for transferring measurements, comparing measurements, ensuring surfaces are parallel.

VERNIER CALIPERS or MICROMETER SCREW GAUGES can be used to take very accurate measurements. Vernier calipers can give precise measurements to within 0.1mm. A micrometer measures to 0.01mm and is used to take more accurate measurements. They can be used for inside and outside measurements. They are very useful for measuring when turning on a lathe or milling on a milling machine. It is important that these instruments do not get warm as they might expand slightly, making readings inaccurate.

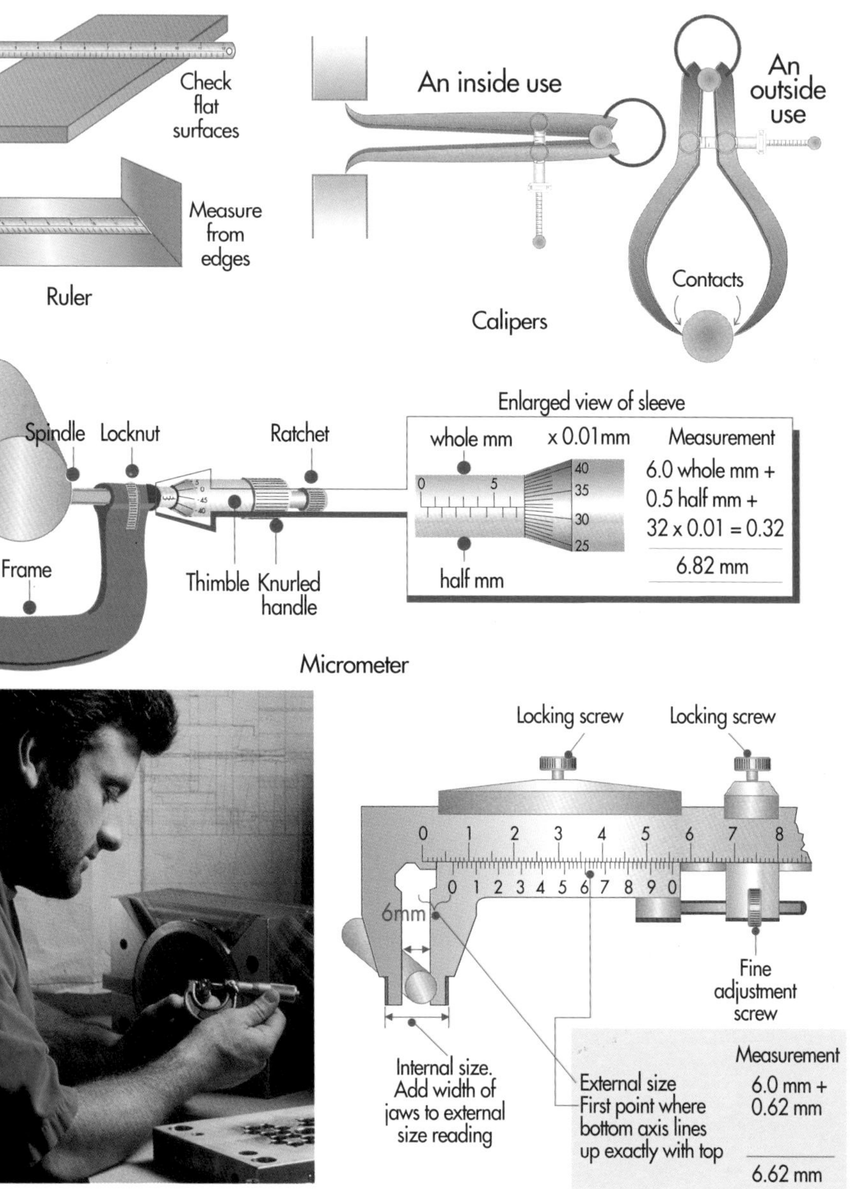

Figure 1 Measuring tools.

Measuring angles, shapes and centres

TRY SQUARES and bevels are used to work out angles. Try squares can also be useful to check that edges are 'true' (straight).

- A **standard try square** will give a line at 90° to an edge.
- A **mitre try square** will give angles of 45° and 135°. It can be used to produce mitred corners (see unit 13).
- A **sliding bevel** can be adjusted to give a range of angles from 0° to 180°.
- A **engineer's sliding bevel** is a small tool used for marking out various angles on metalwork. The blade can be adjusted

and locked with a nut.

- A **combination square** can be used as a try square, a bevel or a depth gauge.
- A **centre finding gauge** is a simple tool that allows the centre of a round metal bar or turned piece of wood to be found. It has a 90° notch cut into one side and a blade that bisects the notch with a straight edge. Rotating the gauge and drawing lines on the rod will show the centre where the lines intersect.
- Some **combination sets** are available which operate as a try square, a mitre square, a protractor, a centre finding gauge, a depth finding gauge and a ruler.

These are shown in Figure 2.

For unusual shapes a TEMPLATE can be constructed. A template is sometimes made out of stiff card or other material, cut to the irregular shape. In industry, templates are sometimes made from wood or sheet steel. They allow irregular shapes to be batch produced (see unit 19), using the template many times.

Figure 2 Measuring angles, shapes and centres.

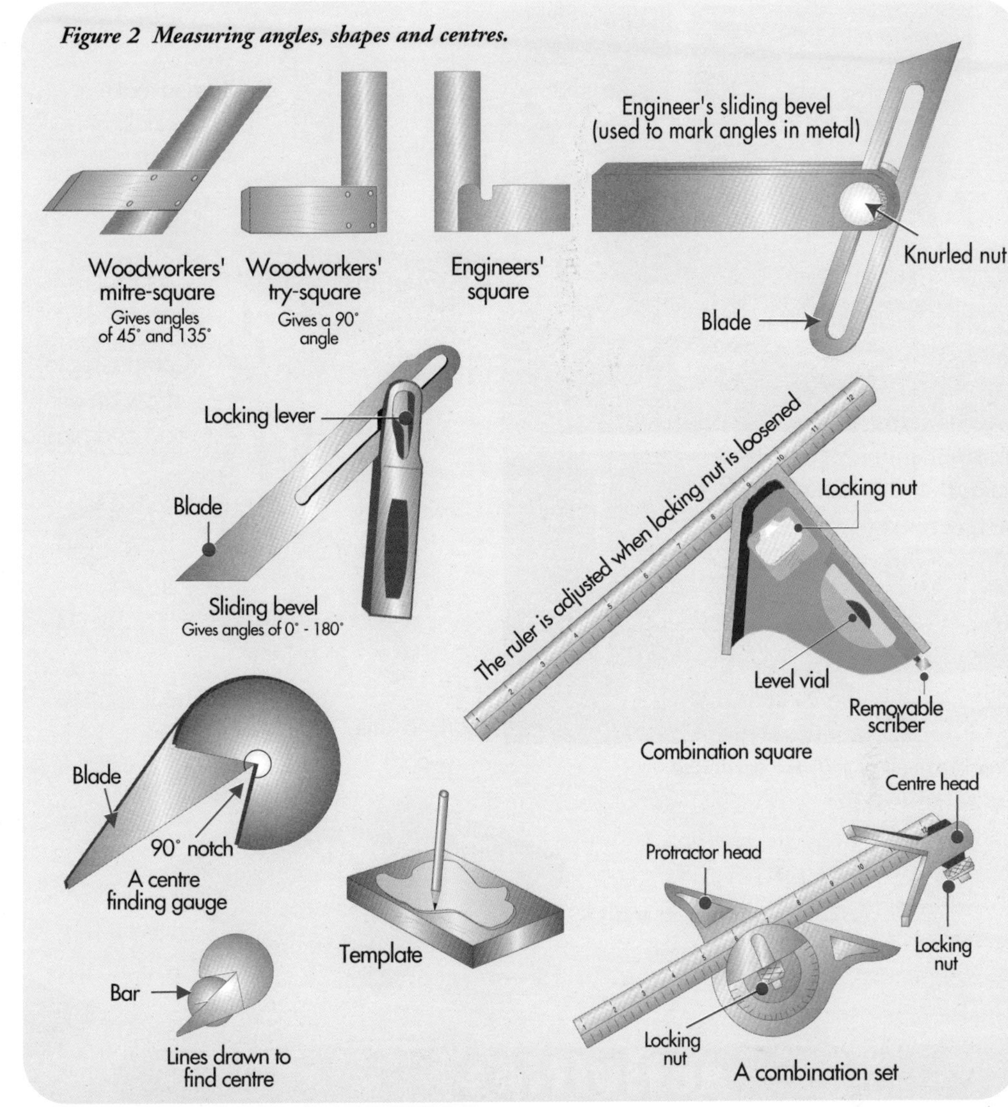

activities

Read the information below.

(a) Suggest THREE products that might make use of precoated steel.

(b) Explain why it is important that sheets must be (i) flat and (ii) accurately cut.

Levelling.

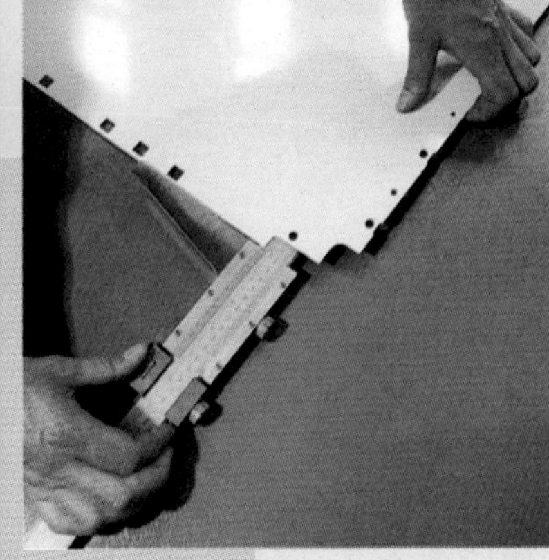

Measurement.

Precoat International is the holding company of Color Steels Ltd, the leading supplier of precoated steel in the UK.

Precoated steel is made by coating wide strip steel with paint or polymer film. It is used in a wide variety of applications. It has established uses in the construction industry as roofing material and is a growing influence in the manufacture of white goods, brown goods and lighting, eg washing machines, refrigerators, video cassette recorders and batten lighting.

It is important that the sheets of precoated steel are cut accurately and also conform to flatness standards. The company uses precision levelling and measurement techniques to ensure its products meet with customer requirements.

Source: Precoat International.

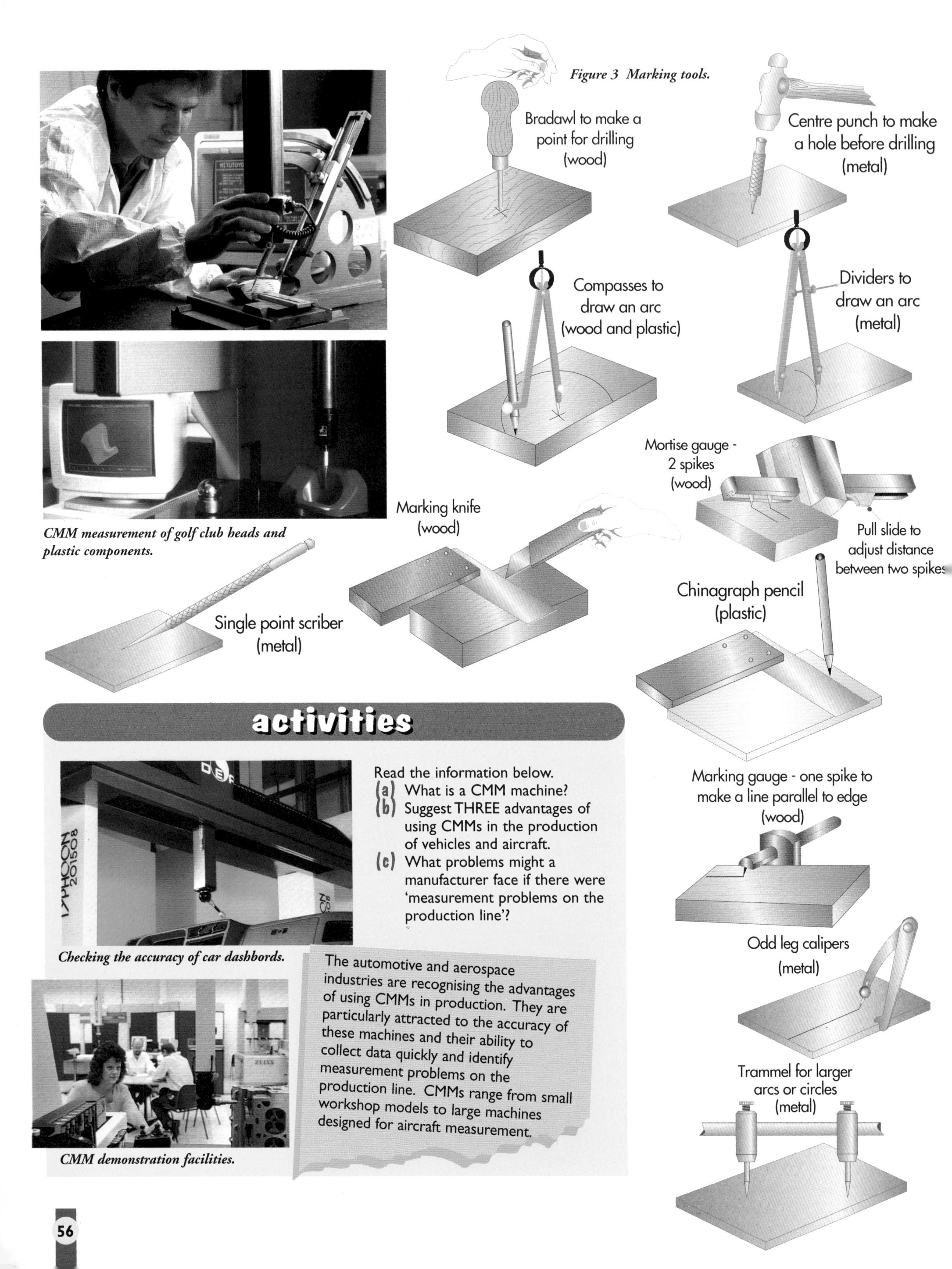

Figure 3 Marking tools.

CMM measurement of golf club heads and plastic components.

activities

Checking the accuracy of car dashbords.

Read the information below.

(a) What is a CMM machine?

(b) Suggest THREE advantages of using CMMs in the production of vehicles and aircraft.

(c) What problems might a manufacturer face if there were 'measurement problems on the production line'?

The automotive and aerospace industries are recognising the advantages of using CMMs in production. They are particularly attracted to the accuracy of these machines and their ability to collect data quickly and identify measurement problems on the production line. CMMs range from small workshop models to large machines designed for aircraft measurement.

CMM demonstration facilities.

Table 1 Rules for marking out.
• Choose the correct marking tool for the line, circle, point or shape to be marked out.
• Choose the correct marking tool for the material.
• Check how accurate the measurement needs to be.
• Check that the edge of the material is straight if marking out from an edge.
• Start all measurements from the same edge or line. This becomes known as the 'Datum Line'.
• To reduce wastage, mark as close to a true edge as possible.
• Make sure that the mark is clear enough for you to use.
• A single clear line is essential.

Coordinate measuring machines

Industry is now making use of COORDINATE MEASURING MACHINES (CMM) in manufacturing. These can make simple or complex measurements, check batches or components one at a time and inspect geometric or irregular shapes. CMMs can be used to check the accuracy of measurements to within microns. Large items such as vehicles or small items such as moulds or components can be checked for accuracy. It is also possible to install CMM probes on CNC machines (see unit 11) to detect wear, for example. They have replaced costly or time consuming manual techniques which rely on the operator's skill. CMMs can be controlled by shopfloor workers using a computer software package or smaller machines can be used by hand.

Calipers - an instrument used to measure the diameter of objects.
Vernier calipers - an instrument used to take accurate measurements to 0.1mm.
Micrometer - an instrument used to measure accurately to 0.01mm.
Try squares - instruments used to check 90° angles and check edges are true.
Template - a means of reproducing the same shape exactly on many pieces of material.
Coordinate measuring machine - a computer operated machine that gives very accurate measurements.
Scriber - a tool used to score metal or plastic.

Marking tools

Marking tools are used to mark out lines, circles, points for drilling or irregular shapes. Rules for marking out are shown in Table 1.

The simplest tool is a **pencil** (HB) for marking wood. However, pencils are of little use on plastic or metal as marks are difficult to see and they rub off easily. A marking knife can also be used for wood and is more accurate than a pencil, but a mark is not easily removed if a mistake is made. A **chinagraph pencil** with a fine tip can be used for plastics. A SCRIBER is the standard marking tool for metal. It is made from carbon steel. **Marking fluid** or layout fluid may be used to make a scriber mark clearer. Felt tip pen or marking fluid must be removed before a product is finished (see unit 14). These marking tools need to be used with a ruler, a try square or a template.

A **centre punch** or **dot punch** can be used to mark out positions for the drilling of metal. The punch must be hammered into the metal to leave a mark. A **bradawl** which can be turned by hand may be used for marking drilling positions in wood. A punch is also used for accurate marking.

For lines that run parallel to an edge:

- a **marking gauge** is used on wood for marking along the grain;
- a **cutting gauge** is used on wood for marking across the grain;
- **odd leg calipers** are used on metal and plastic. These can be adjusted to the right distance and then 'scored down' the material to give a straight line.
- A **mortise gauge** is similar to a marking gauge but it has two pins, one which is fixed and one which is adjustable. It is used to mark out to create mortise and tenon joints (see unit 13).

To mark out a circle, **compasses** with a pencil can be used on wood and a chinagraph pencil (or some felt tip pens) can be used on plastic. For metal a pair of **dividers** is used because pencil will not mark clearly on metal (except aluminium). For longer arcs or circles a **trammel** is used on metal.

activities

The design shown here is made from plastic, wood and metal. To make the design the tubing, plastic and steel have to be measured, marked and cut.

(a) Suggest TWO advantages of a steel over a plastic or wooden ruler.

(b) What equipment might you use to measure: (i) the length of the tubing; (ii) the diameter of the tubing? Explain your answer.

(c) Explain whether you would use a chinagraph pencil, a pencil or a scriber for marking on: (i) wood; (ii) plastic; (iii) mild steel.

(d) What equipment would you use to:
(i) mark out a stated length on the metal;
(ii) mark an unusual shape for cutting out the plastic?

Mild steel dipcoated in LDPE
Tied
5mm acrylic plastic
Thin string, nylon or wire
Copper, bamboo or cane tubing

Wind chime

unit 11

Shaping by cutting

Cutting lines and shapes

The next stage after marking out (see unit 10) a piece of material is to cut it. This removes waste before forming or assembling (see units 12 and 13). Suitable tools must be chosen to ensure material is cut efficiently, without damage to the material or the tool.

Saws are the standard cutting tool for resistant materials, as in Figure 1. Wood saws generally have a broad blade with an attached handle. Saws for cutting plastic and metal have a thin blade fixed in an open bow. The blade of a saw has its teeth slightly bent (or 'set') alternatively left and right to give clearance to the blade and prevent the saw jamming. This makes the saw cut slightly wider than the blade thickness. An allowance has to be made for this when measuring and marking.

After a while saw blades become dull and lose their sharpness. It is important that the saw to be used is sharp enough to do the job. During sawing the teeth of the saw may become clogged with debris. A saw will not cut properly unless the teeth are kept clean. A thin or hard material will require a fine blade in a saw. Soft materials tend to clog the teeth of fine blades and require coarser blades.

In industry, larger power saws and machines are used for cutting. There are strict regulations, legal restrictions and training requirements before operators can use these machines because of the health and safety dangers (see unit 15). Such machines include:

- circular saws to reduce large sections of timber to smaller size;
- fret saws which turn to follow a pattern;
- band saws with a continuous blade for cutting smaller timber accurately;
- table saws for cutting timber to length by cross cutting;
- scroll saws which are pulled across timber for cross cutting to length.

Figure 1 Tools for cutting lines and shapes.

Hand saw
cuts long lengths of wood.
Different saws do different jobs, eg a ripsaw cuts along the grain and a cross saw cuts across the grain.

Tenon saw
cuts smaller sections of wood, eg cutting wood before jointing.
More accurate and teeth finer than hand saw.

Hacksaw
(cuts metal and plastic).
Tension can be adjusted.

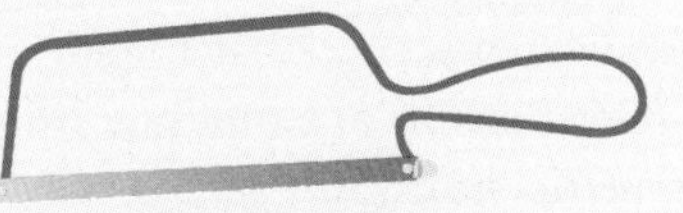

Junior hacksaw
(cuts metal and plastic).
Used for smaller, lighter work than hacksaw.

Tinsnips or shears
(cut metal or PVC sheets up to 1mm thick but not tubing or wire as it does not give a clean cut by hand).

Pliers (metal/wire).

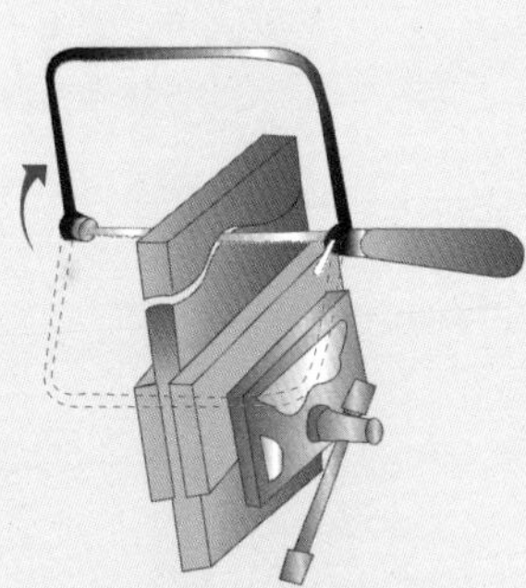

Coping saw
(cuts wood and plastic).
Narrow blade with teeth sloping towards the handle. The frame can be adjusted to cut tight corners.

Electrical jig-saw
(cuts wood and plastic)
Narrow blade, can turn to follow a pattern.

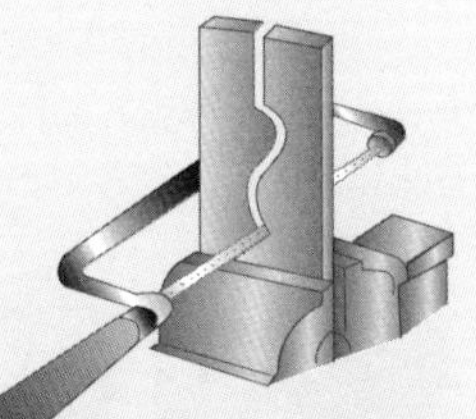

Abrafile (cuts metal).
Round, file-like blade that fits into a hacksaw.
Cuts in any direction.

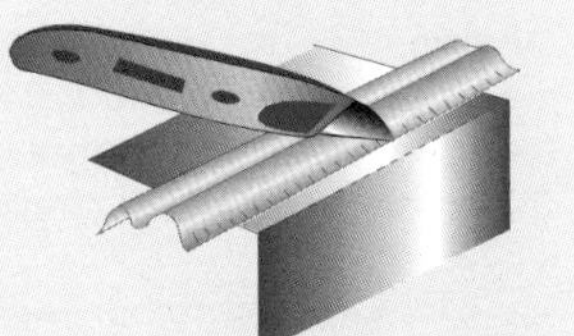

Scoring tool
(hardboard or thin plastic sheet)
Break off board or sheet

Holding tools for cutting

Before cutting, a material must be secured to prevent it slipping. A **bench hook** is used for holding small sections of wood to be cut across the grain. It also prevents the bench from damage. A vice is used for larger pieces of wood or for work that requires more detail, such as joint cutting, chiselling or cutting patterns so that both hands are free to work. When using a **metalwork vice** it is wise to place soft vice jaws onto the vice to protect the material being cut from damage. **Mitre boxes** can be use to hold and guide a saw blade when an angled cut is needed.

Chucks are used for holding either the material to be cut or the cutting tools. The chuck of a pedestal drill, for example, holds the bit for drilling into material which is held in a vice or clamped to a table.

Drilling

Before drilling materials need a location point, made by centre punching (see unit 10). This is because drill bits are chisel edged at the bottom and without a hole

A G-cramp.

A metalwork vice.

A machine vice.

activities

1 The hook is being made and fitted to a metal plate for wall mounting. Explain how you would:

(a) mark out the plate for drilling;
(b) drill the holes for the screws and the hook;
(c) tap the hole.

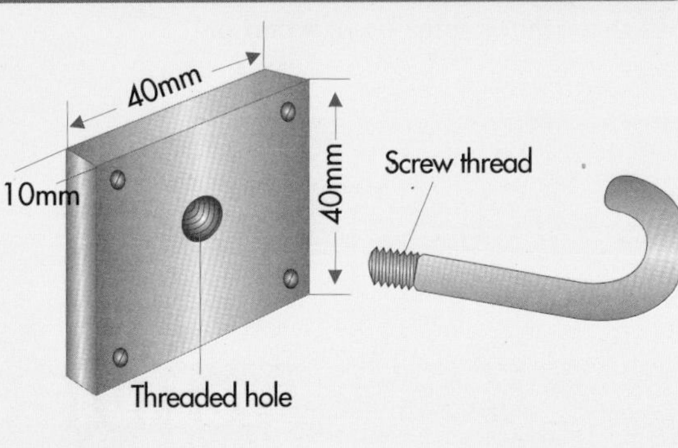

2 The plastic key ring is being made from acrylic using hand held tools.

(a) What tools and equipment might you use to:
(i) cut the outer shape;
(ii) remove the material to get the key shape in the middle?
(b) Suggest how the cutting process could be made more efficient.

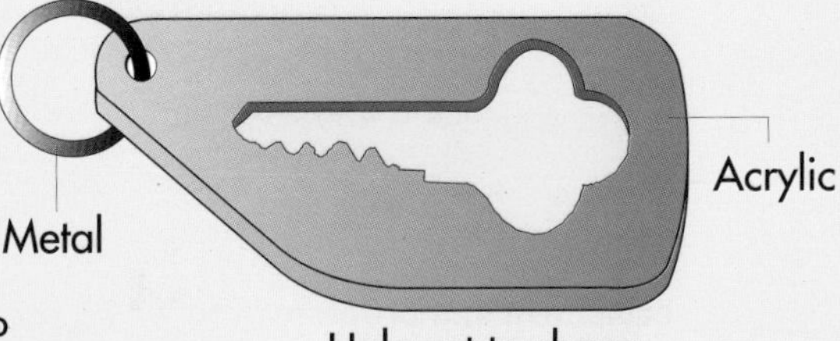

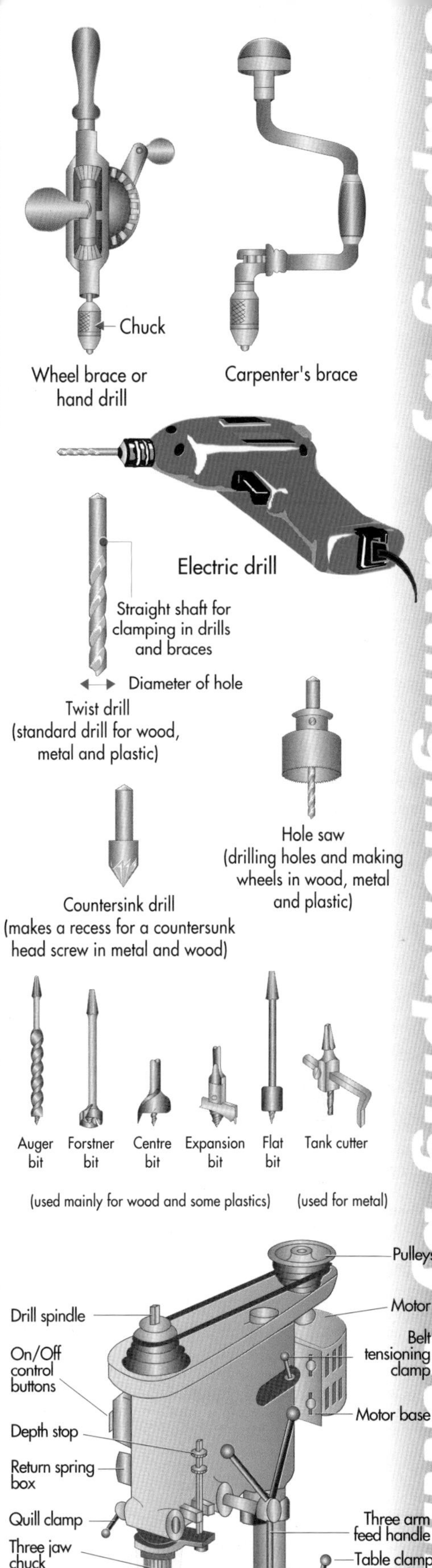

Figure 2 Bits and tools for drilling.

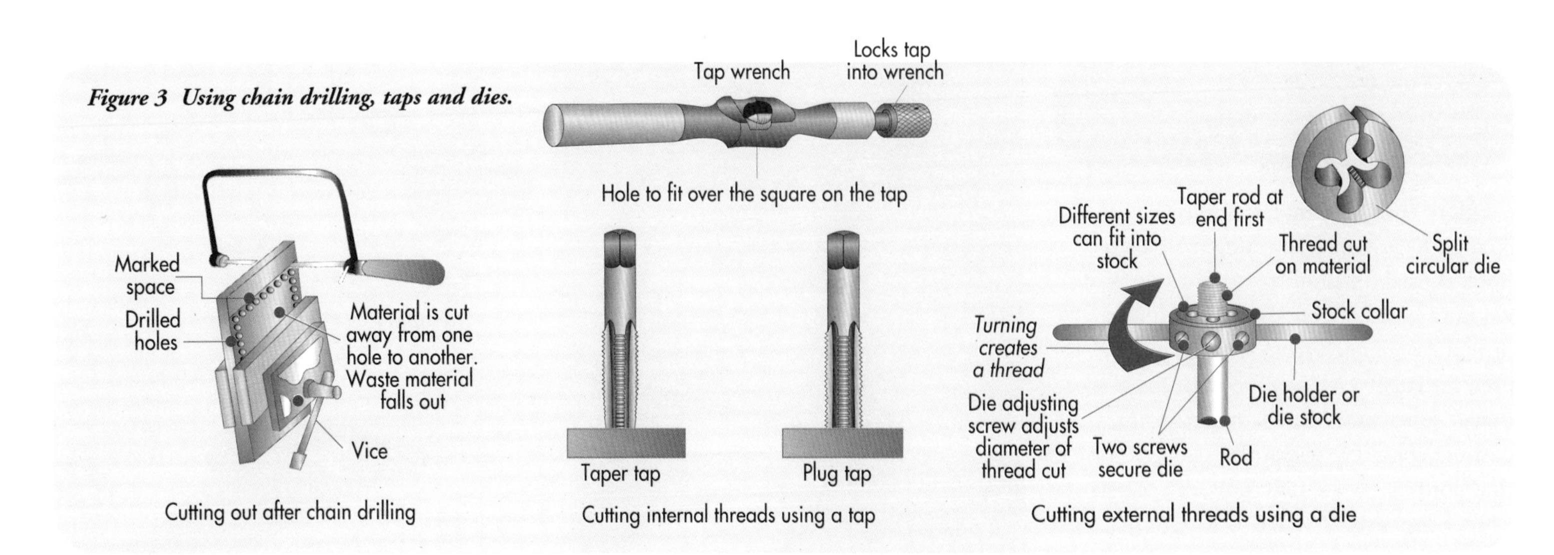

Figure 3 Using chain drilling, taps and dies.

they will swivel to the side and drill in the wrong place.

Materials can be drilled using hand drills or static drills (both manual and electrical). Whichever is used, the correct type of drill bit must be used for a job. The drill bit fits into the chuck and is tightened to hold it in place. The standard drill bit for cutting holes in wood, metal and plastic is the **twist** drill. There is a wide range of drill bits for cutting holes up to 50mm in diameter.

When drilling materials it is important to set the drill at the correct speed and to feed it through the material at the correct rate. Generally, softer materials, such as wood, plastic and softer metals like brass, require fast drill speeds to prevent the drill being clogged. A small drill bit needs a faster drill speed than a larger bit if used on the same material. If the speed is too slow, the waste will not be removed quickly enough and the bit will jam in the material. A slower speed is needed for harder materials, such as cast iron, to ensure that the bit cuts the hole properly.

The feed of the drill should be faster through softer materials and slower through harder materials. Too slow a feed through hard materials may result in the bit rubbing, which dulls its sharpness and can result in overheating. However, when nearly through the material, it is important to slow the feed as the bit breaks through to avoid it cracking the material.

Lubricants are often used when drilling to reduce friction and heat. Examples are paraffin (aluminium), oil or a cutting compound (steels) and turps or paraffin (acrylic). Brass and nylon are self-lubricating.

Holding tools for drilling

When drilling, the material should be held firmly on the drill table. A **G-cramp** is best for large sheets or awkward shapes which cannot be held in a conventional vice. A **machine vice** can be used for smaller pieces of materials because they can be held safely in the jaws. Small sheet materials can be held in a **hand vice**. It is advisable to place a piece of waste wood under the material when drilling to prevent 'burrs' being formed on metal, as the drill breaks through, or splitting of wood or plastic.

Chain drilling, taps and dies

Chain drilling is a process that is used to remove a lot of waste material quickly. Holes are drilled inside the marked space, making sure that the drill does not cut into the workpiece, which causes the waste material to fall out. A chisel, abrafile or coping saw maybe used to help 'join up the dots'. The rough edges can then be filed upto the marking line.

TAPS are used to cut internal threads and DIES for external threads. For an internal thread, the correct sized hole must first be drilled using a tapping drill and the waste removed. In most cases the thread is begun using a taper tap and completed using a plug tap. A second stage tap could be used, but is not essential. The tap is turned using a tap wrench. It is important to keep the tap wrench at 90° to the work or a 'drunken' thread will result. Every half turn forward should be followed by a quarter reverse turn to remove waste. School workshops tend to use 2-12mm threads. In industry threads may be greater than 35mm or very fine (for use in electrical components). 25 mm

activities

The candle holder is to be made using a centre lathe to produce the bar and the base fitted later.

Explain the equipment and processes you would use to:

(a) reduce the bar to the diameter shown;
(b) cut the hole to fit the candle;
(c) cut the thread to fit into the base.

ø20 ø15 ø12 M8

Candle holder (without base)

Figure 4 Different file shapes and cuts.

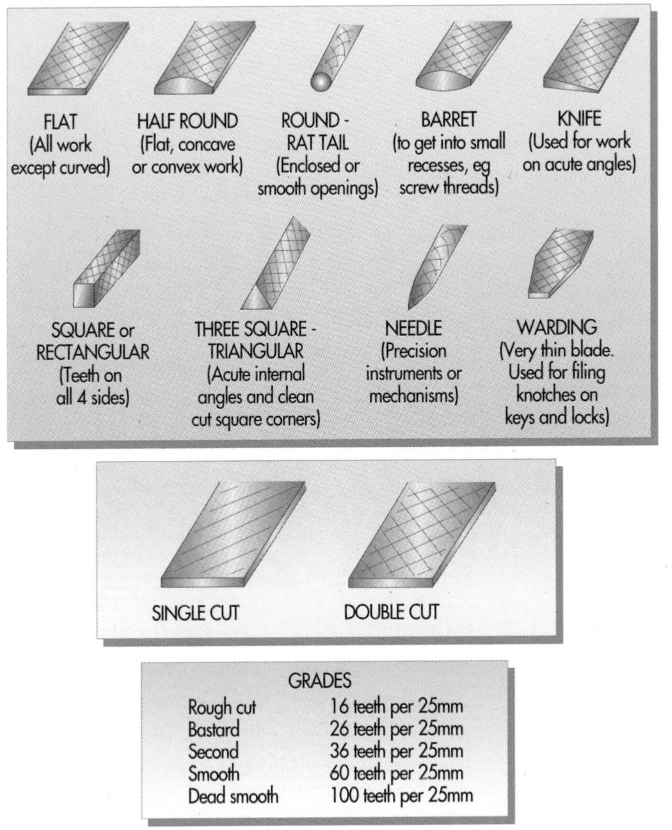

GRADES

Rough cut	16 teeth per 25mm
Bastard	26 teeth per 25mm
Second	36 teeth per 25mm
Smooth	60 teeth per 25mm
Dead smooth	100 teeth per 25mm

threads are very common. British Association taps and dies are used for small work, eg electronics.

A die is used for an external thread. The rod to be threaded needs to be tapered at one end to start the die cutting. The die is held in a die holder and pressed down on the rod turning clockwise. Waste should be removed by forward and reverse turns. Once completed, the die is wound back up the rod. Lubrication is important when cutting internal and external threads.

Filing

Files are used for shaping materials after they have been cut. They smooth rough edges and can be used for more detailed work, such as levelling off a misshapen piece of material. Files are available in different lengths, shapes and cuts, as in Figure 4. The cut of a file depends on how coarse it is (the number of teeth per inch) and the type of teeth it has. Hand files usually have teeth on 3 sides and a safe edge (no teeth) on the other to clean out corners without under cutting. A coarse file is best suited to rapid filing to remove a lot of waste. Finer work requires a smoother file. Files are usually used on metal and plastic, as teeth can become clogged if used on wood.

Planes, rasps, chisels and gouges

Planes are use to cut or smooth wood. They can be used to make wood thinner or to clean up joints after sawing or chiselling. **Rasps** carry out a similar function to files. They look like a rough file and are used on timber and plastic because they have open cupped teeth which do not clog up with material easily. After rasping, wood and plastic are smoothed further with glass or silicon carbide paper. **Chisels** are used to remove waste wood when making joints (see unit 13). They have a sharpened blade at the cutting edge and a handle for holding and striking. **Gouges** are a type of chisel that is used

Figure 5 Examples of planes and rasps and their uses.

Figure 6 Examples of chisels and gouges and their uses.

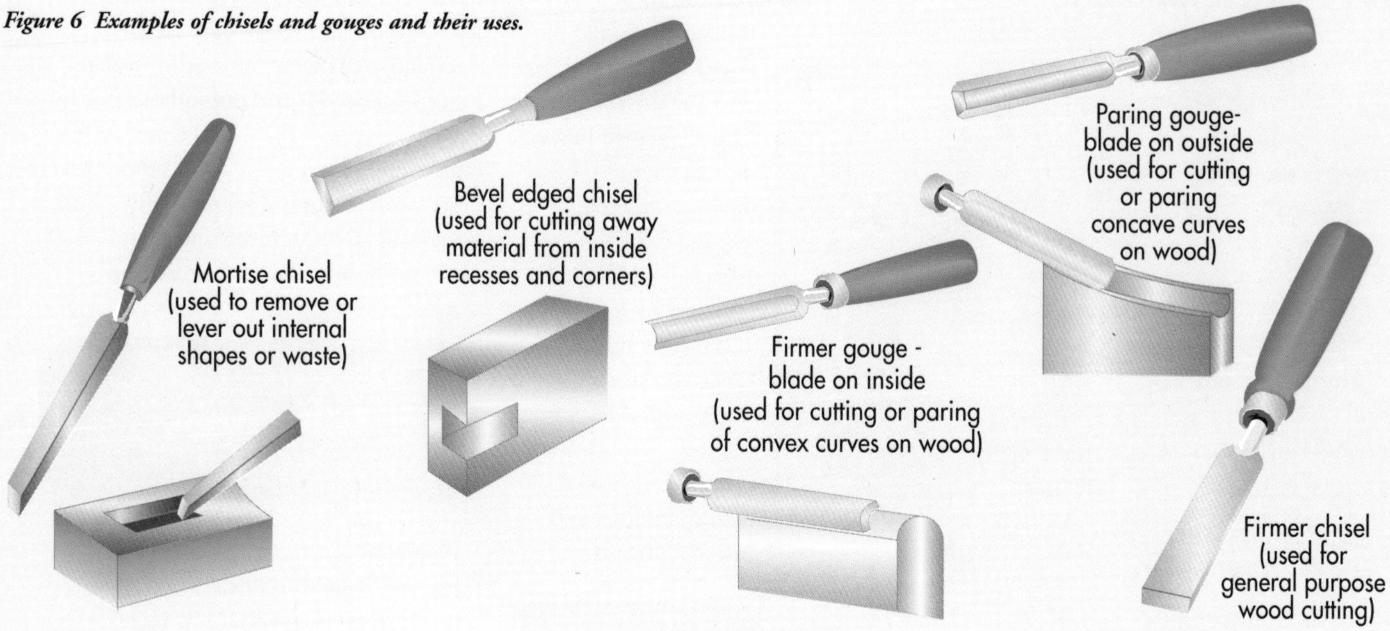

to hollow out and to carve shapes. Cold chisels are used to cut sheet metal that is cold, whilst held either in an engineer's vice or on a cutting plate. **Hand or machine gouges** are used for cutting long grooves in timber (eg housing joints).

Machines and safety

By law all machines, such as pillar drills, milling machines and lathes, must have safety guards fitted around either the cutters, chucks or moving parts. Some are fixed to an appropriate part of the machine table. This depends on the most efficient and safe working method. Guards come in many shapes and sizes. Many of the machines shown in this and other units have guards omitted so that important detail can be shown.

Milling machines

A MILLING MACHINE is used for cutting slits and grooves and for making flat surfaces on large pieces of metal or plastic. Materials are fixed to a table which is moved backwards and forwards as the material is cut. The table can also be raised or lowered to alter the depth of the cut.

Different cutters can be used on milling machines for different jobs, such as side and face cutters, slab cutters, slitting saws and angle cutters. Because of the heat generated as cutters cut the material, a consistent supply of cutting fluid is applied to cool

Figure 7 Horizontal and vertical milling machines.

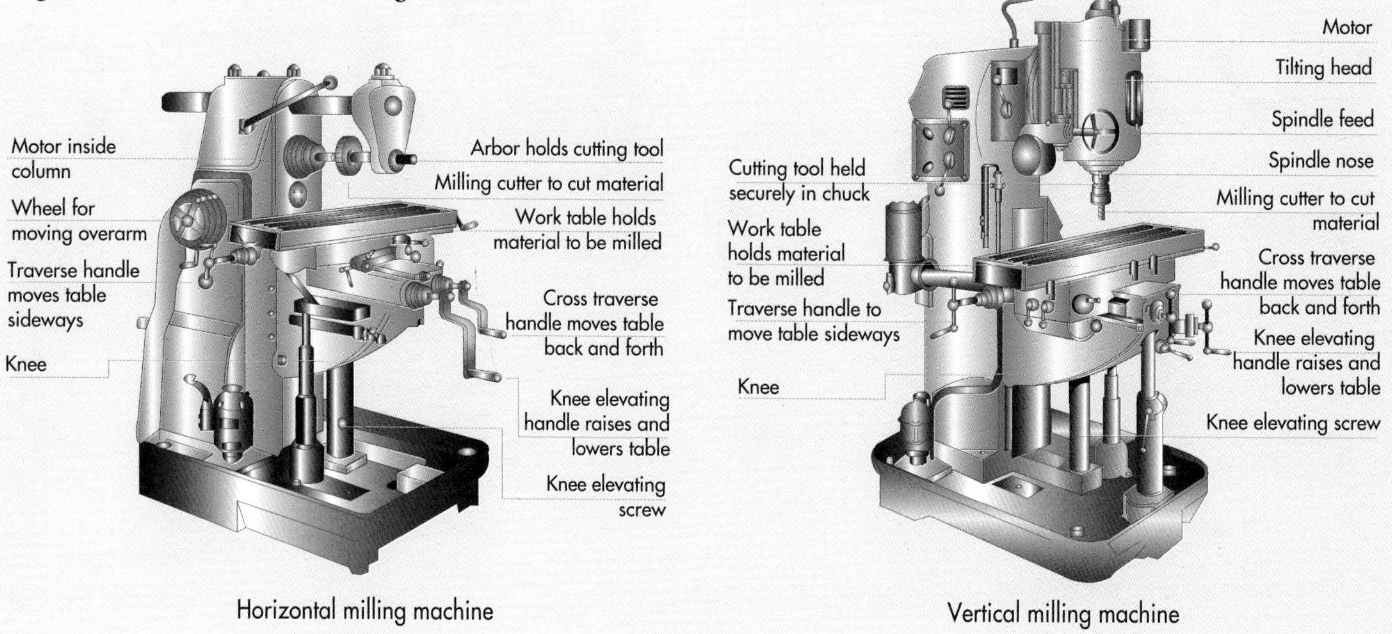

them and prevent 'burn' of the material and dulling of the cutters. The fluid also washes away swarf (cuttings). Care must be taken when cutting thermoplastics (see unit 5) as they can melt (paraffin can be used as a coolant). Other safety procedures include wearing goggles, tying back long hair and keeping hands away from the cutters. Machines should always be properly guarded.

Increasingly computers are being used to control machines. The operator will design a pattern or program on a computer screen using a suitable program. Instructions are then passed to the motor which operates the moving table. This machine is called a COMPUTER NUMERICALLY CONTROLLED (CNC) MILLING MACHINE. The advantages are that it should eliminate human error in the measuring and cutting process, and allow cutting to be carried out quickly and accurately. CNC machines have a surrounding structure for safety during operation.

A CNC lathe.

Lathes

Lathes are used to turn materials as they are being cut. They have a fixed headstock which holds the main drive that runs the lathe. At the other end is the tailstock.

On a WOOD TURNING LATHE cylindrical shapes, such as chair legs, can be made by holding material between two centres. One centre is on the tailstock and does not turn. The other is the driving centre in the headstock which turns, also turning the material. A cutting tool is held still (by hand on a rest) at right angles to the material as it turns. For disc-like objects, such as bowls, the material is attached to a faceplate or chuck on the headstock and the tailstock is not used. The tools used are gouges and chisels (roughing gouges, bowl gouges, spindle or carving gouges, skew chisel) and scraper tools for hollowing. A parting tool can be used when working on a length of wood. Fine grade glass paper is used for smoothing and finishing the wood.

activities

A Japanese spinning top works in an unusual way. If spun with the handle upwards, it turns around and then jumps onto its handle, spinning upside down. One way to make the top is to start with a square piece of wood and drill a wide hole using a forstener bit. A smaller hole is then drilled for a piece of dowel to be fitted as a handle. The top shape is created by turning.

Source: adapted from Good Woodworking, April 1996.

(a) What equipment could be used to:
(i) turn a piece of wood;
(ii) cut the wood as it is turning;
(iii) drill a hole?

(b) Suggest TWO types of drill that might be used to make the top shown here and how they would be used.

(c) Why is turning used when making a top?

case study

STAN GASKELL

The natural beauty of wooden objects gives an interesting and natural look to kitchens, halls and living rooms. Shops sell such crafted products at prices that would often deter the impulse buyer.

One-off, high class, wooden products are the speciality of Stan Gaskell. They are manufactured by turning on a workshop lathe. Many of the products are based on his own ideas from things he sees around him. For example, a wide range of wooden fruit is manufactured by turning, including apples, pears and bananas. So are mushrooms and acorns which can open to reveal balls of string or needles. Other designs include fruit bowls, reading lamps and candle sticks. These are ideally suited to lathe work because of their shape, although more complicated shapes and designs may require hand carving or assembly. A wooden telephone, for example, is made from a turned body and ear piece, with a carved ear piece support.

Designs are made from a variety of woods, such as spalted beech, parana pine, oak, ash, larch and mahogany. Each type of wood has its own grain formation, giving a different appearance to the final product. The original pieces that are worked from are usually off-cuts or waste wood that has been collected from a variety of sources. The designs are finished in beeswax.

Source: Stan Gaskell.

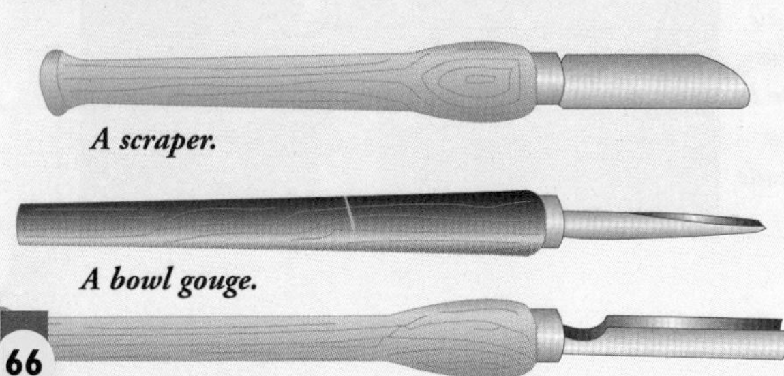

A scraper.

A bowl gouge.

A roughing gouge.

The manufacture of a fruit bowl by turning takes place in a number of stages

1 Decide what to make and determine the size. Use compasses to mark out the circular shape to be cut from the log. Cut the shape using a band saw. This is known as a blank.

2 Drill a hole in the circular blank to accept the pin chuck, which is one part of a combination chuck. This will hold the timber whilst spinning on the headstock of the lathe. Use a roughing gouge to shape the bowl. Rough the outside of the bowl with a small gouge. Cut a dovetail recess in the bottom of the bowl to accept expanding dovetail collets. Develop the outside curve with a bowl gouge.

3 Remove the bowl from the pin chuck. Reverse the bowl and replace the pin chuck with the dovetail collets to fit the recess already cut.

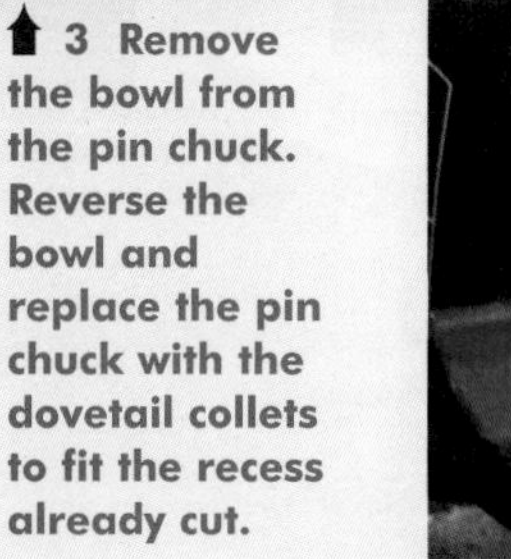

4 Shape the inside of the bowl with a 3/8 inch bowl gouge. The inside can be finished with a scraper chisel and sanded to a fine surface.

5 Sand the completed bowl and finish, for example with beeswax or French polisher's oil.

Questions

(a) What marking tool is used for marking out a shape to be cut for a fruit bowl?
(b) Why is it important to mark out correctly before cutting?
(c) What tools and equipment are used in manufacturing wooden bowls and wooden fruit by turning?
(d) Explain why these tools and equipment are used and the job each does.
(e) A business which manufactures bowls and candle stands in batches operates in the same area. Compare the possible equipment and the production methods to the products manufactured by Stan Gaskell.

TWINBRIDGE PRECISION AND GENERAL ENGINEERS

Whether it's components for road tankers, machine parts for the chemical industry that require acid resistant material or special 'one off' designs, Twinbridge Precision and General Engineers can manufacture and repair to a variety of specifications. The company produces parts for the food, chemical, road tanker, agriculture and packaging industries, such as valves, fittings, machine parts, bolts, shafts and hinges, as well as machines.

It has even been known to produce a one-off machine for putting (edible) nuts onto ice-creams specially designed for a customer's needs. One of the challenges faced was getting the 'hole' exactly the right size! This has since been adapted to drop other food items.

Twinbridge manufactures in most metals, including mild steel, aluminium and brass, but has particular strengths in stainless steel. Production is ideally suited to batches of up to 50 items and 'one off' designs can be carried out to customer drawings. Components are sometimes held as stock and designs are kept on computer for future repeated runs.

The company has both manual and CNC milling and lathe machines. CNC machines were introduced to cope with the intricate shapes and exact measurements required by the industries the business serves. They also enable cost savings, as jobs that would previously have taken days, such as moulds, can be produced far more quickly. The use of CNC machines also keeps make ready times to a minimum for the customer, which is a major advantage in attracting clients.

Source: Twinbridge Precision and General Engineers.

Components.

CNC milling.

Questions

(a) Suggest THREE products that may be made by Twinbrige Precision and General Engineers.

(b) Explain how:
(i) milling;
(ii) lathe machines;
may be used in the manufacture of metal components.

(c) Suggest reasons why CNC machines were introduced into the business.

(d) Do you think that Twinbridge is likely to expand into mass production? Explain your answer.

unit 12 Shaping by forming

Forming

Materials are not only shaped by cutting (see unit 11). They can also be shaped by **forming** and **casting**. To do this they have to be shaped using a MOULD or FORMER. Some materials form more easily than others. Many resistant materials need to be heated before they are shaped or formed around a mould. The material is likely to be in sheet form, although it can be in rod or bar form, or even rectangular sections.

Hanging baskets can be made by steaming thin slats of timber and weaving them around a former to maintain the shape.

Rubber sheet
Polythene sheet
Solid wood or EPS former
Veneers and glue

Figure 1 Shaping wood using a former.

Shaping wood

Wood is a springy material. It can be bent, but it tends to return to its original shape once the pressure is released. Thin 'green' timber tends to be very bendy. Wood such as yew is naturally bendy and was used in the past to make longbows.

Wood can only be bent into a shallow curve. If bent too far it will crack and split. Most solid timber, such as beech, will bend permanently if steam heated, shaped and left to dry. Thin laminate sheets can be shaped around a former made out of solid timber or EPS. The laminated strips are placed in the former. Sandwiched between the strips is adhesive that will bond them together. Rubber or polythene are placed on the outside for protection. The laminations are then pressed together using a G-cramp (see unit 11). The required pressure can also be obtained by using a vacuum bag, which is useful for batch production (see unit 19). Timber curved through lamination is stronger than similar solid timber.

Products made from shaped timber include acoustic guitar bodies and furniture, as well as larger structures such as supports in buildings.

Shaping plastics

For plastics to be shaped in three dimensions they have to be heated and folded around a mould. This is called THERMOFORMING. The working properties of any plastic depend on the temperature to which it is heated. This is shown in Figure 2. Thermoplastics can be shaped in a variety of ways. Thermosetting plastics are more limited because once set they cannot be reshaped (see unit 5).

activities

Look at the information about guitars.

(a) Identify the wooden parts on a guitar that have been shaped and those that have been cut.
(b) Why is a former needed to shape wood?
(c) Suggest why manufacturers may use laminated wood rather than natural wood when making guitar parts.

Acoustic guitars can make a sound without electronic amplification. Some guitar manufacturers make the rims of bodies by soaking wood and then shaping it over a heated pipe. Guitar bodies and sides have been made with woods such as rosewood, mahogany, spruce and maple. However, as the cutting down of certain trees has been restricted and prices have risen, some cheaper models have used laminated 3 ply back and sides.
Source: adapted from The Ultimate Guitar Book, T. Bacon, Dorling Kindersley.

Bending the sides. To make guitar rims, wood is soaked and then shaped over a heated pipe.

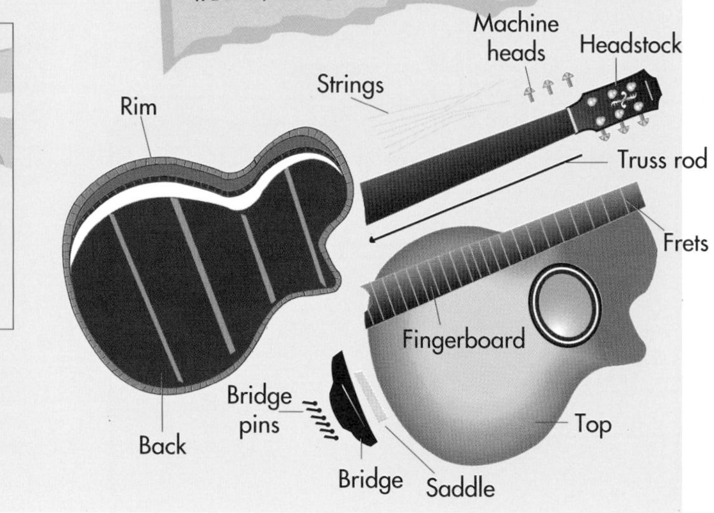

Figure 2 Temperatures and the properties of plastic.

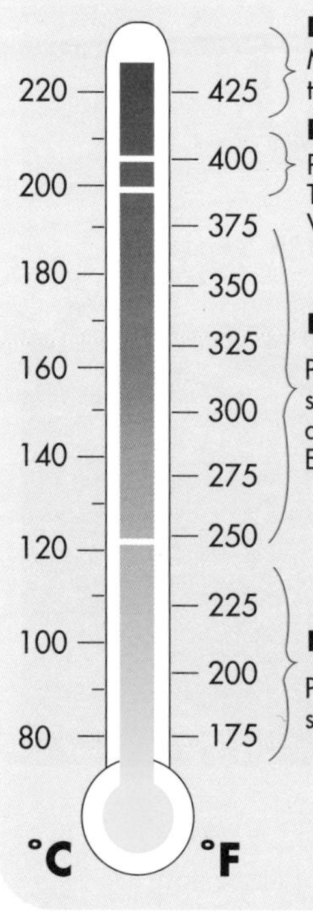

Degrading
Most plastics contain water (hydroscopic). At high temperatures water will boil causing plastic to blister.

Plastic
Plastics become soft and sag under their own weight. They are easy to mould into definable shapes. Vacuum forming and extrusion moulding can be used.

Elastic
Plastics can be bent or folded into permenant shape with force. Line bending, press forming, drape forming and blow moulding can be used. Edges tend to be rounded and angles not so acute.

Rigid
Plastics are bendy and spring back to original shape when pressure is released.

Figure 3 Line bending.

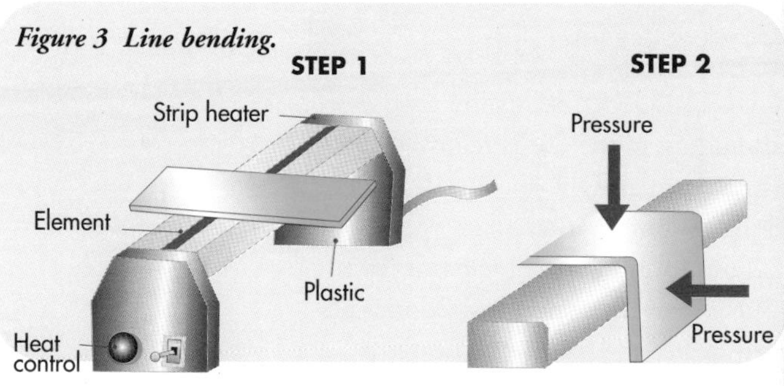

Line bending

LINE BENDING involves the use of a single line of heat from a single electrical element which may be a spiral coil, a tensioned wire or a 'V' blade sword. The part of the plastic to be bent is placed near to the element. It is warmed until it becomes 'elastic', turning each side of the sheet to provide even heat along the line on both sides. Once it is elastic, the plastic is transferred to a cooling jig where it is folded into shape. Shapes will have broad curves rather than sharp edges. The thicker the plastic, the sharper the angle of curve possible. The cooling jig should be designed to apply force on the cool region of the plastic and not on the heated area. This must be allowed to cool naturally so the molecules can arrange themselves evenly, avoiding weak points in the structure. Jigs made from wood or wood composites are best.

A suitable material for line bending is acrylic. Other materials are ABS and PVC which have a very 'elastic' range. Polystyrene is also used, although it requires skilful handling. Line bending is useful because it allows a shape to be formed without the use of corner joints (see unit 13).

Blow moulding

Like line bending, BLOW MOULDING is suited to materials that have a long 'elastic' range. Acrylic, PVC, ABS and HDPE are used for blow moulding. Blow moulding, as its name implies, involves blowing air under pressure onto heated plastic which is held in a moulding jig. The plastic has to be heated and transferred quickly to a jig while still 'elastic'. The plastic is allowed to rise to about half its diameter at which point the blowing stops, trapping the air between the plastic, the mould and the valve. Once cooled, the plastic is released from the mould and finished.

Typical shapes and products made by blow moulding include balls or spheres and plastic bottles.

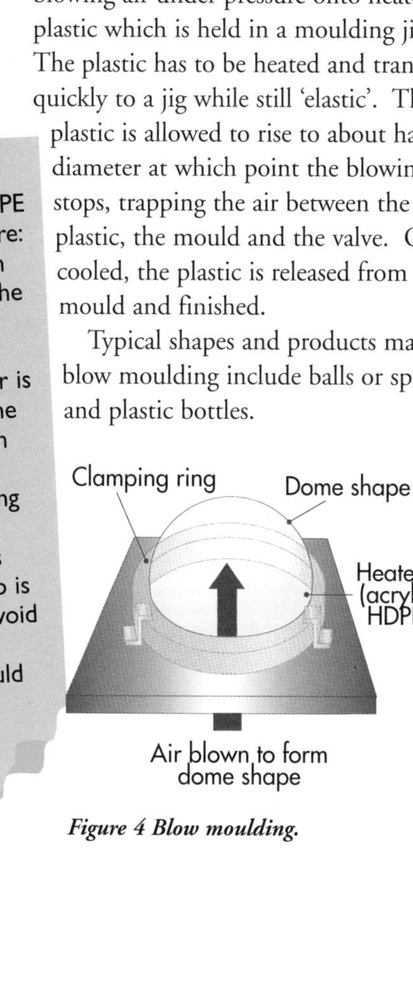

Figure 4 Blow moulding.

activities

Read the article.

(a) Why is blow moulding suitable for producing plastic containers?

(b) Suggest THREE types of container that could be made using this process.

(c) Draw a flow chart showing the steps in blow moulding at Plysu.

Plysu is a manufacturer of blow moulded plastic containers for consumer and industrial use. It uses HDPE for the majority of its production. The steps involved are:

- polymer pellets are fed into the blow moulder, which are heated, mixed to a molten form and pushed to the head of the machine through a die. This creates a plastic tube called a parison;
- a metal mould is clamped around the parison and air is blown into the parison through a blowing pin. As the plastic comes into contact with the colder mould it freezes to the shape of the mould, creating the container;
- after a period the container is taken out of the mould. Scrap is cut away and fed back in to avoid wastage. The containers are tested for pinholes which could cause leakages. Satisfactory containers are then taken to be packed and sealed.

Source: David Howlett, Plysu.

A blow moulding machine at Plysu.

Vacuum forming

VACUUM FORMING is the reverse of blow moulding in that air is removed to create a vacuum and the air outside forces heated plastic onto a mould.

A vacuum forming machine has its own heat source. A plastic sheet is fixed into an air sealed gasket and an electric heater is pulled over the the top of the plastic to make it soft. It is then heated until it becomes 'plastic'. At the correct temperature the heater is removed and the suction begins. At the same time the mould is raised up into the forming position. The remaining air is removed causing the plasticised sheet to form over the mould. As soon as the plastic becomes rigid, the vacuum pump is reversed to 'blow', causing air to fill the seal and lift the formed plastic from the mould. **Drape forming** is similar to vacuum forming except that the former is raised up into the softened plastic, which drapes itself around the former.

High impact polystyrene (HIPS) is popular as a vacuum forming material as it is cheap, has a wide 'plastic' range and comes in lots of colours. Unlike many other plastics it does not need to be pre-dried before forming. Polypropylene gives the best definition if vacuum formed and also does not require pre-drying. Its natural colour is white, but it becomes clear when heated to the 'plastic' range. Other plastics that can be used are extruded acrylic, ABS, polycarbonate and PET.

Products that can be made by vacuum forming include cube shapes, such as alarm boxes, hollow shapes, such as helmets, and irregular shapes, such as chocolate box or biscuit tin 'linings' and bodies of children's toys.

Figure 5 Vacuum forming.

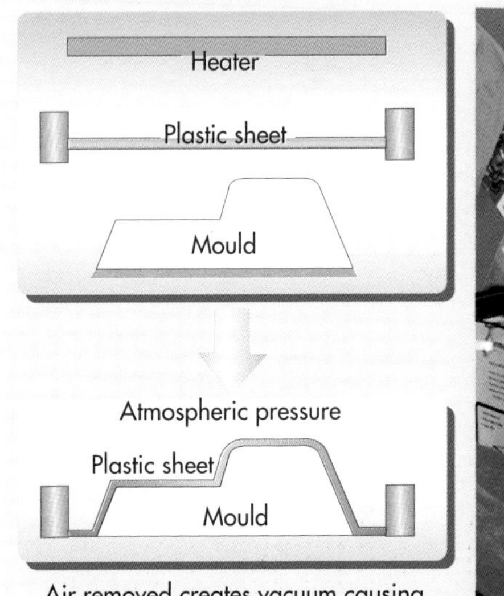

Injection, extrusion and compression moulding

INJECTION MOULDING involves heating granules of plastic until they become fluid. A piston forces the fluid plastic into a mould, where it cools to form the shape of the mould. The product is then removed. This process can be repeated a lot in rapid succession to produce lots of the same product quickly. Injection moulded products can be recognised by the sprue mark where the plastic is injected. Products made by this method include wheels, bowls, crates, storage bins and toys. A wide range of plastics is used including ABS, HDPE, polypropylene and polystyrene.

EXTRUSION MOULDING is similar to injection moulding except that the fluid plastic is forced through a die to produce long continuous shapes. The shape of the die determines the shape of the extruded plastic, which can be trimmed to size.

activities

The design below is being vacuum formed in plastic with the use of a former. It is to be manufactured by a local group to be given away as a free gift for young children whose parents come to a fete.

(a) Explain the steps that would be followed to produce it.
(b) Suggest a suitable plastic that could be used.
(c) Explain how the product might be made in batches.

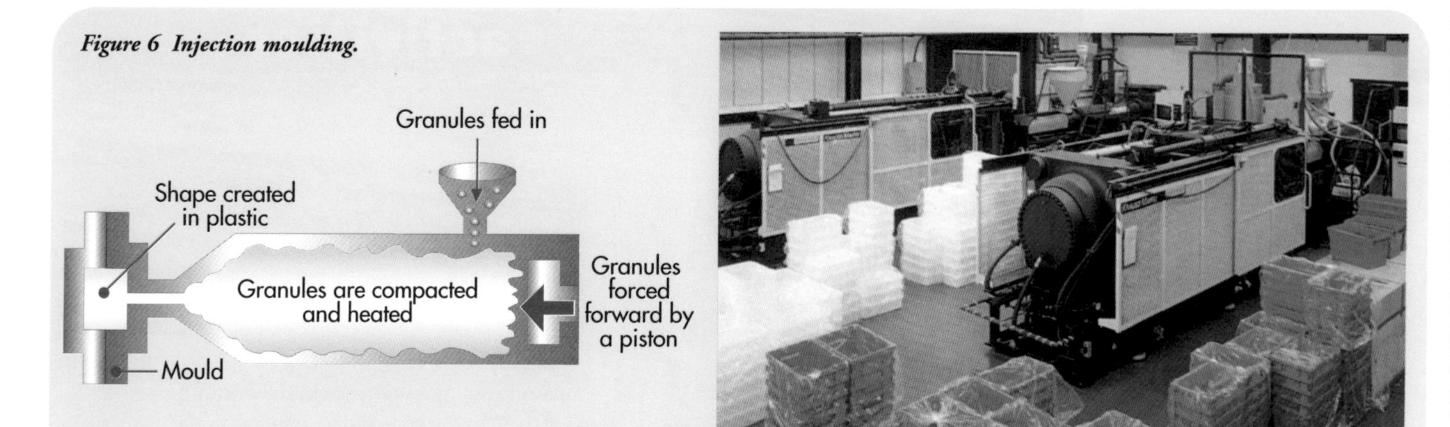

Figure 6 Injection moulding.

An industrial injection moulding machine.

Plastic window frames, curtain rails, pipes, guttering and plastic bags are made by extrusion.

COMPRESSION MOULDING involves plastic being heated into a 'plasticised' form, put into a mould and then compressed. This forces it to take the shape of the mould. It is used for thermosetting plastics (sce unit 5) like phenol formaldehyde and urea formaldehyde resins in powdered form. It is used to make electric fittings (urea formaldehyde) and saucepan handles (phenol).

Cold casting

In this process the plastic is in liquid form as a resin. It is mixed with a hardener and is poured into a mould. The force of gravity allows the mixture to take the shape of the mould. The mixture sets (or cures) and is then removed from the mould. The moulds used can be rigid (made from wood, metal or glass) or flexible (made from rubber or plasticine). Flexible moulds allow for better surface detail and can be used many times. However, they limit the size of the cast and only one cast can be made at a time.

Continuous cell casting is useful for low number batch production. A measured amount of MMA syrup is poured into a glass mould, rotated through 90° and then placed in an oven where the syrup polymerises and cures. If colour is added it tends to settle in the syrup, making one face more coloured than the other.

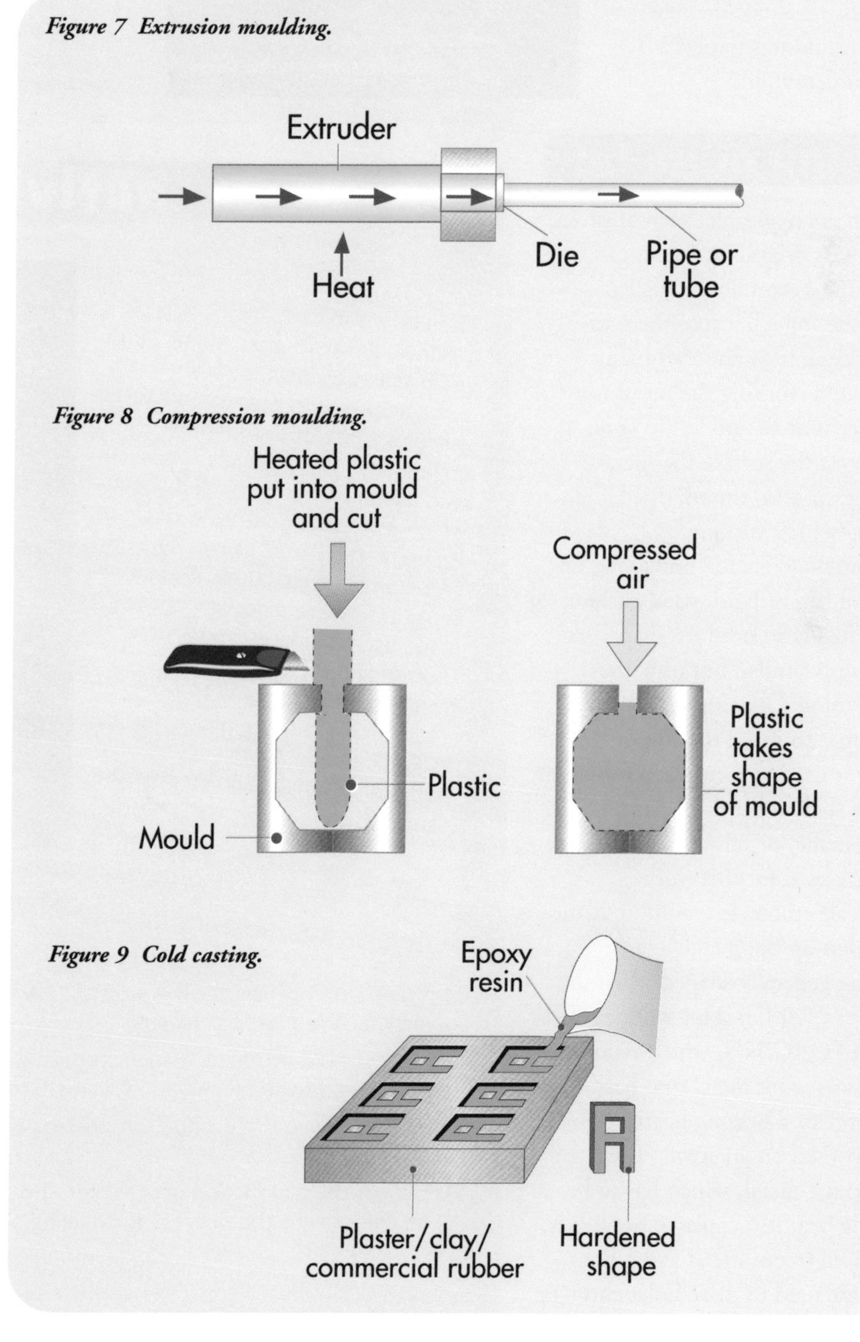

Figure 7 Extrusion moulding.

Figure 8 Compression moulding.

Figure 9 Cold casting.

Plastics memory

Plastics have a MEMORY. Thermoplastics retain information about their original shape when reheated. This can be used to create a raised shape. The plastic is warmed and an indentation put into the hot plastic before it is allowed to cool. The surrounding plastic is then removed to the level of the indentation and the plastic reheated. The plastic will remember the indentation shape and expand again, rising above the new level of the surroundings to give a 3D outline of the indentation.

An injection moulding machine manufacturing video boxes.

activities

Alpha Tech is a company that specialises in high volume plastic injection moulding processes. One of its main activities is the manufacture of video boxes and other related products. The production of video boxes has increased rapidly over several years due to increased demand.

(a) Explain how injection moulding would be used to manufacture video boxes.
(b) Suggest TWO other products that might be made.
(c) What is meant by 'high volume plastic injection moulding'?

Source: BI Group.

Working of metal

Metals which are malleable, such as silver, gold, copper, brass or gilding metal, can be shaped cold using a hammer or mallet. Repeated hammering will cause them to work harden (see unit 6) and eventually crack. Before cold working the metal must be annealed (see unit 6) and left to cool. If oxides develop on the surface the metal must be pickled in acid, rinsed, dried and scrubbed clean before working.

Cold working may include **hollowing** of metal on a sand bag or hard wood cushion and a bossing mallet to produce shapes like dishes. **Sinking** is similar, but only the centre is sunk using a bossing mallet or blocking hammer to make the rim or the edge. Raising is used to form deep or wide shallow shapes such as bowls or pans. A wedge shaped mallet or raising hammer and raising stake are used for this work. **Planishing** is carried out to smooth out the work and harden up the metal.

Hot steels are generally shaped when the metal is red hot (700°C). Hot working of metal is called FORGING, which requires a variety of tools to work metal that has been heated in a forge or a brazing hearth. The hot metal is worked on an anvil. Tongs are needed to grip the metal, which has to be returned to the heat if it cools. Chisels (see unit 11) are used to cut metal along lines and punches are used to drive holes through

activities

The Heywood Williams Group plc is a manufacturer of glass, aluminium and plastic products.

Plastic products are manufactured using a variety of production techniques. Granules are manufactured into extruded sheets which form the foundation of Door Panels' PermalPanel range. The group also manufactures drainage vents and waste pipes for housing, made using the latest extrusion technology. Pipes are manufactured from PVC.

Injection moulding processes are used for plastic containers to hold paint, for example, and to produce plastic wash basins.

Source: Heywood Williams Group plc.

(a) What TWO processes mentioned here are used to manufacture plastic products?
(b) Suggest FIVE products manufactured by companies belonging to the Heywood Williams Group.
(c) Briefly explain the production process used to make pipes.
(d) How is the production process for sheets likely to be different to the process for making pipes?

Figure 10 Cold working of metal. Tools and their uses.

Figure 11 Forging tools.

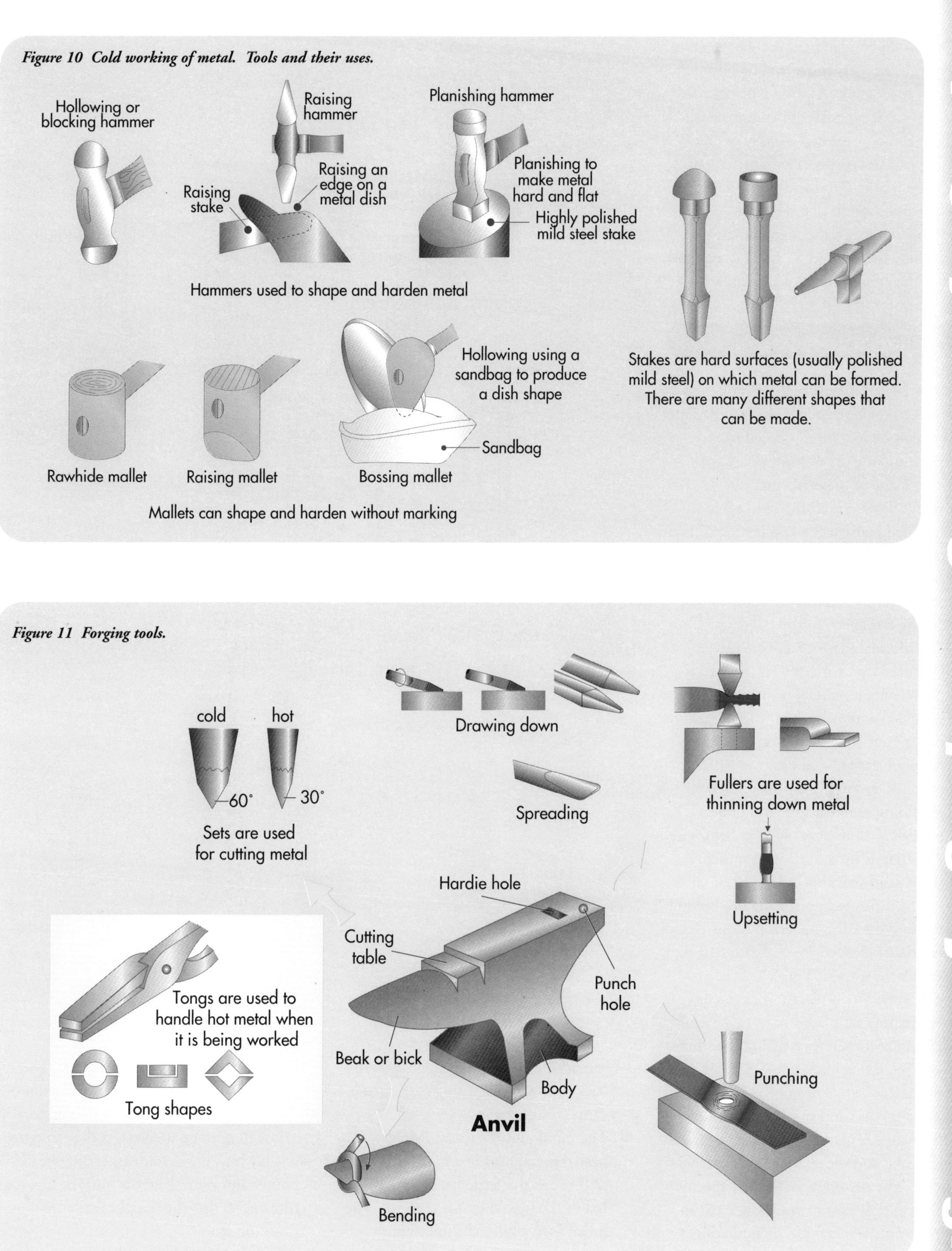

hot metal. **Fullers** are used to fuller metal in preparation for 'drawing down' (reducing the width of the metal). A swage block can be used for punching holes or bending metal. Hot metal can be twisted with tongs or a twisting bar. A process called upsetting or jumping up is used to increase the thickness of a bar or section in a certain area.

Forging is used in the manufacture of parts where the strength of grain is required, such as the crank shaft of a car engine.

Sand casting

When heated metals become molten, it allows them to be cast into shapes. Because of the high temperatures needed to melt metals, moulds used to form the shapes must be made of materials that can withstand heat. Moulding sand sifted to the required consistency and texture is used for green SAND CASTING. Green sand is sand which is just damp enough to hold its shape. There is a number of stages to producing a shape.

- The external shape of a casting is produced by a pattern. The pattern is placed on a moulding board and sprinkled with parting powder to ease the pattern out of the mould at a later stage.
- A **drag** box is placed over the pattern, which is covered with finely sifted moulding sand (facing sand or a moulding compound such as bentonite). The drag is then filled with ordinary sifted sand (backing sand). Sand is rammed firmly into the drag to hold it in place once the pattern is removed and the drag is turned over. Again parting powder is sprinkled on.
- The **cope** box is placed onto the drag. Sprue pins are placed in to make a pourer and riser, then facing sand (or compound) is placed over exposed areas of the pattern. The cope is filled with backing sand and rammed in firmly.
- The cope is marked and removed from the drag and the sprue pins are taken out. The pattern is removed from the drag and gates (or runners) are cut so that molten metal can be poured in.
- Repairs are made to the mould using smoothing tools. The cope is placed back onto the drag using marks made earlier to line them up.
- The mould is now ready. Molten heated metal held in a crucible is poured in through the feeder filling the space left in the mould by the pattern. The metal used could be aluminium, bronze, cast iron or steel. Once cool, the runners and risers are removed. The casting is cleaned and sharp edges and excess metal are removed (fettled).

It is important at all stages that sand does not fall into the mould, especially the pourer and riser. Patterns must be tapered (drawn) so that they can be easily removed from the sand.

It is also possible to make more

Figure 12 Sand casting.

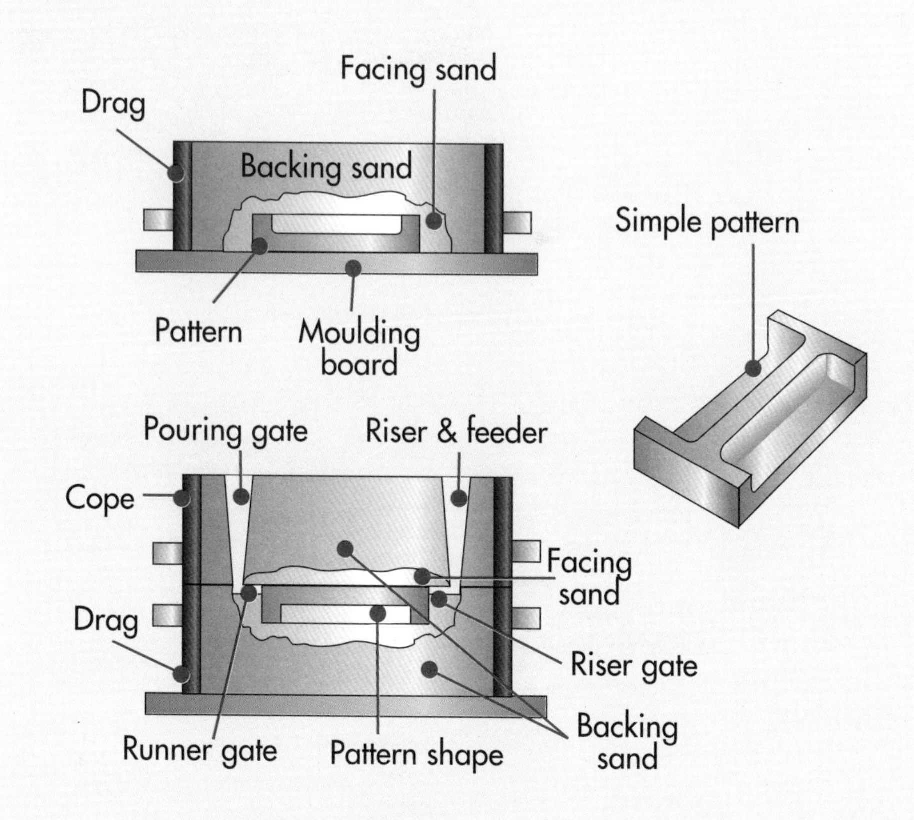

Figure 13 Die casting of a pipe/wall fixing unit.

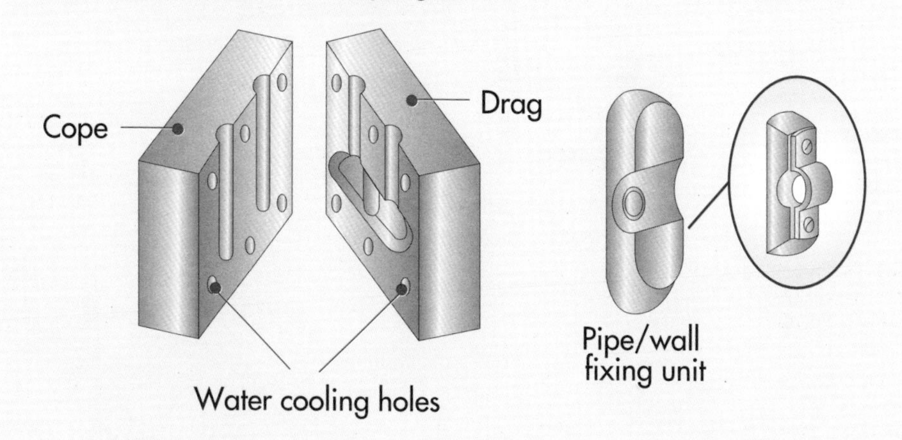

complicated shapes using sand casting techniques with split patterns. Also, hollow shapes can be made with the use of a **core**. The core is placed into the mould in the drag and the cope lowered onto it. The core forms the inner space or hollow required in the casting and the mould in the sand forms the outer shape required. Molten metal is poured into the space between.

Die casting

The problem with sand casting is that the mould needs to be made over and over again, which is time consuming. DIE CASTING using aluminium alloys, brasses, bronzes or nickels solves this. One half of the metal die is fixed to a die casting machine and the other half is moved on to tie bars so that the mould can close during casting. Molten alloy is injected into the die under high pressure while hydraulic pressure keeps the die together. Cooling channels allow oil or water to cool the metal. The die sticks to the side of the mould once released. These casts are then tipped into a bath of cool water and the die is ready to use again. Large numbers of casts can be made in this way, making it suitable for large batch production (see unit 19). Products made using die casting techniques include ships' propellers and model cars.

Continuous steel casting.

Continuous casting

Molten metal, like copper, bronze and aluminium, can be 'tapped' straight into long moulds which have a retractable base. As the mould fills up the base lowers and the cast is cooled with water jets. This is CONTINUOUS CASTING. Steel is cast in a similar way but, because of the high temperature needed to keep it molten, it is run vertically from a ladle. As it cools and solidifies it is run along rollers and cooled further using water spray. This generally produces casting ingots for further refining.

Extruding and rolling

Like plastics, metals can be extruded. High temperatures keep the metal molten and different dies are used to make different cross sections. Extrusion can be used to make metal rods, bars, tubes and strips. Metals are rolled when hot or cold to make thinner sheets or strip metal (see unit 6). Rolled metal can be converted into tubing by rotation. Wires can be made by drawing hot metal rods through a die.

Mould or former - used to shape materials.
Thermoforming - shaping or forming in 3D using a mould.
Line bending - using a single line of heat to bend plastic.
Blow moulding - blowing air under pressure onto a sheet of heated plastic.
Vacuum forming - removing air to create a vacuum so that the air pressure forces the heated plastic onto a mould.
Injection moulding - forcing 'fluid' plastic into a mould.
Compression moulding - putting heated plastic onto a mould which is then compressed.
Extrusion moulding - forcing 'fluid' plastic through a die.
Plastics memory - plastic retaining information about its original shape.
Forging - hot working of metal.
Sand casting - using sand to make moulds which are used in the manufacture of products.
Die casting - using metals to make dies which are used in the manufacture of products.
Continuous casting - using long moulds to produce casts.

activities

Look at the information below.

(a) What is continuous casting?
(b) Why might bronzes be used for continuous casting of tubes?
(c) Why is the process suitable for the manufacture of tubes?

Delta Encon Ltd operates a continuous casting process, producing rod, tube and complex sections in a form close to the required finished shape (Near Nett Shape), resulting in extremely low material wastage when making the final component.

The continuously cast products are made in specific lengths, up to 12ft, in phosphor bronzes, leaded bronzes and gunmetals. Major end uses for these products are for water fittings (excellent corrosion resistance) and bearings, bushes and thrust washers. It is also possible to cast certain of the 'cast' brasses by the same production route.

Specifications involved are BS1400: 1985 and equivalent National Specifications as well as the European Standard CEN EN 1982.

Steps in the production process involve:

* machining of graphite dies;
* melting of the alloys in induction furnaces;
* casting through the graphite dies;
* straightening by reeling and roller straightening.

Source: Delta Encon Ltd.

HATTERSLEY NEWMAN HENDER

What do your central heating system, hot and cold water taps on a sink and pipes to transport water or oil have in common? They all contain valves which control the volume of fluid that passes through the system.

Hattersley Newman Hender make fluid control valves. Three castings are used in the manufacture of each valve. The castings are produced using the green sand moulding technique. Castings are used to make valves for a number of reasons:

* the ease of making complicated shapes;
* the low cost of manufacture (one casting costing £35 would cost hundreds of pounds to machine from solid metal);
* components of the exact size can be made repeatedly;
* the variety of materials that can be used in the process, for example cast iron, bronze or cast steel.

Hattersley's castings are manufactured in cast iron because the material gives good definition of detail, has the required mechanical strength and is relatively cheap to produce.

Source: Maurice Hamer, Hattersley Newman Hender.

Stages in the casting process

1 The internal shape of the cast is formed by a **core**.

2 The external shape is formed by a pattern in two moulding boxes - the **cope** and the **drag**. Here the pattern in the drag is covered in sand which is compressed by a machine.

3 The drag is upturned, the pattern removed, and the feeder and vents are cut.

4 The cope is lowered onto the drag with the core in position.

5 The cavity left by the pattern, but not filled by the core, is filled with molten metal. The finished casting is then fettled and dressed before any necessary machining required to complete the component takes place, for example, drilling holes to bolt the valve parts (not shown here).

Questions

(a) What metal does Hattersley Newman Hender use for casting?
(b) What are the advantages of using that metal?
(c) State TWO other metals that could be used in casting.
(d) What are the possible benefits of sand casting for a manufacturer?
(e) Draw a flow chart to show the processes that take place when sand casting.

Case study: LEGO GROUP

In some Western European countries nine out of ten families with children under 14 years of age own 'Lego'. The Lego Group is famous worldwide for its manufacture of plastic children's modelling bricks, kits and other elements. The word 'Lego' is taken from the Danish *leg got* meaning 'play well'.

The first stage in the production process is working closely with suppliers of raw materials (plastic granules) for manufacture. The granules must conform to certain specifications, such as colour matching and non-toxicity. The next stage is to transfer the granules to injection moulding machines where the plasticised granules are heated and passed through moulds that have to be accurate to 0.005mm. The factories manufacturing the bricks are fully automated. When the required number of bricks have been manufactured they are taken from the machines and packaged.

Thermoplastics are used for all Lego elements. They are melted at approximately 235°C after which they are moulded and left to harden as they cool. In principle they can be melted down and remoulded an infinite number of times, although in practice there is a limit to this process before the material is damaged. The main type of plastic used is ABS. It is used as it is resistant to scratching and can hold its shape. It is also resistant to other substances that Lego comes into contact with, such as perspiration.

Lego buckets are made from polypropylene and transparent parts are made from polycarbonate. Packaging before 1990 was made from PVC, but this was changed to PET, which had the effect of reducing thickness by 30%.

Source: Lego Group.

Row after row of injection moulding machines manufacture elements.

Lego brick moulds

Questions

(a) List the different thermoplastics used to manufacture Lego products.

(b) Draw a diagram of an injection moulding machine showing the production process used to manufacture Lego parts. Label the diagram using information from the passage.

(c) Suggest THREE other products that could be made by injection moulding.

(d) Why might injection moulding be a suitable method of manufacturing Lego products?

(e) Are Lego products likely to be mass produced? Explain your answer.

unit 13 Assembling and joining

Joints

Some products are made in one piece. Others, however, are made up of two or more parts. JOINTS are the places where parts of a product meet. Joints can be **fixed** or they can **move**. For example, the joints on a cycle frame are fixed together whilst the joints on its chain are designed to **move**. In addition, joints can be **temporary** or **permanent**. Temporary joints are designed to be removed, such as on interlocking tent poles or snooker cue extensions. Permanent joints are fixed joints that will hold pieces firmly in place, giving a product strength. They cause damage if separated. Permanent joints can be achieved by glueing, soldering, welding, and using nails or rivets.

Using adhesives

There is a wide variety of glues or ADHESIVES that can be used to bond a joint. Most are permanent. Non-permanent adhesives are masking tape, sellotape or materials like 'blu tack'. These are sometimes used to protect materials as they are being worked or to hold materials in place while permanent joints are made.

Some adhesives are made up as pastes or cements, while others are straight gums. Many are kept fluid by being dissolved in water or another solvent. Once applied and left to set (cure) the solvent evaporates, leaving the adhesive to hold the materials together. Solvent-based glues need a well aired room in which to work and time for fumes to dissipate. Some adhesives (usually water based) take hours to cure, whilst some set instantly (called impact adhesives). This can affect the planning of a job. Slow drying adhesives need clamps so the material does not slip out of place before the adhesive sets. Fast drying adhesives require caution as they can stick to the skin. High impact adhesives have little room for error as they set immediately.

'General purpose' adhesives can be used to glue a range of materials. Others work best on specific materials. Examples are tensol cement for acrylic, polystyrene adhesive for solid polystyrene, PVC adhesive and balsa cement for balsa wood. **Polyvinylacetate** (PVA) is specifically for timber products. It comes in a paste form and is used to make permanent joints. Pressure is required on the joint for at least the first 2-3 hours of glueing, generally applied by a G-cramp or sash cramp (see unit 11).

Epoxy resins usually come as a two-part glue. A hardener is mixed with adhesive to form a paste. The paste is applied to a joint and cramped until it sets. Curing time is around 20 minutes, but rapid versions can dry in 5 minutes. Epoxy resins can join

Joints are held in clamps as adhesive dries.

activities

Look at the photographs. For each product:

(a) explain whether the joints are temporary or permanent;

(b) suggest whether the joints are fixed or movable;

(c) explain whether the joints are likely to have been glued, welded or brazed, fixed using fittings or fixed using other methods.

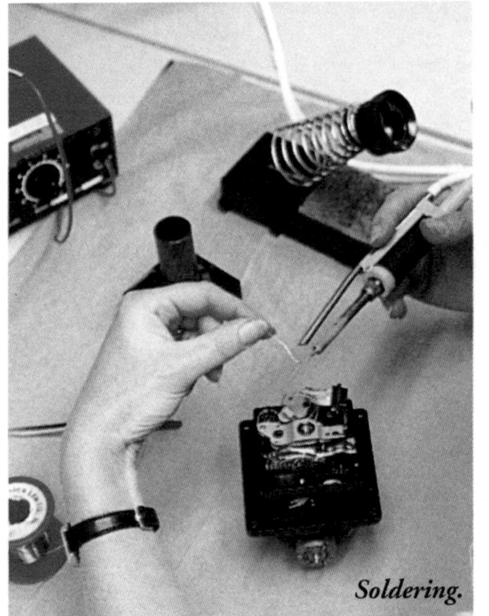

Soldering.

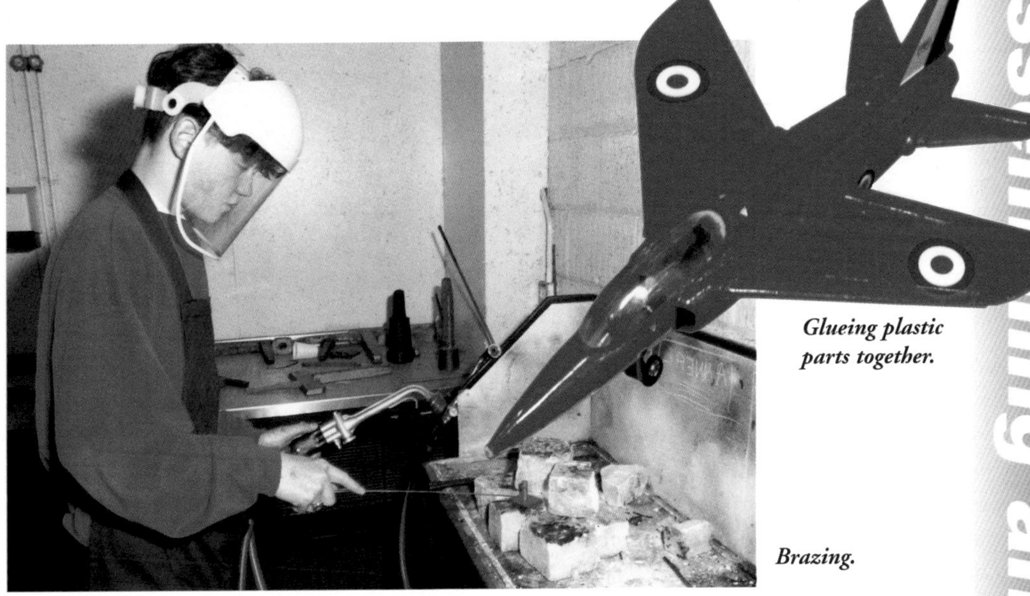

Glueing plastic parts together.

Brazing.

materials such as wood or metal to ceramics. Industrial versions are toughened with rubber and have an 'impact performance'. In some processes glues have replaced traditional welding and riveting techniques to give smoother finishes and lighter products. **Super glues** (cyanoacrylates) are epoxies which cure in seconds, responding to moisture on the surface of material. They are often used for small joints and can glue materials such as rubber, ceramics, glass and fabrics. **Contact adhesives** are used to fix other materials to wood, especially non-wood laminates. The glue is rubber based and is spread onto both faces to be bonded. It is left until it is touch dry when the two surfaces are pressed together. The bond is instant, so there is little room for error.

Soldering and brazing

SOLDERING is a process used to join metals. It involves heating an alloy that has a lower melting point than the metal it is to join. When molten, the solder spreads to 'wet' the area heated by filling in the 'gaps' at the molecular level. Once cool, it forms a thin alloy layer that holds the metals together. Metals to be joined must be cleansed to remove surface film. Fluxes are used with solders to keep surfaces clean and prevent oxide layers forming. They dissolve oxides, allowing the solder to run freely.

Soft solder (an alloy of tin and lead, and some have flux added) is used extensively in electrical and electronic work to join components to copper tracks, for example when making light bulbs, cameras and computers. It is also used to join large areas of tin plate, copper or brass together. A soldering iron is generally used to melt the solder. The solder comes in a range of melting points depending on the alloy mixture.

Silver solder (an alloy of copper, zinc and silver) melts at 600°C-800°C. Originally used in jewellery manufacture, it is now used in high quality engineering products because of its strength, high melting point and neatness of finish. It is preferred to brazing when making frames of mountain cycles because it is lightweight and has better shear strength. It is used to join high melting point non-ferrous metals. Gas and air or oxy-propane are used, but not oxy-acetylene.

Brazing (sometimes called hard soldering) is an alloy of brass (copper and zinc). It melts at 870°C-920°C and is only used to join metals like mild steel which have a high melting point. A gas torch is used to melt the brazing rod. Gas and air or oxy-acetylene are used. Standard frames made from mild steel tubing are brazed together. Brazing is cheaper than silver soldering. **Aluminium brazing** uses an alloy of aluminium and silicon. It is used to join aluminium and its alloys, which are

activities

The mild steel tubular sections are part of a frame to be used for a television stand. The sections are to be soldered together.

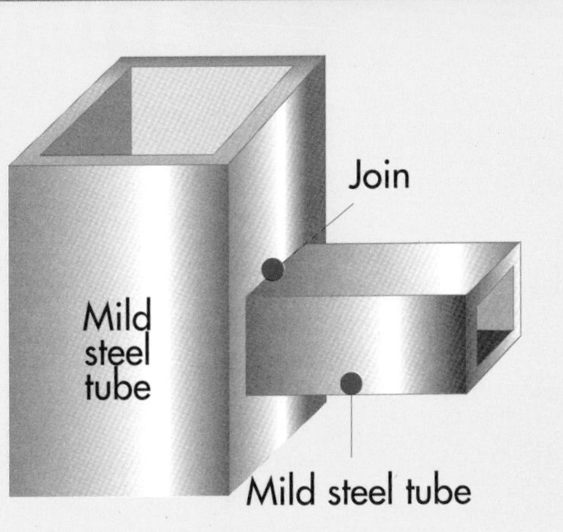

(a) What is meant by soldering?

(b) (i) What solder would you use to join the parts?
(ii) Explain why you might use this solder.

(c) (i) Explain why the use of a flux is important in soldering.
(ii) Suggest a type of flux that should be used when soldering these two parts together.

difficult to 'wet' because of the rapid development of an oxide layer during soldering and the close melting points of aluminium and its solder alloy. Fluxes have been developed to help solve this problem.

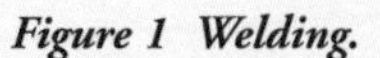

Figure 1 Welding.

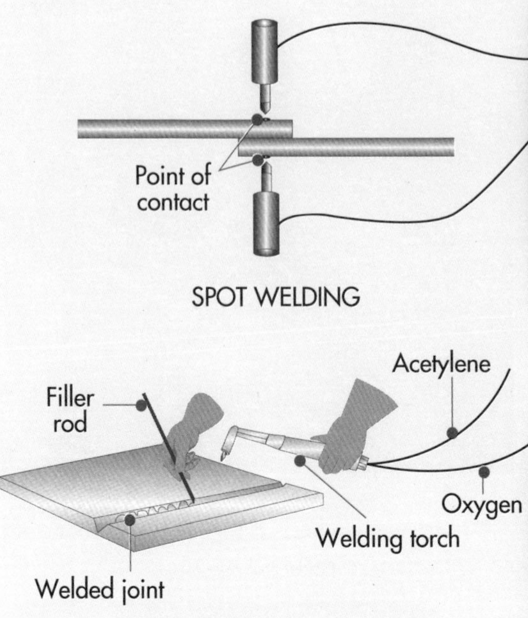

Robotic welding on a production line.

Fluxes

FLUXES are essential with all soldering otherwise the solder will not adhere to the metal to be joined. Different fluxes are used depending on the type of soldering taking place (soft, silver or brazing). It is important to use the correct flux for the type of soldering process being used. They can be put onto the joint before soldering or mixed with the solder, as in soft solder for electronic work. Fluxes dissolve any oxides that form on the metal or solder as they are heated. They allow the solder to run freely into the joint.

Active fluxes chemically clean the metal. They are easy to work with but must be rinsed off to prevent metal corrosion. **Protective** fluxes only prevent oxidation and so the area around the joint must be cleaned thoroughly.

Welding

WELDING is the fusing together of two pieces of the same material (usually metals although thermoplastics can be welded). When hot, molecules at faces of materials that meet become fluid, mix and then cool, joining the materials together. Some welding involves just the materials. A filler, however, is generally used to fill in the trough that results at the welded area on materials over 16 swg thick.

Spot welding is where a high electrical current is sent through two pieces of metal butted together which overlap. The current heats the metals up at their point of contact. Increasing the pressure forms the joint. Spot welding is used for sheet metal work in the motor industry and to make fridge and washing machine bodies. Seam welding uses a similar method.

Electric arc welding is where an electrical spark is used to melt a 'filler' rod which heats up the two surfaces to be joined to their melting point and fuses them together to make a join. Tungsten inert gas (TIG) and metal inert gas (MIG) are two different arc welding methods. The inert gas protects the tungsten (or metal) electrode where the spark is created and the metal to be welded from oxidising, giving it a longer life. These methods do not require fluxes. They have made the joining of non-ferrous metals far easier (particularly aluminium with its oxide layer) and have replaced riveting methods in much of heavy industry. Production lines that use robot technology use MIG welding.

Oxygen/fuel welding is used mainly for smaller joints on thinner material. A torch is used. Oxygen is mixed in the torch with acetylene, propane or butane. Oxygen and acetylene is most popular as it gives a higher temperature. The temperature and flame quality is controlled by altering the gas mixture. This makes it very versatile and useful to weld many metals.

Other types of welding are:

- cold welding (see unit 12) - hammering metals with low melting points where they are to be joined, such as gold, lead or silver. It is a specialist process;

activities

Look at the information about CAC Gates.

(a) What type of construction is used to make the gate?

(b) What type of joint is used to fix the horizontal rails to the end post?

(c) Why might this type of joint be used?

(d) Suggest advantages and disadvantages of joining two pieces of wood by:
(i) adhesive;
(ii) screws;
(iii) nails.

CAC Gates manufactures traditional garden gates from timber. Part of the range is a simple gate made from vertical planks fixed to 3 horizontal rails as shown in the diagram, with a diagonal rail for support and two thicker end posts.

- heating and then hammering metal to create a weld, eg making sword blades by hammering low carbon steel around high carbon steel;
- ultrasonic welding - the use of vibrations to put wires into semi-conductors or to seal explosives cans;
- friction welding - the use of friction to heat and fuse metals, eg welding hard steel tips onto mild steel shafts;
- the use of lasers;
- hot air welding - a process used to weld plastics and to seal polythene bags at one end using a heated press.
- tensol used to 'weld' acrylic.

Joining wood

Wooden joints are used to give a strong bond between timber which adhesives alone do not provide. Most joints are permanent. Once made, timber joints are usually glued or fixed with other fittings. There are many different types of timber joint, so it is important to choose the right one for the job. The joint chosen depends on the the size of timber being used and the position where the wood is to meet.

Because of the angled nature of wooden structures, there are 3 basic types of timber construction. **Frame construction** is often used to hold thinner sections of material, such as plastic or timber panels and materials like plywood and plasterboard. The joints are at the corners of a rectangular section, eg in windows, doors and picture frames. Joints used are halving, bridle, mortise and tenon, dowelling and butt. T-joints may also be used across the frame. **Stool and table frameworks** are really a type of frame construction which has two joints at the corners. Many of the joints have to be mitred (angled cuts) so edges are flush.

Figure 2 Frame construction, stool and table frameworks and box or carcass construction.

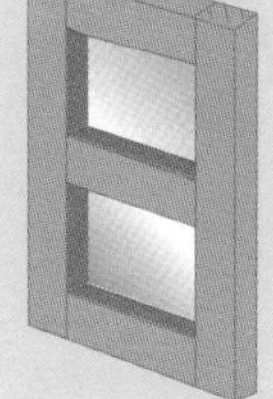

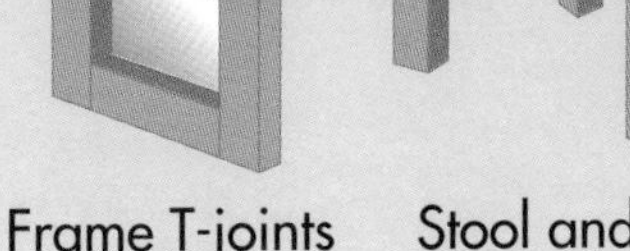

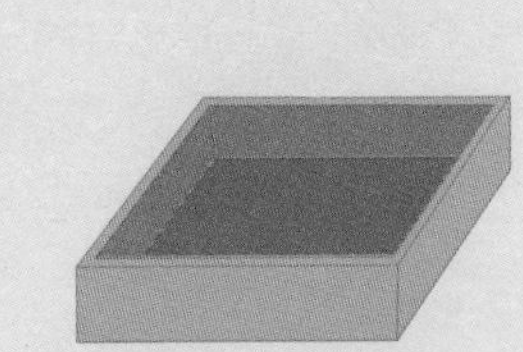

Figure 3 Wooden joints.

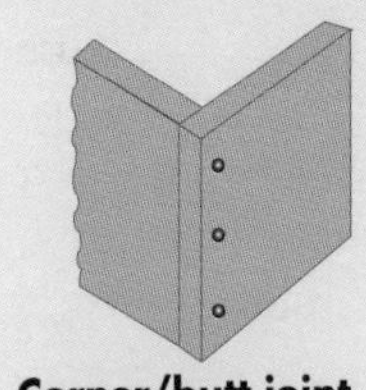

Corner/butt joint
Weak because no overlap. Screws, plywood triangles and metal fastenings can add strength.
For rough work and constructions, eg crates, eaves of buildings.

Cross halving joint
Used where members cross each other, eg same table and chair constructions.

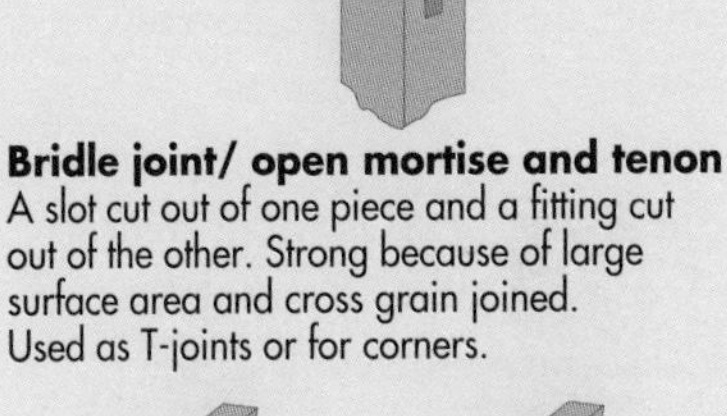

Bridle joint/ open mortise and tenon
A slot cut out of one piece and a fitting cut out of the other. Strong because of large surface area and cross grain joined. Used as T-joints or for corners.

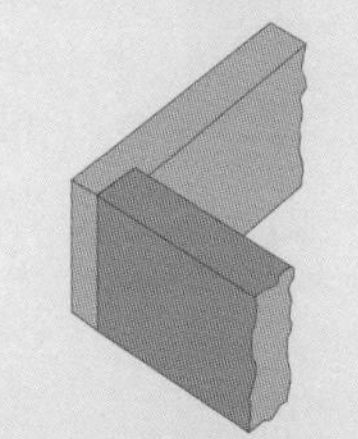

Rebate (lap joint)
Small section of one face is removed to fit end of another piece. Still weak, but stronger than butt joint.
Rebate with groove is stronger as grain crosses at joint.

Housing joint
A groove is cut to fit the end of a piece of wood.
Access to centre of wood makes it stronger than a rebate.
Used in T-form constructions, eg DIY furniture.

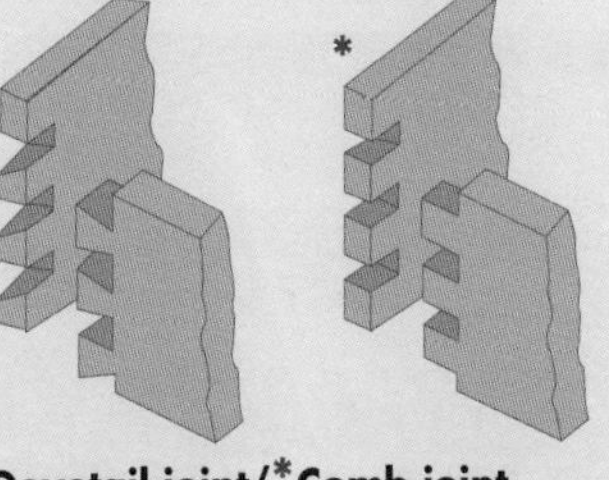

Dovetail joint/*Comb joint
Angles or 'tails' cut at end of both pieces. Strong as surface area is large and grain crosses. Used in quality wood products. Also lapped and through dovetail and dovetail bridle.
A comb joint is easier to make but less strong as it is not wedged.

Halving joint
Each section has $1/2$ of its thickness removed at the joint. Surface area where grain crosses is greater. Gives a good glueing surface. Cross halving and dovetail halving are most common.

Dowel joint
Holes drilled to fit dowel rods which can be glued. Dowelling jig can match holes in each piece.
Used on DIY furniture

Mitred joint
A joint at an angle. A butt joint used for picture frames. Stronger joints can be mitred bridle or mortise and tenon

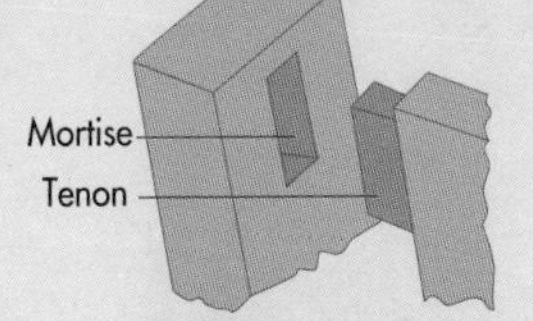

Mortise and tenon
Strongest joint because of surface area touching and crossing of grain. The tenon fits into the mortise (hole)and is glued.
Used in T-form constructions, frames and stools.

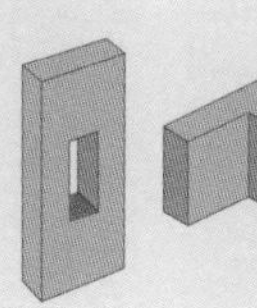

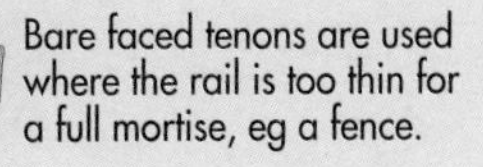

Bare faced tenons are used where the rail is too thin for a full mortise, eg a fence.

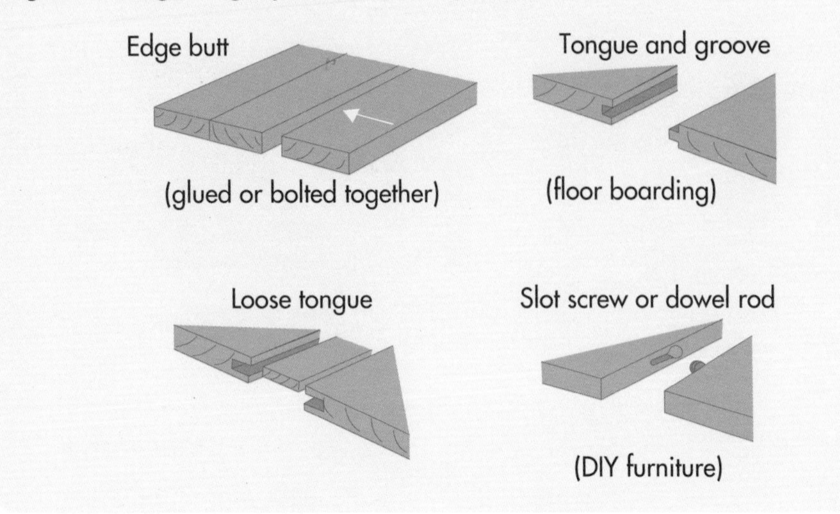

Figure 4 Joining the edges of wood to make larger boards.

Examples of products using these frames are stools, chairs and table legs and rails. Common joints are butt, single dovetail and mortise and tenon. **Box or carcass constructions** have joints at the ends or edges, but the timber used is wider than in a framework construction. Examples are found in boxes, crates, shelving, cabinet work and storage containers. Common joints are butt, rebate, finger, housing and dovetail. T-joints may also be used in box construction.

Linkages.

Hinges.

The joints used in the manufacture of wooden products are shown in Figures 3 and 4.

Movement

Movable joints should offer strength and support as well as movement. Like other types of mechanism (see unit 17) moving joints can offer reciprocating, linear and rotary motion. A sliding mechanism, where a panel runs along grooves cut into material, has linear motion. An example would be a cupboard drawer which slides open along a track. Telescopic joints like those in car aerials and extending ladders are used on collapsible, easy to store designs.

Hinges offer a type of oscillating arc. They are usually bought as a set. One side is attached to a structure. The other is attached to a door or lid that holds it in place and allows it to swing open and shut. Collapsible structures such as camera tripods have hinges or linkages to allow them to be folded and stored in a small space. Linkages provide a permanent joint, keeping materials in place, but can also allow movement around a pivot as in a car window handles. Self-locking plates allow materials to be adjusted or moved, but when locked in position they do not move, giving strength and support.

activities

DAT Ltd is a contract joinery business that manufactures furniture. Many of the wardrobes it makes have internal drawers. The sides, back and front of the drawers are made from 18mm plywood and the base from 6mm plywood. The sides are joined to the back and front as shown in the diagram (joint A). The base is joined to the back, sides and front by a groove cut into each to accept the base (joint B).

(a) What type of joint is: (i) joint A; (ii) joint B?

(b) How would you secure a wooden joint in a drawer?

(c) Suggest TWO ways in which joint A might be adapted to make it stronger.

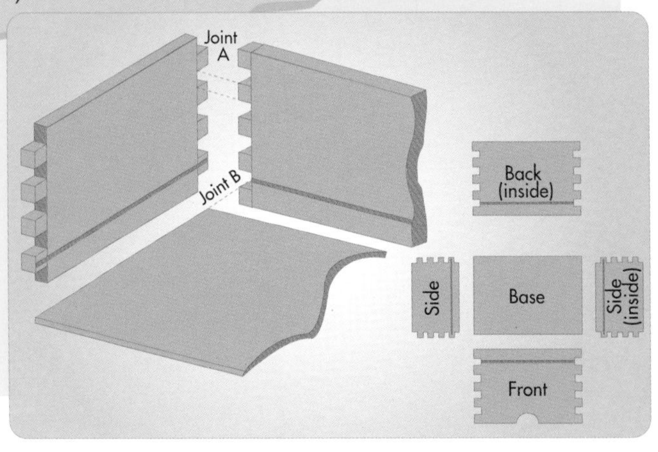

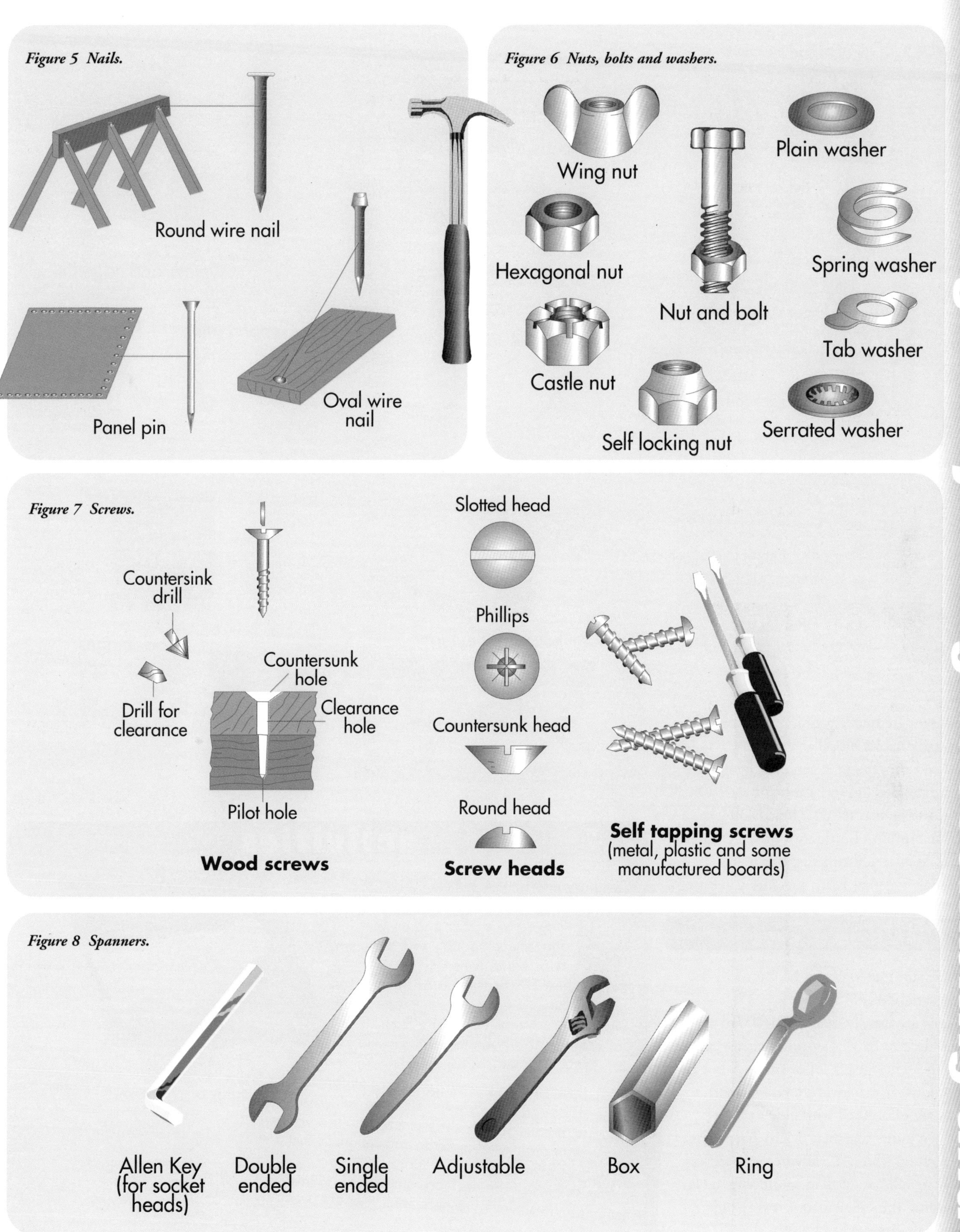
Figure 5 Nails.
Round wire nail
Panel pin
Oval wire nail
Figure 6 Nuts, bolts and washers.
Wing nut
Hexagonal nut
Castle nut
Nut and bolt
Self locking nut
Plain washer
Spring washer
Tab washer
Serrated washer
Figure 7 Screws.
Countersink drill
Drill for clearance
Countersunk hole
Clearance hole
Pilot hole
Wood screws
Slotted head
Phillips
Countersunk head
Round head
Screw heads
Self tapping screws
(metal, plastic and some manufactured boards)
Figure 8 Spanners.
Allen Key (for socket heads)
Double ended
Single ended
Adjustable
Box
Ring

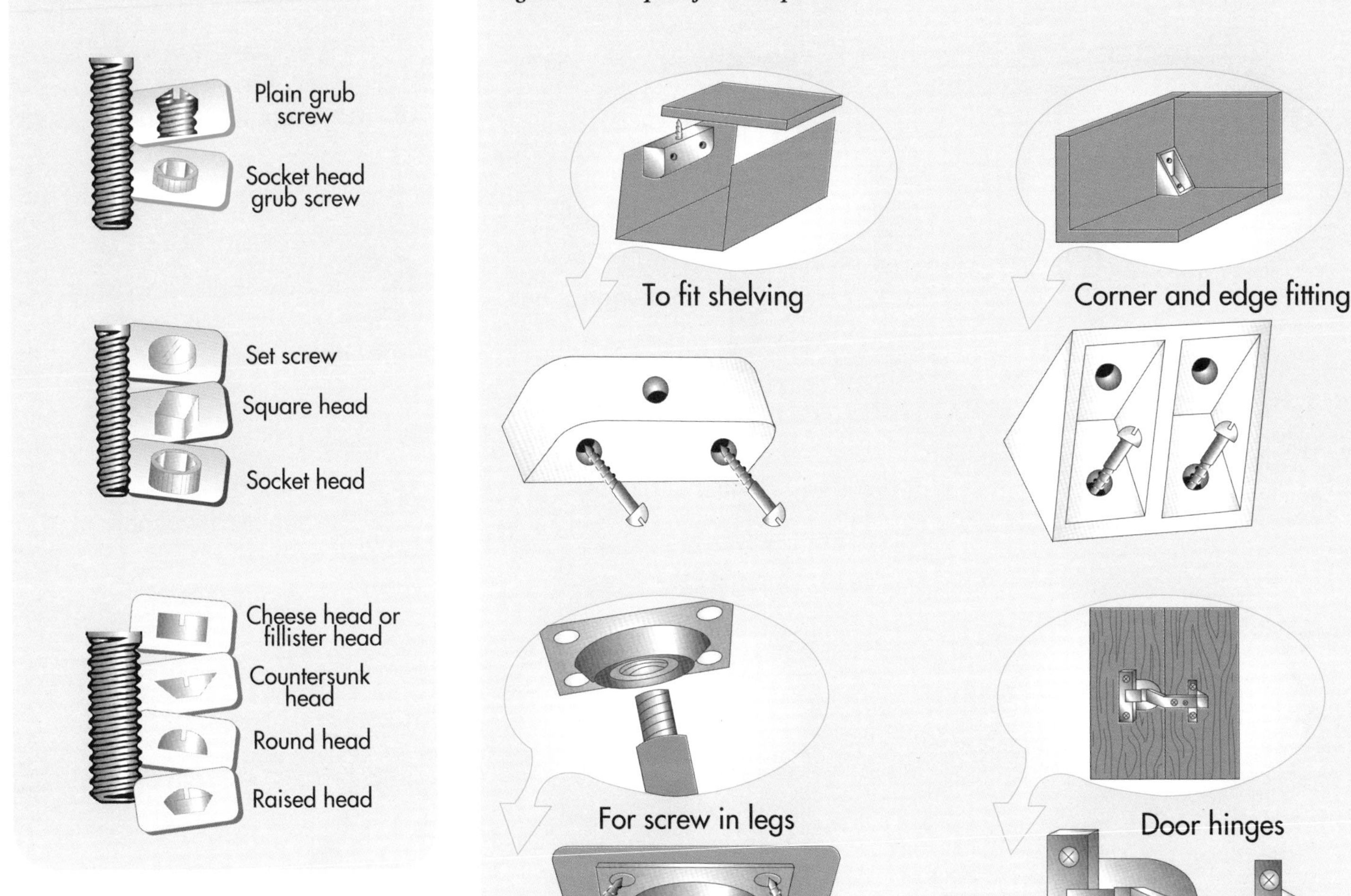

Figure 9 Grub screws and set screws.

Figure 10 Examples of KD components.

Examples are rotary washing lines and adjustable tables on pillar drills.

Rotary movement is achieved by circular clips tightened around a tube or rod. Once tight, the joint is fixed. Threads offer a similar motion. Bottle tops or screw threads allow circular adjustments, but hold materials together when pressure is released.

Fittings

Resistant materials can be joined by a wide variety of FITTINGS.

Nails are usually made of steel and are often used to fix timber products together quickly. They give a lot of strength but can work loose if materials are pulled apart. Nails are often used with glue to hold wooden joints together. Many have turns to catch on fibres. Oval wire nails are less likely to split wood than round wire nails providing they are nailed across the grain. Panel pins are used to fix thin sheet

activities

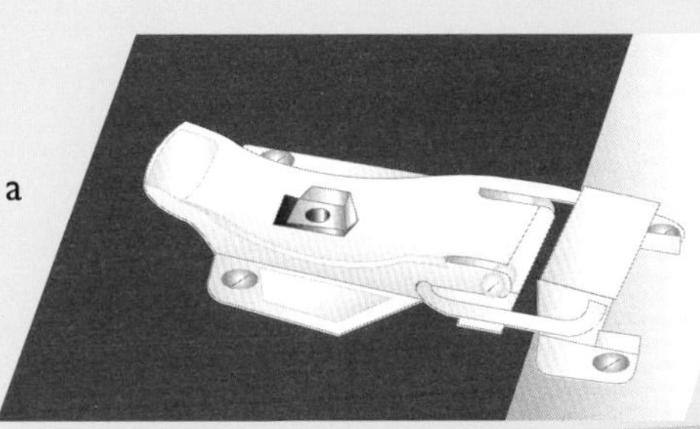

Read the information below.

(a) Explain how a latch:
   (i) is fixed to a door and panel;
   (ii) allows a temporary join between a door and a panel.

(b) Suggest SIX possible uses for a ProLatch.

(c) What advantages might a latch have over a hook in holding two pieces of material together?

Pretax manufacturers produce a quick action surface fitting fastener called the ProLatch. It acts as a drawer latch and will also close a door or panel against a seal or gasket with considerable pressure and hold it in place. A safety catch keeps the ProLatch in the closed position and can be secured with a wire or safety pin. A version is available which accepts a padlock.

Applications of the latch are hinged doors, gates, flaps, covers or guards on agricultural machines, cabinets, vehicle bonnets and boat hatches.

Source: adapted from Engineering.

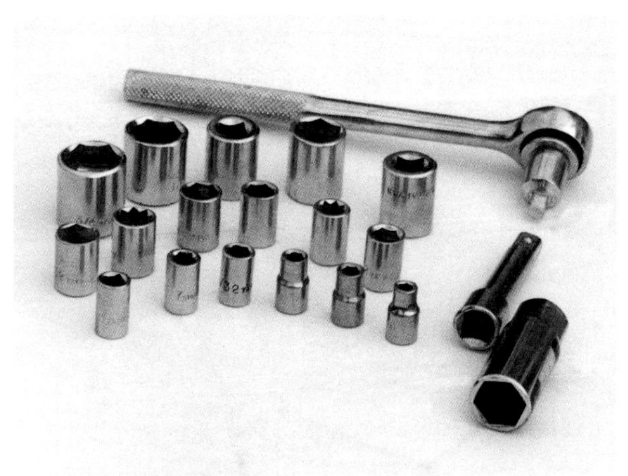

A socket set.

material. Drawing pins, split fasteners and safety pins are other types of temporary fasteners.

Screws are methods of fixing either permanently or with an option to dismantle if needed. Screws have a thread. They need a clearance hole in the material which houses the screw thread and a pilot (or guide) hole drilled in the other part before fitting. Too large a pilot hole means the screw will not grip; too small will make it hard to screw in. Wood screws have a thread cut part way along their length and tapered at the end. Self tapping screws are threaded the hole length. They cut their own thread and are used on sheet metal, soft plastics and some manufactured boards, eg chipboard. Some screws are 'countersunk' head screws. Drilling with a countersink bit means the head will not stand 'proud' above the face of the material.

Nut and bolts and **set screws** can be used with wood, metal or plastic. Most bolts have a hexagonal shaped head to allow a **spanner** to tighten them. Spanners come in many shapes as shown in Figure 8. Socket sets are also used to tighten bolts. Two clearance holes have to be drilled and the bolt put in place. Once in place, a nut of the correct size is attached to lock the materials together. Carriage bolts have a domed head and are used to attach metal to wood. Wing nuts can be used where the joint just only needs to be hand tight. Some nuts, bolts and screws are used with washers. A flat washer prevents surface damage by the fitting and spreads the bearing load, giving tighter joint. Coiled, spring or serrated washers are used where the product vibrates, such as in washing machines.

Set screws are used to tighten one part to another. Grub screws are headless screws used for safety when holding parts that revolve. They can have different heads. They can also have different shaped points, eg oval, cone, flat or extended (known as full or half dog).

Riveting is an old process that has been used to join metal together to form armour, ships, towers and bridges. Today it has largely been replaced by welding techniques and adhesives like epoxy resins. Pop riveting is still used for small scale work with thinner sheet plastic and metal, and sometimes hardboards. The rivet is 'popped' through the material using a pop-rivetting tool.

The growth of DIY products has lead to a wide range of newer fittings. They are generally known as **knock down** (KD) fittings because they allow products to be assembled and disassembled many times without damage. They are used to make products such as furniture. Examples are shown in Figure 10.

Standard components

It is possible, when designing and making a product, to purchase components in standard sizes. Some examples are:

- latches - which allow two parts of a design, such as a door and a frame, to be temporarily joined together;
- handles - which are gripped and turned to allow doors or lids to be opened;
- brackets - used to support shelves;
- hooks - which can screw into materials and allow items to be hung from them.
- locks - which prevent two parts of a design joined temporarily, such as a door and a frame, from being opened without force.

Joint - **a point where materials meet.**
Adhesive - **a substance used to stick materials together.**
Soldering - **using molten metal to bond two metals together.**
Welding - **fusing together of two pieces of the same material.**
Flux - **a chemical used with solder to prevent oxides forming and allow the solder to flow.**
Fittings - **removable components used to join materials together.**

activities

LRE Relays and Electronics manufacture Pan-L screws. This is a range of specially finished coloured alloys or corrosion resistant steel screws that come with slotted recesses or Phillips heads. The screw is available in any colour to match any surface. The base metal is high tensile steel and the special coating material is highly resistant to chipping, corrosion or abrasion. The one piece screw has a 'captive' washer which creates a complete seal against dirt, moisture and vapour.

Source: adapted from Engineering.

(a) What types of head are available for this screw?

(b) Suggest why this screw might be used:
(i) for assembling coloured panels made of anodised aluminium;
(ii) for products used outside.

(c) What advantages does using the captive washer with the screw give to a product?

unit 14

Finishing

Glasspaper
Cork block
Sanding wood by hand

What is finishing

Once a product has been made from wood, metal, plastic or a composite material it has to be 'finished'. This means that materials' surfaces will be improved in order to make them last longer or look better. The type of finish chosen depends on whether it is designed to:

- protect the material from chemical attack, weathering or disease (see unit 9);
- protect the material from scratches and abrasions;
- improve the appearance of the surface of the material.

Finishes may be **temporary** or **permanent**. Temporary finishes can be wiped away or rubbed off over time and need replacing. Permanent finishes are likely to be difficult to remove without causing damage to the material. The finish on many materials needs regular maintenance to preserve their appearance and quality. Most timbers need polishing. Metals needs cleaners to remove tarnishing and plastics require detergent or degreasers.

Preparing the material

Before a finish is applied to a material its surface has to be prepared. This ensures that the finish will not be easily removed. Preparation involves surface abrasives or cleaning materials. It is an important stage that can take a lot longer than applying the final finish.

Wood is **sanded** smooth to remove rough edges. Glass or garnet papers are used (sheets of paper with crushed glass or garnet glued onto the surface). A cork block should be used to give even pressure during sanding by hand to give a level surface. Powered sanders (see unit 11) using electricity or pneumatics may also be used with care. The abrasive paper is graded from coarse to fine. Sanding should start with a coarse grain and finish with a fine grain. Sanding should always be done with or along the grain and never across it, otherwise it could leave scratches and may destroy delicate graining if not used correctly.

Emery cloth is used on metals to reduce friction and give a smooth finish. Again this abrasive material will leave scratch marks if used incorrectly.

Silicon carbide papers are used on hard plastics (eg acrylic). They are usually wet (with water). They are also graded from tough to fine.

To remove grease or oil from a surface it may have to be **cleaned** with a degreasing agent such as white spirit. Some metals,

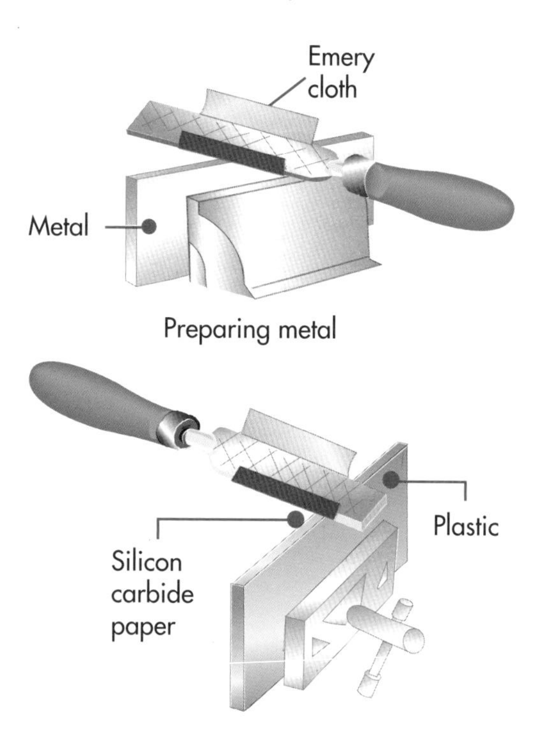

Figure 1 Preparing materials.

activities

Read the text in this unit.

(a) Suggest THREE methods that could be used to finish metal tube.

(b) What advantages would finishing have?

(c) Chose ONE finish for:
(i) a rotary clothes line and
(ii) a child's swing and explain why it is suitable.

Metal tube is used in the manufacture of many products. These include children's swings, clothes poles and rotary washing lines.

such as copper, brass and silver, may have to be dipped in acid to remove oxide layers. These should then be washed in water to remove the surplus acid and left to dry to create a clean, dirt free surface ready for finishing.

Temporary finishes

Wood has a natural grain and a lot of finishes are used to emphasise the grain and to keep a 'natural' appearance.

Oiling, for example, is when oil is rubbed gently along the grain of the wood with a cloth, brush or silicon carbide paper. It is sometimes used for products that come into contact with food. Olive oil is colourless and has no odour. Linseed oil is used on other types of wood. It is used to treat cricket bats. These oils replace 'natural' oils lost through treating and help to prevent the timber from drying out and splitting. They need to be applied periodically. Steel can be treated with oil in a similar way. The steel is heated and then dipped in engine oil, which gives the metal a 'blue' finish and protects it from dampness. There are also special oils and greases which are sprayed onto metals and machines to give long term, temporary protection.

Today **waxing and polishing** of wood is often done with the wood being sealed with a cellulose sealer before being waxed. A fine grade glass paper is used to rub the sealant down. The wax, usually Carnauba, is worked into the surface. It can then be polished. Spray waxes are also available. Silicone wax gives protection where hot drinks are likely to be used. A 'traditional' waxing method is where the wax only (beeswax) is put onto bare wood. The lustre is built up over time.

For outdoor use creosote can be applied to wood. It tends to stain and has a strong odour. Newer types of weatherproofing are odourless and less likely to stain or damage plants.

Some plastics such as acrylic can be given a high gloss finish by buffing with special plastic polishes. Another way is to quickly melt the surface with an intensive heat, called flame polishing. Slight scratches can be removed by rubbing with metal polish.

Permanent finishes

Varnishes Shellac based polishes are traditionally known as varnishes. They are 'painted' onto timber using specially made cloth rubbers or are sprayed. They harden to give permanent protection against moisture and light knocks or abrasions. Some varnishes contain coloured pigments or 'skins' which enhance the grain. For outdoor use varnishes with a higher percentage of oil are best. French polishing is a highly skilled way of varnishing. It is built up from many layers of 'shellac' polish. The surface has to be prepared using wood grain filler before the polishing begins.

A polished metal finish.

Lacquers Lacquers are similar to varnishes. Polyurethane lacquers are very tough, and resistant to moisture and heat. Some have to be mixed before use. Cellulose lacquers can be sprayed onto a surface, but are not as tough as polyurethane lacquers. Lacquers are best applied in several thin coats rather than a single thick coat.

Metals can also be lacquered. Their surfaces must be degreased first or cleaned with a mild abrasive like 'Brasso'. The lacquer can then be applied. It is not used industrially and tends to be limited to jewellery and other 'decorative' work. After a while the lacquer starts to flake off and has to be replaced.

Metal polishing and buffing Metals can be polished by hand if the product is small. Awkward shapes can be polished by hand or industry would use ultrasonics. Usually metals are polished with a polishing or buffing machine. It has 'mops' which are spun around an axle. A wax is used which has a fine grit embedded in it. Machine polishing helps the metal to obtain a good 'shine'. Once 'buffed', the metal will need regular polishing to prevent tarnishing. It is usually non-ferrous metals such as brasses, bronzes, nickel, silver and gold that are polished by buffing. Steels are buffed

activities

The furniture shown here has been made from timber for use in a children's library.

Read the text in this unit.

(a) Explain TWO finishing processes that could be used if the product was made from natural wood. State whether the finishing processes are temporary or permanent.

(b) Explain TWO finishing processes that could be used if the product was made from manufactured board.

to a high finish before electroplating. Metals can also be planished (see unit 12) before polishing. Some buffing polishes actually help to melt the surface of the metal. These are usually 'finishing' polishes which give the metal a mirror surface.

Enamelling GLASS ENAMELLING is used on brooches, rings and jewellery. The metal is cleaned in an acid bath, scoured using pumice powder and rinsed before gum arabic or tragacanth is applied. Powdered enamel is shaken on evenly and allowed to dry. The metal is then heated slowly so as not to crack or blow off the enamel. At 800°C the enamel fuses. After being allowed to cool very slowly, oxides are cleaned off and polishing of the metal back takes place. Metals used are copper, gilding metal, gold, silver and bronze. STOVE ENAMELLING is used on washing machines, cookers and fire fronts. It is a similar process to glass enamelling, but fusion takes place at much lower temperatures. Metals used would be steels.

Being resistant to air, water and chemicals, enamelling offers great protection. Colours can be added to the powder for a decorative finish.

Dip coating DIP COATING involves metal (usually tubing or metal rods), being heated in an oven. The hot metal is then dipped into a powdered suspension of plastic. The plastic 'powder' is 'fluidised' by blowing air through it. The plastic melts and sticks to the metal covering it. The coated metal is returned to the oven for a few minutes until the plastic becomes smooth and glossy. It is then removed and allowed to cool slowly in the air. Dip coating offers a lot of protection to the metal so it does not rust or tarnish, and can provide a wide range of colours if the pigment in the plastic is changed (see unit 5). It is often used where the product has to be handled for hygienic reasons or to protect against water, eg garden tools.

Table 1 Dip coating.

Plastic	Uses
Polythene	Vegetable racks, garden furniture, washing up drainers, clothes maidens
Cellulose, acetate, butyrate	Car steering wheels, hand rails, coat hooks, door knobs
PVC	Electric fittings, tool handles, pans
Nylon	Motorway barriers, artificial limbs

Electroplating ELECTROPLATING (through electrolysis) involves protecting metals by coating them with another metal. This 'coating' metal may be less reactive and more resistant to chemical attack. This is why metals are sometimes gold or silver plated. Other types of plating include chromium, tin, copper, nickel and zinc. The metal to be plated is placed as the cathode in a solution containing 'ions' of the plating metal and a low d.c. current is applied.

GALVANISING is where iron or steel parts are coated with a thin layer of zinc. This is done by dip coating in zinc powder, electroplating or spraying with molten zinc. Galvanising is an example of sacrificial protection. The zinc and the iron form a 'cell' or battery. The chemicals attack the

activities

Products such as supermarket trolleys and motor vehicle wheels are often plated (electroplated). Supermarket trolleys made from mild steel rod may have zinc plating and car wheels made from aluminium alloys may be chromium plated.

Source: adapted from Canning, Annual Report and Accounts.

(a) Explain what is meant by electroplating.
(b) Suggest why electroplating is likely to be a suitable finishing method for these products.

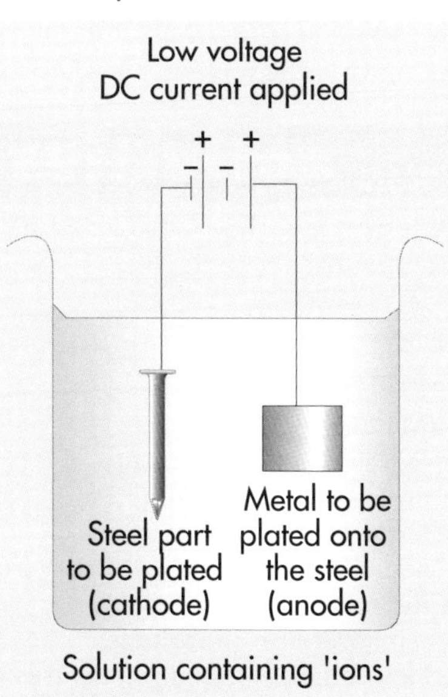

Figure 2 Electroplating.

Doors with different finishes.

Industrial spray painting.

zinc in preference to the iron, leaving the iron untarnished. Steel hulls of ships and underground piping can have lumps of magnesium attached to them. The magnesium is attacked, leaving the hull or the piping unblemished.

Aluminium can be protected using **electrolysis**, but in this case the aluminium is made the 'anode', hence the process is called 'anodising'. The electrolyte used is sulphuric acid. A thin film of aluminium hydroxide is placed on its surface. This is then washed and can be coloured by placing in a water based dye before the surface is hardened chemically by changing the hydroxide to oxide.

Colouring

Wood can be coloured by **staining** (semi-permanent). The stain is brushed on and left to dry. Staining changes the timber colour yet still emphasises the grain. More than one coat may be needed. The timber will have to be sealed in order to 'fix' the stain permanently. Common stains are often different shades of red or brown, but today many different colours of stains can be purchased.

If timber is **painted** (permanent) the natural grain of the wood will be hidden. Hardwoods have a good grain texture and are best treated with a clear finish. Softwoods have a less attractive grain, on the whole, and painting is unlikely to spoil their aesthetics. Manufactured boards like plywood and hardboard have little in the way of texture so painting is likely to improve their appearance.

Any type of paint, from emulsion to gloss, can be used on timbers. If painting onto fresh timber the wood may have to be primed and undercoat applied and then the final colour painted on. Before each layer, a light sanding helps the paint 'stick' onto the previous layer. MDF is sometimes painted with spray paints. It has no grain, so block colour can be easily applied without brush strokes on a surface finish. Metals are painted in the same way. The surface should be degreased first and any rust traces removed. 'Hammer finish' paints give metal a shiny appearance. 'Crackle paints' give a textured finish, as on cameras or binoculars etc. Painting can be done with a hand brush, a spray gun/aerosol or using industrial painting machines.

Anodising can give aluminium a range of colours, as can tempering metals and quenching oil (see unit 6). This also gives the metal the added protection of an oxide layer.

It is also possible to paint plastics, although it is unlikely as they have a natural finish built in and are self protected.

Other decorative finishes

Veneering (permanent) VENEERING the surface of poor quality timber (chipboard, plywood etc.) can be improved by glueing a thin sheet of timber over it. Thin sheets of timber (usually hardwoods like teak, mahogany or 'exotic' timbers such as African walnut) are cut from logs. Different cuts give different textures. The logs can be rotary cut around the perimeter of the log or thin slices can be cut down the log. The surface of the timber and back of the veneer are glued using PVA (see unit 13). The veneer is laid onto the timber carefully and pressed on using a flat press or clamped between boards. Other 'cheaper' types of veneer include plastic laminates like melamine which have a photograph or print of a pattern sealed inside the plastic.

Edging strips or beading (permanent) These can be used to finish the edges of manufactured boards. Some of these are pre-glued with a hot-melt adhesive and can be 'ironed' on using a hot iron.

Wood veneer and PVC edgebanding.

These edges can then be trimmed. For solid wood similar edging strips called lippings can be used. These are thicker than veneers and the corners have to be mitred (see unit 13) to give a satisfactory fit.

Inlay motifs (permanent) These are highly decorative 'designs'. They can be glued directly into timber surfaces or into veneered surfaces. The appearance of edges can be improved by inserting into grooves around their edges (edge inlay).

Etching (permanent) This can be used to create patterns in metal. The metal is covered with molten or heated wax. A

activities

Paint is all around us and has many uses. It can be applied to a variety of resistant materials. It can be bright or dull and can survive the heat and cold. Paints are used to protect and decorate surfaces. They place a film around a product that separates it from its surrounding environment. Modern paints are a mix of several ingredients.

Paints can be distinguished by their use. Architectural paints are used inside and outside of buildings. Industrial paints are used on factory production lines. Speciality coatings are used to protect against corrosion, as flame retardants, as antibacterial paint and as slippery paint to deter burglars from climbing drains.

Traditional paints use an organic solvent, but concern over solvent emissions and their environmental effects has led to new developments. Water based coatings use water as a solvent. Powder coatings contain no solvent and are used in motor manufacturing.

Source: adapted from New Scientist, 17.2.1996.

What is in paint?

Resin - when dry it gives a hard surface film. Types of resin include:

- polyester resin - decorative, industrial, marine, anticorrosion and wood uses
- polyurethane resin - automobile, industrial, anticorrosion and wood uses,
- epoxy resin - automobile, industrial, marine and anticorrosion uses

Pigment - provides colour

Solvent - controls application and helps paint to dry

Additives, such as driers or fungicides

Look at the diagram and read the article.

(a) Suggest THREE uses for:
(i) architectural paints;
(ii) Industrial paints;
(iii) speciality coatings.

(b) Explain how paint protects a product.

(c) Why have water based paints and powder coatings been developed?

(d) How might:
(i) additives;
(ii) pigments; and
(iii) resins;
protect a product and change the appearance of a product?

design is drawn on carbon paper and the print transferred to the wax. The pattern is then cut or scratched, exposing the surface of the metal through the wax. The metal is then dipped into ferric chloride solution or nitric acid. The acid will etch away the exposed surface making the pattern on the metal. When finished the remainder of the wax can be removed, the metal washed and lacquered.

Engraving (permanent) This involves cutting decorative shapes into resistant materials. First the pattern has to be drawn onto the material using transfer, carbon, or drawn straight onto the piece. Then 'chasing tools' are used to remove the thin layer of metal. For wood a chisel and mallet are used. For metal a metal chisel or punch is used. There are different shapes of punches to give decorative shapes. Punching using shapes is called repousse. Most engraving today is carried out using machines.

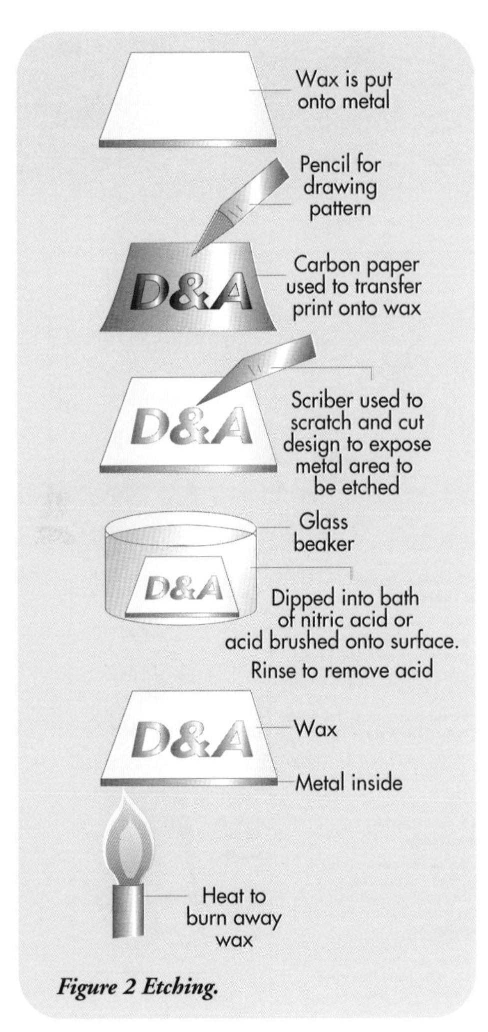

Figure 2 Etching.

Finishing and movement

Some products may have moving parts. A finish needs to be chosen that will help these parts to move efficiently and not catch or stick. For metals, there is a variety of oils and greases that can be used to cover moving parts. These are called **lubricants** (see unit 7) and will also protect the materials from attack by chemicals, air and water. Lubricants will also reduce friction and protect the metal from wear. For wooden surfaces some are required to be non-slip, for example, furniture tops or flooring, whilst others are needed to be slippery, for example, a dance-floor or sliding parts. Beeswax is used to reduce slip and paraffin wax to improve slip.

Glass enamelling - fusing glass onto heated metal.
Stove enamelling - Enamelling at lower temperatures than glass enamelling.
Dip coating - covering metal in plastic powder whilst hot.
Electroplating - passing electricity through an electrolyte to cover the surface of the metal to be plated.
Galvanising - using zinc to coat or cover steel or iron.
Veneering - glueing a decorative layer of timber or plastic onto a cheaper piece of timber or manufactured board.

activities

Table 2 Uses of finishing techniques in various industries.

Industry	Coatings £m Organic	Plating	Galvanising	Total-£m	Share-%
Motor vehicle	308	170	13	491	28
Construction	324	5	123	452	26
Electrical/Electronic	109	230	-	339	20
Retail consumer	138	150	18	306	18
Aerospace	59	73	-	132	8

Read the table and the information below.

(a) Which industry uses finishing techniques the most?

(b) Suggest how:

(i) organic finishes could be used in the motor industry;

(ii) electroplating could be used in the electronics industry;

(iii) galvanising could be used in the construction industry.

The three main types of finishing used in industry are organic finishes (paints and powders), electroplating and hot dip galvanising. Table 2 shows the main uses of these finishes. A study by the DTI has shown that finishing will be used even more in the UK motor and electronics industries as Japanese and US companies set up and invest in the UK.

Source: adapted from Engineering, December 1994.

case study: FLYMO E300 SPRINTER MOWER

Flymo Limited manufacture garden maintenance equipment. The information here relates to the parts of a Flymo E300 electric mower and how to assemble the handle.

Source: Flymo Limited.

PART	DESCRIPTION	QTY
1	SCREW	2
2	HANDLE/LABEL ASSY	1
	HANDLE, UPPER	1
3	CORD GUIDE	1
	CORD GUIDE	1
4	RETAINER, SWITCHBOX	1
	RETAINER, SWITCHBOX	1
5	WASHER	2
6	KNOB WING	2
7	HANDLE BOLT	2
8	HANDLE, LOWER	1
9	CLIP CABLE	2
10	LABEL, AUTOSTOP	1
11	SCREW	5
12	COVER ASSY	1
	COVER ASSY	1
	COVER ASSY	1
13	FILTER	1
14	CLAMP, PLASTIC	1
15	LABEL, WARNING	1
	LABEL, WARNING	1
	LABEL, WARNING	1
	LABEL, WARNING	1
16	LABEL - FLYMO	1
17	HOOD 30CM	1
18	PIN SPLIT	2
19	PIVOT PIN	2
20	PIN RETAINING	2
21	PIN	2
22	MOTOR - 240V BRAKED	1
	MOTOR - 240V	1
	MOTOR - 220V	1
	MOTOR - 230V	1
23	MOTOR MOUNTING PLATE	1
24	SCREW PLASTITE	4
25	INSERT, IMPELLER	1
26	IMPELLER	1
27	BLADE SPACER PEGGED	3
28	BLADE 30CM	1
29	WASHER ANTI FRICTION PTFE	1
30	SPANNER/SCRAPER	1
31	BLADE BOLT C/W PTFE WASHER	1
32	MAINS LEAD 20MT	1
33	LOCK OFF	1
34	SPRING-LOCK OFF	1
35	SWITCHBOX UPPER	1
36	LEVER	1
37	SPRING-TORSION	1
38	THERMAL CUT-OUT	1
39	CUT-OUT COVER	1
40	SWITCH	1
	SWITCH	1
	SWITCH	1
41	PIN RETAINER	1
	PIN RETAINER	1
42	LEAD	1
	LEAD	1
	LEAD	1
	LEAD	1
43	LEAD-INTERNAL	1
44	SWITCHBOX, LOWER	1
	SWITCHBOX, LOWER	1
	SWITCHBOX, LOWER	1
45	SCREW	4
46	CABLE RETAINER	1
47	PROTECTION SLEEVE	1
48	CONNECTING LEAD	1

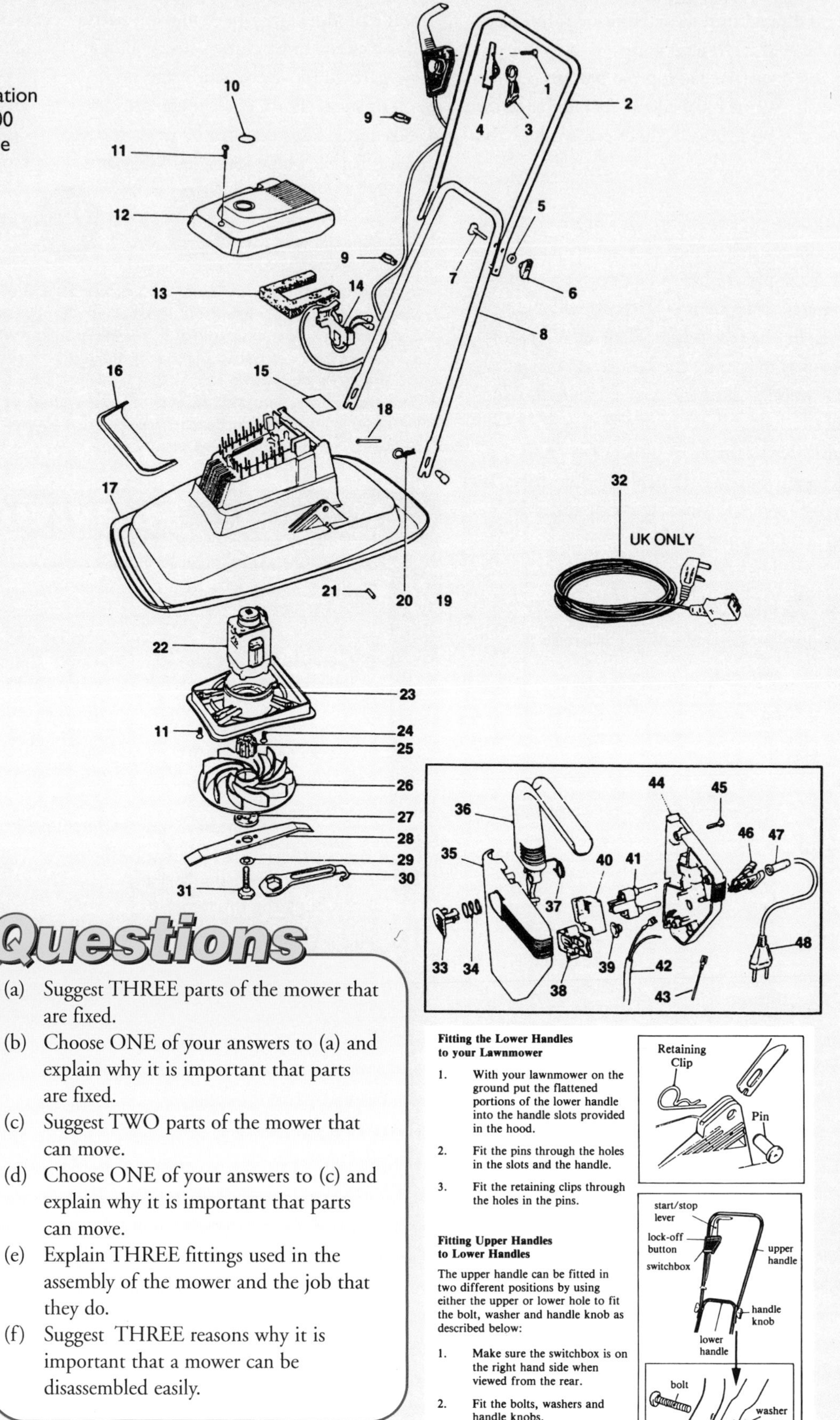

Questions

(a) Suggest THREE parts of the mower that are fixed.

(b) Choose ONE of your answers to (a) and explain why it is important that parts are fixed.

(c) Suggest TWO parts of the mower that can move.

(d) Choose ONE of your answers to (c) and explain why it is important that parts can move.

(e) Explain THREE fittings used in the assembly of the mower and the job that they do.

(f) Suggest THREE reasons why it is important that a mower can be disassembled easily.

Case study: FAIRLINE BOATS PLC

Fairline boats plc manufactures a range of luxury cruising power boats from 28 foot to 60 foot. The company is renowned for the sophistication of its designs and finishes. Quality is vital at all stages of production. The boats are production boats, but with a large degree of customisation, and so ability to cope with maintaining quality with this variety is essential.

The hulls are made from glass reinforced plastic (GRP). The hulls are laid up in a mould using an outside skin of gel coat and a laminate of resin and glass fibre. They require no finishing; the quality of the hull depends on the quality of the mould.

Galley work surfaces made from Avonite.

The interiors are manufactured from a choice of timbers. Cherry is used to give a feeling of warmth in the interior. Maple is chosen by customers who want a lighter interior - often for boats going to sunnier climates. The highly lacquered finish both protects the timber in the marine environment and also gives a high quality appearance. The wood is first tinted with a water-based stain, followed by a coat of polyester lacquer to give a hard and even finish. This is then sanded down and additional layers of melamine lacquer are added to give the final finish. Tint may be added to one of these coats of lacquer to enable panels where where the colour is slightly different to be matched.

Teak is used for external timber on decks and cockpits. This is very hard wearing and resists the marine environment. It is initially finished in teak oil, but subsequently needs very little attention.

Galley work tops are made from Avonite. This is a resin based composite that can easily be fabricated to fit complex shapes. The high gloss surface is achieved by sanding and polishing.

Stainless steel is used extensively internally and externally in boats. It is important to use the best quality stainless steel (316) as this is resistant to marine corrosion. Chrome is mainly used for internal fittings, particularly where stainless steel is not available, eg showers, taps. Chrome would not be used externally as it is less resistant to corrosion.

Source: Fairline Boats plc.

Questions

(a) What method of wood finishing is used in the manufacture of internal joinery on luxury boats?
(b) Explain THREE advantages of this type of finishing.
(c) Why might the hull of a boat require little finishing?
(d) Explain ONE finishing method that might be used on metal parts of a boat.
(e) Explain why finishing is likely to be vital in luxury boat manufacture.
(f) What evidence is there to suggest that Fairline Boats is unlikely to mass produce luxury boats?

Finishing of internal joinery.

Hulls manufactured from GRP.

unit 15

Health and safety

Importance of health and safety

Accidents and injuries that take place in a work environment can cause discomfort to people. They can also lead to temporary or permanent injury and absence from work. They can even lead to the loss of limbs or loss of employment in extreme cases. The prevention of injury in the workplace is also important to employers because:

- time is lost if somebody is off sick or injured;
- the temporary replacement of injured staff costs extra;
- equipment repairs may have to be carried out;
- equipment may be out of use until checked or repaired;
- of possible legal costs and compensation.

Protection at work

The Health and Safety at Work Act (HSWA) 1974 has had three main effects on health and safety in the work place.

- It imposes criminal liability on employers for failing to meet regulations.
- It set up the Health and Safety Executive (HSE) to be responsible for checking the act is being followed. HSE and local authority inspectors visit work places to check health and safety regulations are being met.
- It gives employees rights to be represented on health and safety matters.

The Workplace (Health, Safety and Welfare) Regulations (WHSWR) 1992 implemented EU regulations regarding health and safety. They also set out an Approved Code of Practice (ACOP) for employers. Other regulations include:

- The Management of Health and Safety at Work Regulations (MHSWR) 1992, which relates to the implementation of health and safety arrangements;
- The Provision and Use of Work Equipment Regulations (PUWER) 1992, which relate to the safe use of equipment and machinery;
- The Personal Protective Equipment at Work Regulations (PPEWR) 1992, which relates to protective clothing and equipment;
- The Health and Safety (Display Screen Equipment) Regulations 1992, which relate to workers using computer screens and technical requirements of workstations;
- The Manual Handling Operations Regulations (MHOR) 1992, which relates to the transport and handling of loads by hand.

Your employer has a duty under the law to ensure, so far as is reasonably practicable, your health, safety and welfare at work.

In general, your employer's duties include:

- making your workplace safe and without risks to health;
- keeping dust, fume and noise under control;
- ensuring plant and machinery are safe and that safe systems of work are set and followed;
- ensuring articles and substances are moved, stored and used safely;
- providing adequate welfare facilities;
- giving you the information, instruction, training and supervision necessary for your health and safety.

Your employer must also:

- draw up a health and safety policy statement if there are 5 or more employees, including the health and safety organisation and arrangements in force, and bring it to your attention;
- provide free, any protective clothing or equipment specifically required by health and safety law;
- report certain injuries, diseases and dangerous occurrences to the enforcing authority;
- provide adequate first-aid facilities;
- consult a safety representative, if one is appointed by a recognised trade union, about matters affecting your health and safety;
- set up a safety committee if asked in writing by 2 or more safety representatives

As an employee, you have legal duties too. They include:

- taking reasonable care for your own health and safety and that of others who may be affected by what you do or do not do;
- cooperation with your employer on health and safety;
- not interfering with or misusing anything provided for your health, safety or welfare.

Source: HMSO.

***Figure 1** An extract from The Health and Safety Executive's poster found in workplaces which explains the obligations of employers and employees towards health and safety.*

activities

The Provision and Use of Work Equipment Regulations 1992 contains regulations applying to the safe use of 'work equipment'. The term work equipment is used to cover:

* single machines, such as a lathe;
* tools, such as a portable drill;
* any equipment assembled to work together, such as an assembly line to manufacture televisions. It also states that work equipment must be used only for operations for which they are suitable. This takes into account the internal integrity of the equipment, the place where it is being used and the purpose for which it is being used.

(a) Suggest THREE examples of: (i) single machines; (ii) portable tools; (iii) equipment working together to carry out tasks.

(b) Choose TWO portable tools and suggest one task that might be suitable for using the tool and one task that would be unsuitable. Explain your answers.

Risk assessment

The Health and Safety At Work Act requires that businesses make a RISK ASSESSMENT of their activities. The assessment should point out what must be done to ensure all aspects of the working environment comply with health and safety legislation. An employer or person delegated by the employer (the safety officer) checks the working environment for possible risks. That person then puts into action procedures and/or equipment that will reduce risks to the employees.

Risk assessment will cover the layout of a workshop or work area; dust and fume extraction; chemicals, use and storage; operating machinery; safety procedures. The employer is also responsible for regular checks to ensure standards are maintained and must display the results of these checks.

The work environment

The layout of a work area, whether it is the whole building, a room or a work bench, needs to be organised to minimise risks. Areas should be designed for certain tasks and be clearly marked as such. Examples are areas where heat is involved (furnaces etc.), areas for machinery (lathes, drill etc.) and areas for working by hand (work benches). Others include specific storage sites, gang ways (walkways) and traffic routes that are clearly marked and kept clean and free of blockages. There are recognised colour codes for all of these areas. Most factories place the markings as indelible lines on the floor.

Work areas should have sufficient floor area, height and unoccupied space for people to get to and from work stations. The size of the work room will depend on the number of people in it. Work areas also require suitable lighting (natural if possible), emergency lighting and ventilation. Temperatures should be reasonable inside buildings (at least 13°C where strenuous activity is carried out and at least 16°C where the majority of work is sitting or non-strenuous). They should be warm or cool enough to provide comfort so that there is no need for special clothing.

Figure 2 Protection at work.

Helmet
(Filtered to avoid eye damage when electric arc welding of metals)

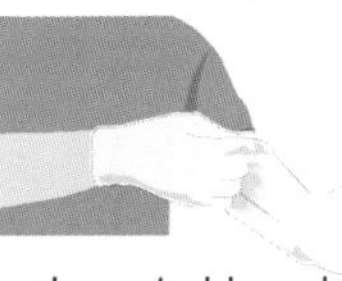

Plastic/rubber gloves
(Sometimes disposable. Used for enamelling, annealing and when using chemicals such as acids)

Overalls
(Increased protection for clothing)

Goggles
(Eye protection when using drills and lathes and when polishing and grinding)

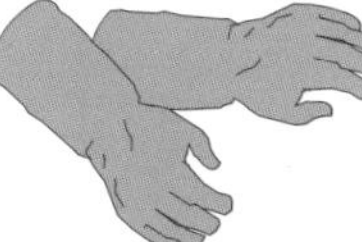

Gauntlets
(Used when casting metals. Usually leather. Also used with 'heat' work such as line bending)

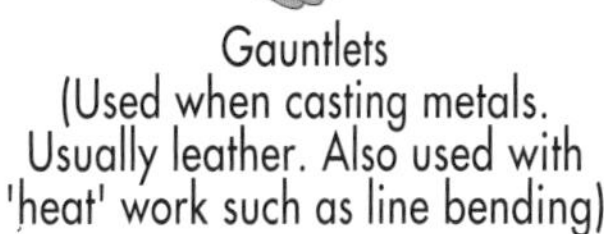

Steel capped shoes
(For general heavy work in workshops to protect toes. Usually used in forge work and casting)

Leggings
(Protection of legs when casting, for example)

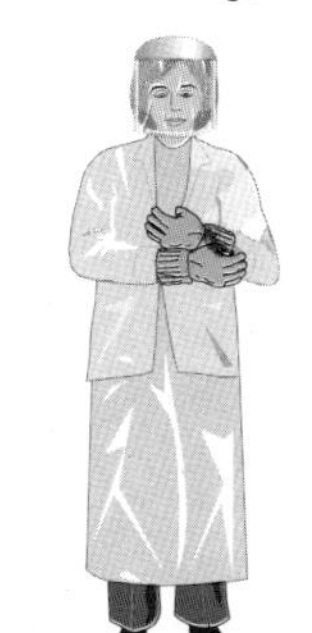

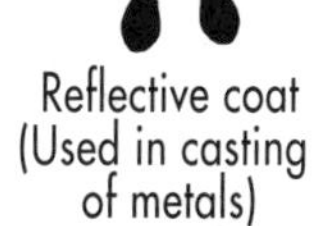

Reflective coat
(Used in casting of metals)

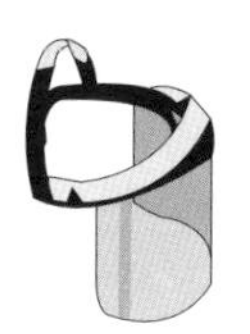

Visor
(Eye and face protection)

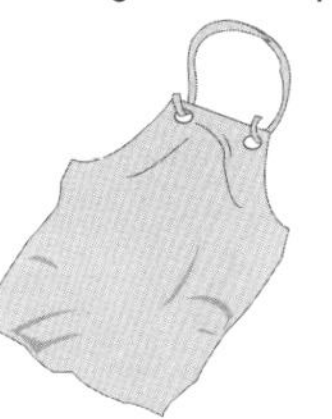

Apron
(General purpose protection of clothing. Leather aprons give heat protection)

Hard Hat
(Used for head protection)

Respirators and face masks
(Used with machinery that generates dust and for painting)

Ear defenders
(Used when drilling or cutting and with heavier machinery)

Chemical suit and hood

Dust and fume extraction

When working with resistant materials there will be occasions when dust or fumes are released as a product is being manufactured. These 'airborne' dangers need to be removed before they are inhaled as some may cause injury to the body immediately or at some time in the future. Many new machines have their own dust and fume extraction units. Older machinery may not and may require an approved portable 'extractor' to be alongside and in operation whilst work is taking place.

Some glues are contained in solvents which are dangerous and should only be used in a fume cupboard or under an extraction canopy. It is important to carry out such work in a well ventilated room where air is circulating which can allow the fumes to dissipate. Dust is one substance that is dealt with by COSHH regulations (see later).

Protective clothing for dust and fumes is likely to include an apron to cover clothing and goggles to protect the eyes from dust and splinters. Dust respirators are also recommended.

Chemicals

Virtually all chemicals in a workshop provide some sort of danger. They may be toxic (poisonous) if ingested (inhaled or swallowed). Others may be damaging to the eyes. They may burn the skin, or cause irritation, for example solutions used for developing and etching PCBs or fumes released when cleaning ferrous metals with sulphuric acid.

The Control of Substances Hazardous to Health (COSHH) Regulations 1994 form part of risk assessment. They require employers to assess risks arising from substances hazardous to health. They set out likely hazards of toxic, harmful, irritant and corrosive substances, eg chemicals, resins, paint strippers,varnishes, stains, preservatives and dust, how they can be safely stored/handled and how they can be dealt with in case of accidents.

Machinery

Instructions for the safe use of machinery should be clearly displayed by the machine. They should be clear and precise to help the machinist operate the item safely and efficiently. Warnings should be displayed to show the potential hazards of machines, and any essential protective clothing to be worn. All machines should have an emergency 'shut off' button that operates properly and is clearly marked. When not in use all machinery should be switched off, isolated and secured to avoid accidents possibly by inquisitive people or unqualified staff. Employers must provide adequate health and safety training (and retraining) in the correct use of equipment, either verbally or by demonstration.

General clothing for use with machinery should be aprons, secured properly so that no loose ends can get caught in the operating machinery. Loose clothing should be removed and long hair should be tied back. Goggles should be worn to protect eyes, and possibly ear defenders if the machinery is particularly loud or is used for any length of time. Any item to be used in a piece of machinery should be held securely using clamps or fixing bolts. Most machines have protective guards which need to be in place prior to operation.

Machinery should be serviced regularly to make sure it is working efficiently. Saw

Table 1 Colour codes.

Colour	Area	Signs
Red	Areas where heat is used (eg a furnace)	Prohibition signs
Blue	Machinery that doesn't use heat (eg a lathe)	Mandatory signs
Yellow/Black	Gangways; areas to be kept clear	Warning signs

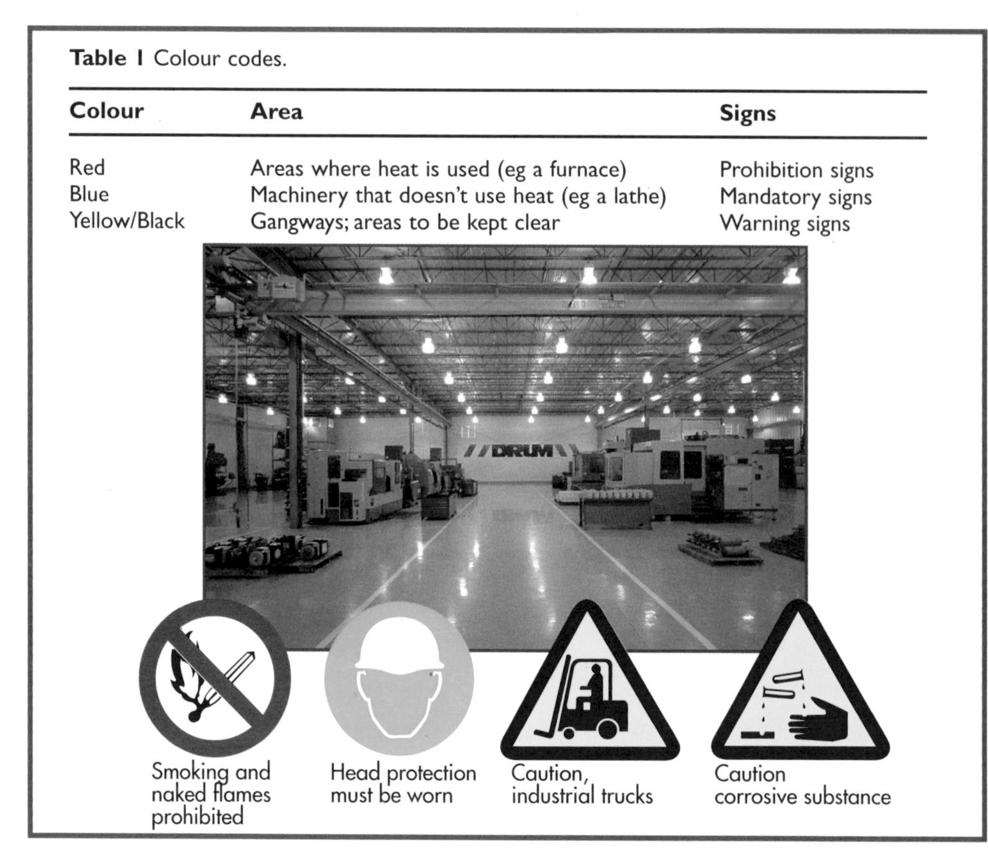

activities

Look at the photographs.

(a) Identify the possible health and safety problems that may occur in each activity.

(b) Suggest what protection may be used to ensure that the tasks are carried out as safely as possible.

Casting.

Drilling.

Welding.

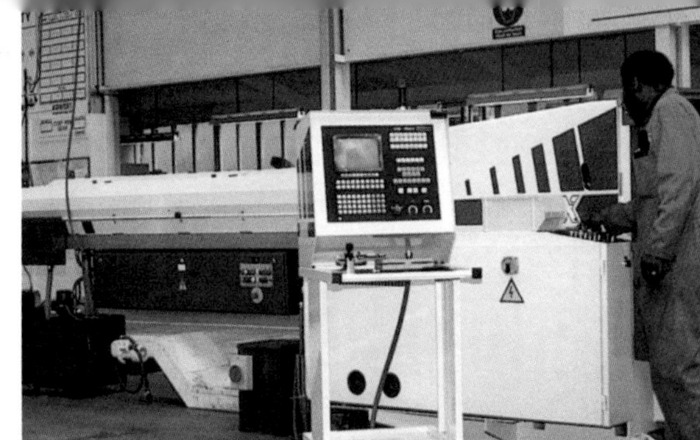

CNC lathes are enclosed to protect operators.

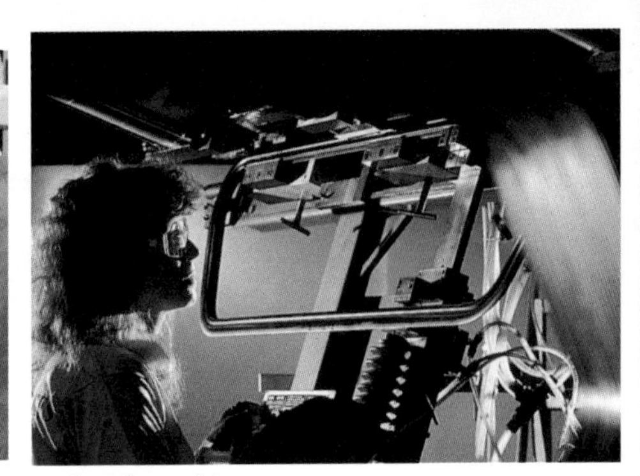

Goggles and ear defenders are used with machinery.

blades and drill bits need to be sharp. A dulled blade may 'jam' and cause serious problems for the operator. A service record must be kept for each piece of machinery. Faulty or broken machinery must be clearly labelled as such and put out of use.

Workstations should be arranged so tasks can be carried out safely and comfortably, without undue bending and stretching. Seating should meet regulations. Work carried out for long periods, with continuous repetitive tasks, requires rest and recovery time.

Procedures

All working environments should have clearly displayed procedures for a number of eventualities. These are:

- fire drill which will include the orderly evacuation and closing down of workshops;
- guidelines for conduct in the work area, such as safe and proper behaviour and legal responsibilities;
- general instructions in case of accidents such as first aid for foreign bodies in the eye or limb injuries.

It is important that people in a work area are well acquainted with all these procedures and have had practice at carrying them out.

First aid

All work areas should have a person appointed to be in charge of first aid. Businesses with more than 50 employees require some qualified in first aid. Workplaces need to have a clearly marked and well stocked first aid box. Essential items to be kept in the box will be:

- a printed card listing contents and a leaflet giving first aid guidance;
- individually wrapped sterile dressings;
- sterile eye pads with attachment;
- triangular bandages;
- safety pins;
- selection of medium, large and extra large sterile unmedicated wound dressings;

Some people are allergic to certain medicines (eg aspirin, paracetamol). In a business, medicines, tablets and creams should not be administered by the person in charge of first aid.

Cleanliness and waste

Work areas, work rooms and equipment should be clean and tidy. Waste materials should not be allowed to accumulate and should be placed in appropriate disposal units. Floors and stairways should be cleaned regularly in a way that prevents slipping. Care must be taken that materials used for cleaning do not cause a hazard themselves, for example if they are flammable, slippery or cause risk if they inhaled. Cleaning materials are subject to COSHH Regulations 1994. Waste should be disposed of in a suitable manner. Waste wood can be either recycled into manufactured boards or turned into sawdust. Chemicals must be disposed of by contacting a supplier or waste disposal company that will dispose of the chemicals legally.

activities

A worker employed by a local company had tendons in his hand severed by a metal cutting circular saw. His injury needed micro surgery and he was off work for nine months. The accident occurred as the worker was cutting short lengths of angle iron when the saw blade swung back onto his left hand.

He had been employed with the company for about a month and received virtually no instruction on the use of the pivoting head circular saw. He only knew how to turn the machine off and on and was asked to use it because the normal operator was absent. The machine was in a poor state of repair and did not have a safety guard properly attached so the saw blade was exposed.

The company was fined for failing to train the operator and for inadequately guarding the machine.

Source: adapted from Health and Safety Executive Newsletter.

(a) What, according to the article, were the TWO main reasons for the accident?

(b) Suggest problems for the:
(i) worker;
(ii) company;
as a result of the accident.

(c) Suggest ways in which the company may prevent such an accident in future.

Risk assessment - **an assessment to point out what is required to ensure all aspects of a working environment comply with health and safety legislation.**

unit 16

Systems

What are systems?

Systems are activities or parts that, when linked together, carry out a specific task. A SYSTEM can be mechanical, electrical or electronic, or an activity to produce a product. A hand whisk is a **mechanical system** (see unit 17) that is used to mix food. A calculator is an **electronic system** (see unit 18) that is used to carry out calculations accurately. A production line in a factory is a system that is used to manufacture products, for example televisions or furniture (see unit 19).

The purpose of a system is to change the nature of a task. It may make the task:

- easier;
- more efficient;
- faster or slower.

Materials, energy or movement are transferred through a system as it operates. The end result is a product, a signal (eg sound or light) or movement, perhaps in a different direction.

Designing systems

When designing systems it is important to ask:

- what do I want the system to do (make a product, act as an alarm)?
- what will be transferred through the system (materials, energy, movement)?
- how will the system operate (manually, mechanically, electrically)?

At its simplest every system is made up of three parts. INPUTS:

- can activate the system;
- can be a signal;
- can be a switch;
- can be materials;

depending on the system. They are usually the link between the outside world and the system. The PROCESSES are the series of operations which alter or change the material, energy or movement to achieve an end. The OUTPUTS are the outcomes of the system - what is produced. Systems can be shown as flow diagrams, as in Figure 1.

Complicated systems can be simplified by designing **sub-systems** within the main system. For example, an electronic system such as an alarm may have a time delay. A mechanical system such as a cycle may have a gear train or a brake sub-system. The advantage of having sub-systems is that it allows complicated systems to be produced. Each sub-system carries out its own smaller task effectively.

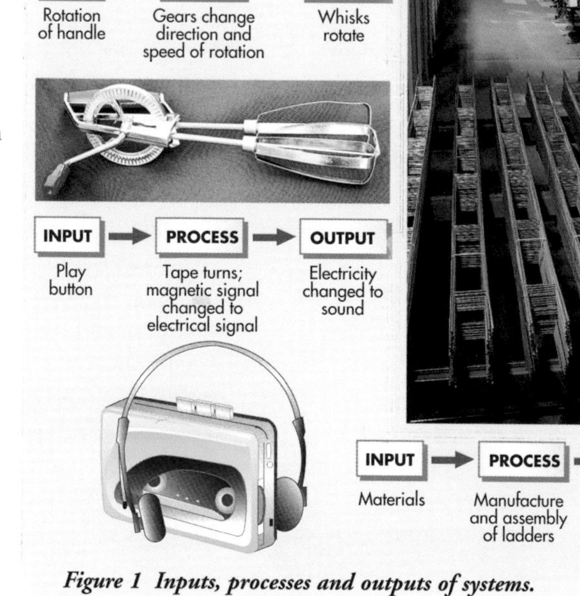

Figure 1 Inputs, processes and outputs of systems.

activities

Look at the photographs. In each case:

(a) explain whether a mechanical, electrical or production system is shown;
(b) identify the inputs, processes and outputs;
(c) suggest how the system might be controlled.

Lighting with a control panel used to set and time a flash light.

A paper cutter

Production of doors. An operator uses a CNC router to cut shapes into MDF as part of the production process.

Figure 2 Feedback in a system.

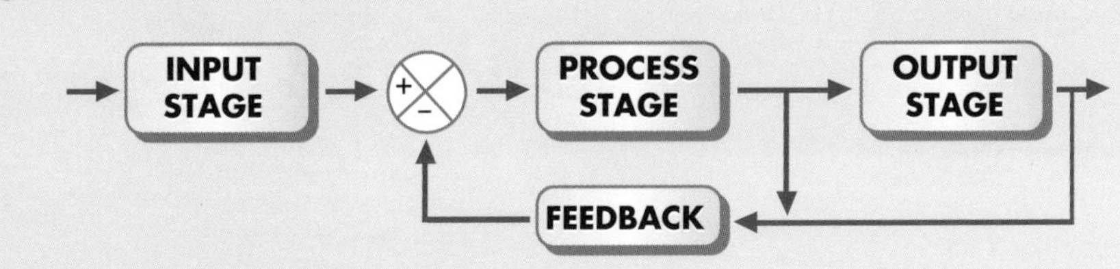

Control

As materials, energy or movement pass through a system they may be **controlled**. The advantage of being able to control a system is that work can be done more efficiently, accurately, faster or slower. For example, the speed of an assembly line needs to be controlled. Too fast and workers may not be able to complete tasks. Too slow and workers may waste time.

A simple system can be controlled by setting an input such as an on-off switch or a variable control such as a water tap or a volume dial. A more complicated system may be controlled by a timer, for example.

A system of production can have many methods of control and be broken down into many sub-systems. Switches, dials, sensors, templates, gauges and tests can be used to control the speed of production, the quality of production (see unit 23) and the rate at which stock is ordered (see unit 19). Some manufacturers make use of computers to manufacture and assemble products, such as:

- computer aided design, CAD (see unit 2);
- computer aided manufacture, CAM (see unit 19) and computer numerically controlled, CNC, machines (see unit 11);
- computer integrated manufacturing, CIM (see unit 19), where the entire production process is controlled by computers.

Feedback

FEEDBACK involves information being passed back from later in a system to an earlier part, as shown in Figure 2. It is an important part of a system because it can ensure that it is operating efficiently and can alert the system if a desired outcome is not being achieved.

Feedback can be used to control parts of a system. If a piece of metal or plastic is being cut too deep by a milling machine, the information can be fed back to the operator to make the necessary adjustment. A quality check at key stages of production may indicate that something has gone wrong. Feedback systems that involve people are called **open feedback systems**.

Sensors can be used to monitor levels in a system. If the temperature level rises too high (or too low) in an oven the sensor detects this and sends back the information so that the level can be lowered (or raised). Thermostats in heating systems are an example of this. The temperature is set and the heater continues to work until the temperature reaches the desired value. The sensor detects this value and acts to switch the heater off. When the temperature falls below the set value, the sensor sends information back along the system to turn the heater on again. This type of system that works automatically is called a **closed feedback system**.

Feedback in a system can be either positive or negative. Positive feedback occurs when the information fed back acts to increase the signal (ie to step up production). One problem is that this can get out of control and the system may become unstable. Negative feedback is when information is fed back to reduce the output which tends to produce stability.

activities

(a) Explain why a building alarm is a system.

(b) Suggest how an operator could control the system.

(c) Identify TWO methods of feedback in the system and the uses to which it could be put.

Many businesses are protected by the use of internal alarm systems against burglary and vandalism. Typically most alarms have a control panel linked to a series of sensors. These sensors can be in the form of :

- contact pads on windows and doors which detect if they have been opened;
- vipers on windows which detect movement of the window;
- sensors which use an infra red beam to detect movement in a room.

If a sensor detects movement an alarm is set off in the building and sometimes in a local police station. It is possible to adjust the system so that different areas can be alarmed. It is also possible to adjust the length of the alarm and the delay before it is set off. Most systems allow an operator to check in which area the alarm has been set off and also detect any faults in the system.

A viper (vibration sensor).

A control panel.

Key Terms

System - **a set of smaller tasks that combine to carry out a larger task.**
Inputs - **activate or enter a system.**
Processes - **operations which alter or transfer the input into the system.**
Outputs - **outcomes from a system.**
Feedback - **information that is returned from one part of a system to an earlier part.**

unit 17

Mechanical systems

Mechanisms

Many devices that are used at home, at work or for recreation are called MACHINES. Machines are made from moving parts called MECHANISMS. There are four groups of mechanism: **levers** and **linkages**; **wheels** and **pulleys**; **gears**; **screws** and **threads**. Mechanisms combine to make up mechanical systems (see unit 16). Levers, for example, can join together to make linkages; gears can be meshed to make gear boxes; pulleys can be combined to make a 'block and tackle'.

Mechanical systems have an input, a process and an output. The input force is often described as the effort. This makes the system move. The output is a force that has to be moved - the load. This may be a weight that needs moving or a resistance to movement (eg a lid fixed on a can or a screw tightened into a piece of material).

Mechanical systems need energy to work. This energy may come from burning fuels (eg a steam engine), a clockwork spring, an electrical motor or our own muscles. Mechanical systems have to do work. Machines are designed to make work easier or more efficient. They are often described as 'labour saving' for this reason. Mechanical systems can carry out a number of jobs. They can change the type or direction of movement, take movement from one place to another, change the amount of force and change the distance moved.

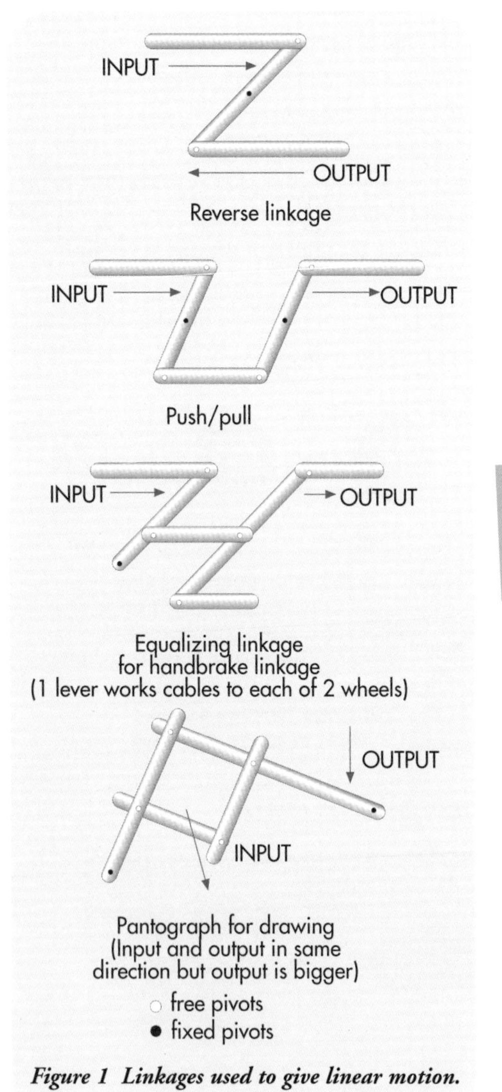

Figure 1 Linkages used to give linear motion.

Changing the type of movement

Mechanisms move in different ways.

Linear motion Some mechanisms move in one direction only, forwards or backwards, like a bolt on a door, upwards, downwards or sideways. This is linear motion. Linkages are often used to give linear motion. Linkages are levers that are connected together. They can have fixed pivots that are attached to a backboard or a machine body and moving

activities

The drawing below shows a mechanism which could be used as part of a game or a toy.

(a) What type of mechanism is shown?
(b) What type of output motion does it give?
(c) Suggest TWO types of game or toy which could use this mechanism.
(d) What might be added to make the figures move smoothly within the toy?

pivots. The load of one lever becomes the effort of the next lever in a linkage system, so that force is transmitted through the system.

Reciprocating motion Some mechanisms move forwards and backwards in one movement, like the needle of a sewing machine. This is called reciprocating motion. It can be achieved simply by adding a return spring or elastic to a device, such as a door closing mechanism. When stretched the spring moves in the direction of the force. Once the force has relaxed the spring returns to its normal size, pulling the object back into position.

A CAM with a 'follower' attachment can also achieve reciprocating motion. The cam may be a circle, where the axle of a wheel is off centre. This gives an 'up and down' motion. The amount of rise and fall of the follower and the length of the cycle can be altered by adjusting the shape of the cam. The distance between the highest and lowest points on the cam cycle is called the stroke. Many cams operate using circular motion as the input. Pear shaped cams are used in vehicle engines. The cam shaft controls the opening and closing of fuel/air inlet valves and exhaust gases outlet valves of the cylinders.

Figure 2 Cam shapes.

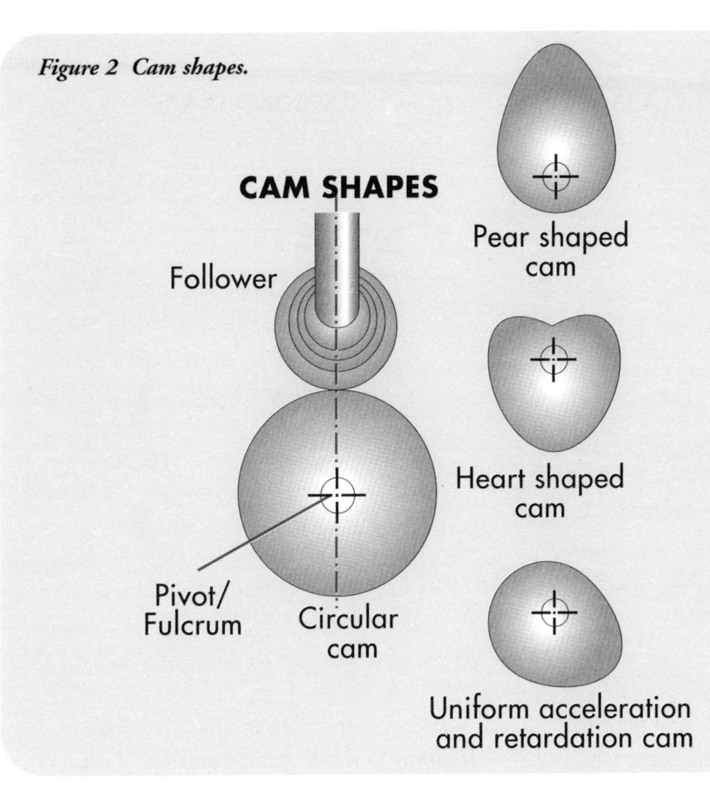

Oscillating motion Some mechanisms swing to and fro like a pendulum. This is called oscillating motion. Machines that have an oscillating motion are metronomes and robotic arms that carry out repetitive moving tasks as they swivel on a dais. The arms of robots and hydraulic grabs also have a pivot on the arm that swings in an oscillating fashion.

Mechanisms that give an oscillating action can be levers and linkages as they swing around a pivot. Levers are beams which turn on a PIVOT or FULCRUM. There are 3 types of lever (1st, 2nd, and 3rd class) as in Figure 3. These differ in the position of the pivot, the effort applied and the load. Bell cranks are often used to give an oscillating movement. These also swing around a pivot.

Steering A simple steering mechanism involves a pin in a pivot. The push and pull action causes the wheels and axle to turn in an arc. More complicated systems, as in motor vehicles, use links at the ends of the axle or a rack and pinion mechanism.

Rotary motion Some mechanisms turn round in a circle, like a record turntable or a wheel. This is called **rotary** motion. Wheels are not only used in many forms of transport, but can be adapted to suit a wide variety of

activities

Look at the information.

(a) Identify the input, process and output to this system.

(b) Suggest TWO other systems that might make use of keys and levers.

(c) Draw a flow chart to show how movement takes place from the key to the wire.

(d) What types of movement are taking place in the system? Explain your answer.

A piano produces a sound when keys are played. Pressing a piano key causes a movement in a system of levers, which results in a hammer hitting a wire. Each lever has a pivot or fulcrum on which it turns. When the hammer hits the wire it drops back and the wire resonates. Letting go of the key will drop the damper onto the wire, stopping the sound.

Source: adapted from The Way Things Work, D. Macaulay, Dorling Kindersley.

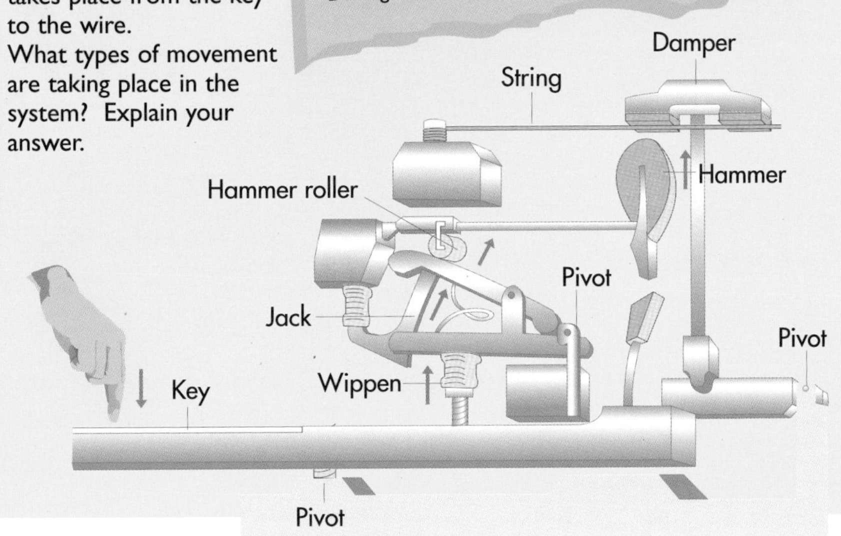

Figure 3 Levers.

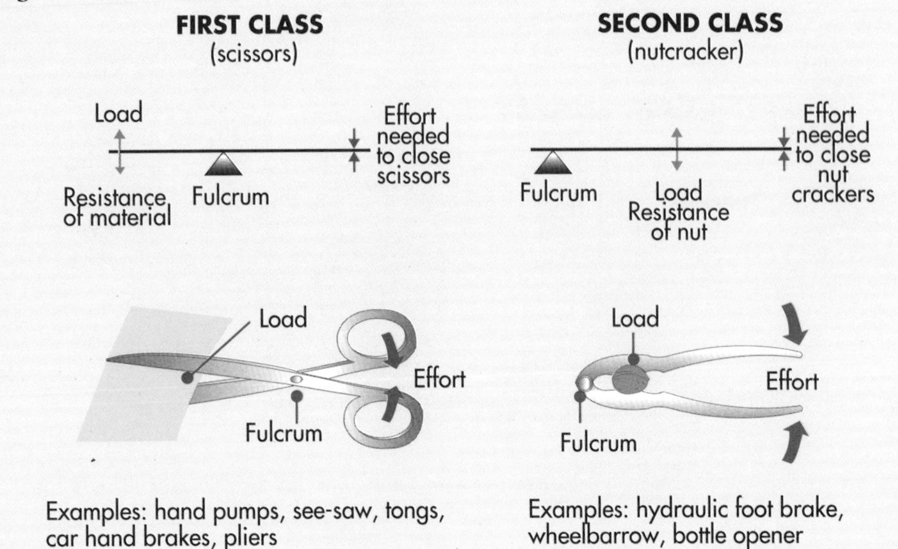

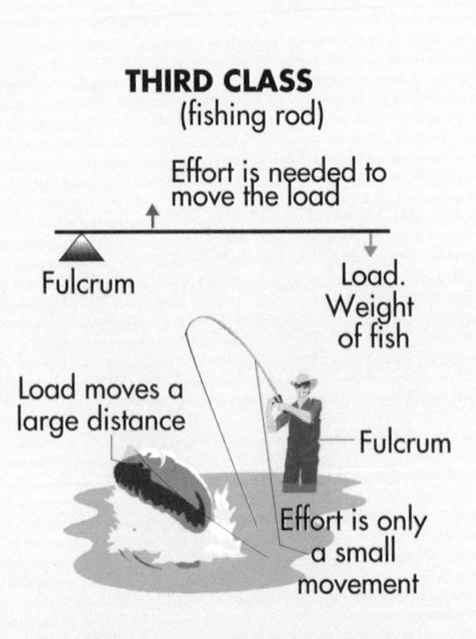

needs. With a centred hole and fixed to a frame by an axle around which the wheel turns, the construction becomes a cart, bicycle or any other type of vehicle. The wheel can be given shock absorbing qualities by fitting it with a tyre or a suspension.

Pulleys are wheels that are used to turn a belt. Pulleys can be flat, grooved or have teeth cut into them. Grooved and toothed pulleys prevent the belt from slipping. Gears are wheels with teeth. The teeth are cut at regular intervals. These are called spur gears. Bevel gears have teeth cut at an angle so that they can fit together at different angles to change the direction of motion. A worm gear has a gear in the shape of a cylinder, with one spiral tooth which operates along with a spur gear called a **pinion**.

Changing direction of movement

Mechanisms can be combined to change the direction of movement in a mechanical system. For example, the steering wheel shaft of a vehicle is at 90° to the axle. A hand operated car jack has its crank at 90° to the vehicle to be lifted, mainly for safety reasons. Linkages can be arranged to alter the direction of linear motion. For example, a pushing action on a lazy tongs system gives a linear motion at 90° to the force.

A cam with follower converts **rotary motion to reciprocating motion**. Linear cams change the direction of reciprocating motion at 90° .

Linkages combined with CRANKS change **linear or reciprocating motion to oscillating or rotary motion** (or vice versa depending on which is being driven). For example, a crank can be used to turn a rod attached to it (oscillating to linear) or the rod can be used to turn the crank (linear to oscillating). Car engine crank shafts work in this way.

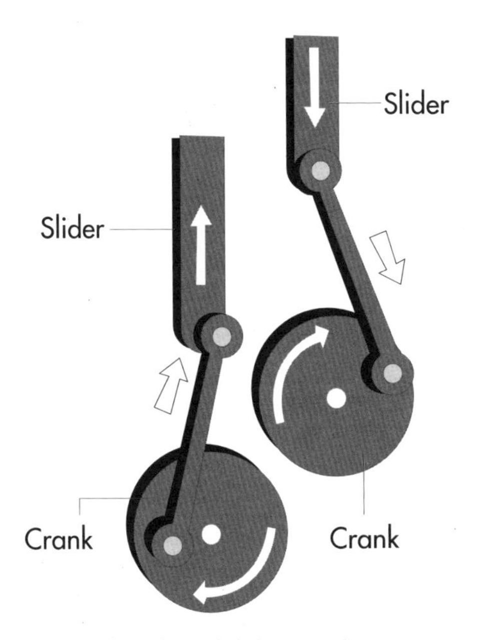

Figure 4 Cranks and sliders turn linear motion into oscillating motion and vice versa.

A rack and pinion changes linear to rotary motion or vice versa.

To change **linear to rotary motion** or vice versa there are a number of mechanical combinations available. A screw mechanism like a car jack or bench vice is one way. A RACK AND PINION, where one of the gears is shaped along a length or 'rack', can be used in canal locks, bottle openers, scales and steering systems. A simple cable wound around a winch is another.

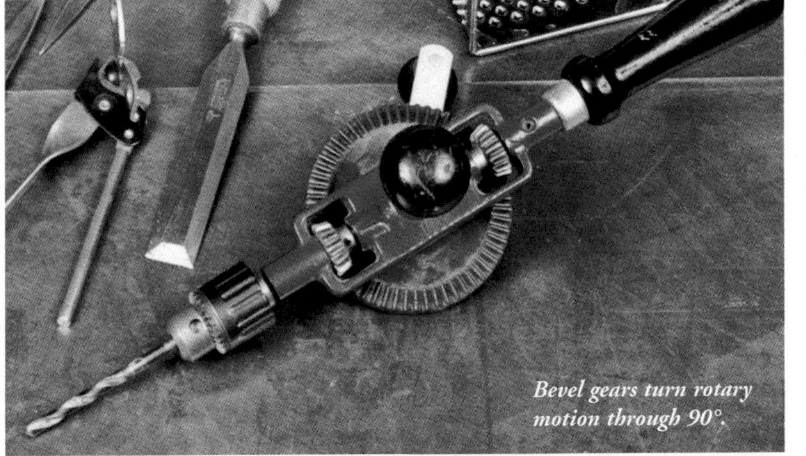

Bevel gears turn rotary motion through 90°.

Spur gears can be made to turn rotary motion in opposite directions.

Worm gears turn rotary motion through 90°, but only the worm is the driver.

Rotary motion in different directions can be achieved using a variety of mechanisms. SPUR GEARS meshing together turn in opposite directions. If the driver is turned clockwise the driven gear turns anti-clockwise. BEVEL GEARS, crown and pinion and worm gears convert rotary motion through 90°. WORM GEARS only allow the worm to be the driver. If the pinion is turned the driver in the mechanism locks. For bevel and crown and pinion gears, either gear can be the driver.

activities

1 Look at the photograph of the wine bottle opener.
 (a) Identify the type of mechanisms being used.
 (b) Suggest ONE other design that might make use of each mechanism.
 (c) Draw TWO diagrams.
  - The corkscrew is being screwed into the cork and the handles are rising.
  - The handles are pressed down and the cork is pulled out.

 In each case explain how the direction of movement is changing, putting arrows on the diagrams to illustrate the answer.

2 Look at the photograph of the tin opener.
 (a) Identify the: (i) load; (ii) fulcrum; and (iii) effort.
 (b) What class of lever is being used? Explain your answer.

Taking movement from one place to another

Most mechanical systems take movement from one part of a system to another, but some transfer movement from one system to a different or adjacent system. In transferring movement they also transfer energy and force. Pulley systems do this as in Figure 5. Each system is joined by the belt that is attached to the pulleys. The pulley that is turned by a motor or by hand is called the 'driver'. The pulley that follows is called the 'driven' or follower. Both pulleys travel in the same direction. Vacuum cleaners, washing machines and walkmans use a two pulley system like this.

Figure 6 shows a sprocket and chain system. The chain is itself a set of linkages, each joined by a pivot. The teeth of the gear fit into the chain. Chains do not stretch or slip. Like belt and pulley systems,movement travels in the same direction.

Figure 5 A pulley system.

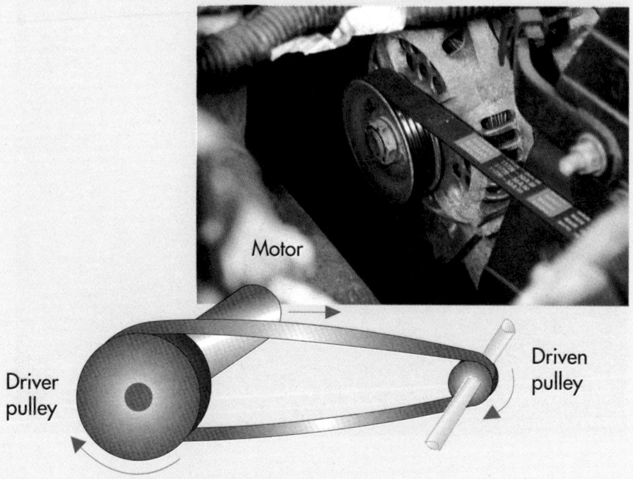

Motor

Driver pulley

Driven pulley

Note: the driven pulley can be larger than the driver pulley.

Figure 6 A sprocket and chain system.

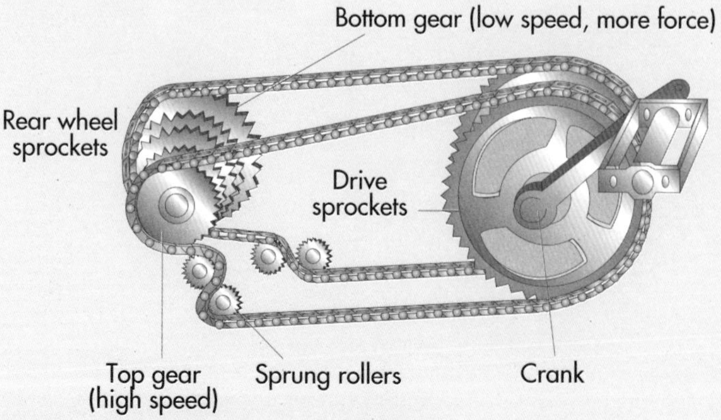

Bottom gear (low speed, more force)

Rear wheel sprockets

Drive sprockets

Top gear (high speed)

Sprung rollers

Crank

The chain acts as a belt to make the wheels turn faster than the feet. Normally the rear wheel sprocket needs to be small for high speed. To climb hills it needs to be large so the back wheel has less speed and more force.

Pneumatic and hydraulic systems

Movement, energy and force can also be transmitted in mechanical systems using air or fluids like water and oil. Transmission using air is called PNEUMATICS and using fluids it is called HYDRAULICS.

Pneumatic and hydraulic systems are contained in cylinders. Movement is transmitted by the action of **pistons** which compress the air or fluid. The force is transmitted equally throughout the system, pushing other output 'pistons'. These output pistons may be used to push or lift an object, as in hydraulic ramps, pneumatic drills or car brakes.

activities

Look at the photograph of the turntable.

(a) Identify the type of mechanical system used in the turntable.

(b) Explain what is meant by the 'driver' and the 'driven' using the turntable as an example.

(c) How is movement taken from one place to another?

(d) Suggest THREE other designs that might make use of this system.

Force multipliers

Mechanical systems can be used as FORCE MULTIPLIERS or DISTANCE MULTIPLIERS, but not both at the same time. As a force multiplier, a system will use a small input force and convert it to a larger output force. However, as it does this the input will have to move a greater distance than the output. If a machine uses a small force to move a larger force then it is said to have a MECHANICAL ADVANTAGE. The mechanical advantage can be calculated by:

$$\frac{\text{output force moved (load)}}{\text{the input force needed to move it (effort)}}$$

A simple sloping structure, like a wedge or a set of ramps gives a mechanical advantage. They can be used to lift or separate a heavy weight. Trying to raise a heavy weight vertically may be very difficult. Rolling it up an incline makes the job easier. However, it has to be moved a greater distance. A **screw thread** concentrates an incline in a smaller space by wrapping it around a cylinder as a helix. The motion is rotary rather than linear. When turned, the screw (and the load) move a distance equal to the pitch of the thread.

Trying to loosen a nut by hand may be difficult. To make the job easier a spanner is used. This increases the distance between the effort force and the load, acting like a lever with the nut acting as a pivot.

Pedals and cranks increase TORQUE (turning effect of a force). A **crankshaft** has two or more cranks joined together. Crankshafts convert reciprocating motion to rotary motion. In a child's pedal car the crankshaft is turned by pedals and drives the wheels. Pistons in a car engine turn a crankshaft to drive the wheels.

Distance multipliers

As a distance multiplier a mechanical system will move an input a short distance to move the output a larger distance. However, to achieve this, the input force will have to be greater than the output force. Comparing the distance the input moves with the distance the output moves is called the VELOCITY RATIO. It is calculated by:

$$\frac{\text{input distance moved}}{\text{output distance moved}}$$

activities

As a brake pedal is pressed the piston creates a force that is transferred through the fluid to the brakes. This forces the piston outwards and onto the wheel. The master cylinder is bigger than the brake cylinder, making the system a force multiplier. The brake pedal moves further than the brakes.

(a) What type of system is a brake system?

(b) How is force transferred in a brake system?

(c) Suggest THREE other designs that make use of force multipliers.

(d) Explain why a brake system is an example of a force multiplier.

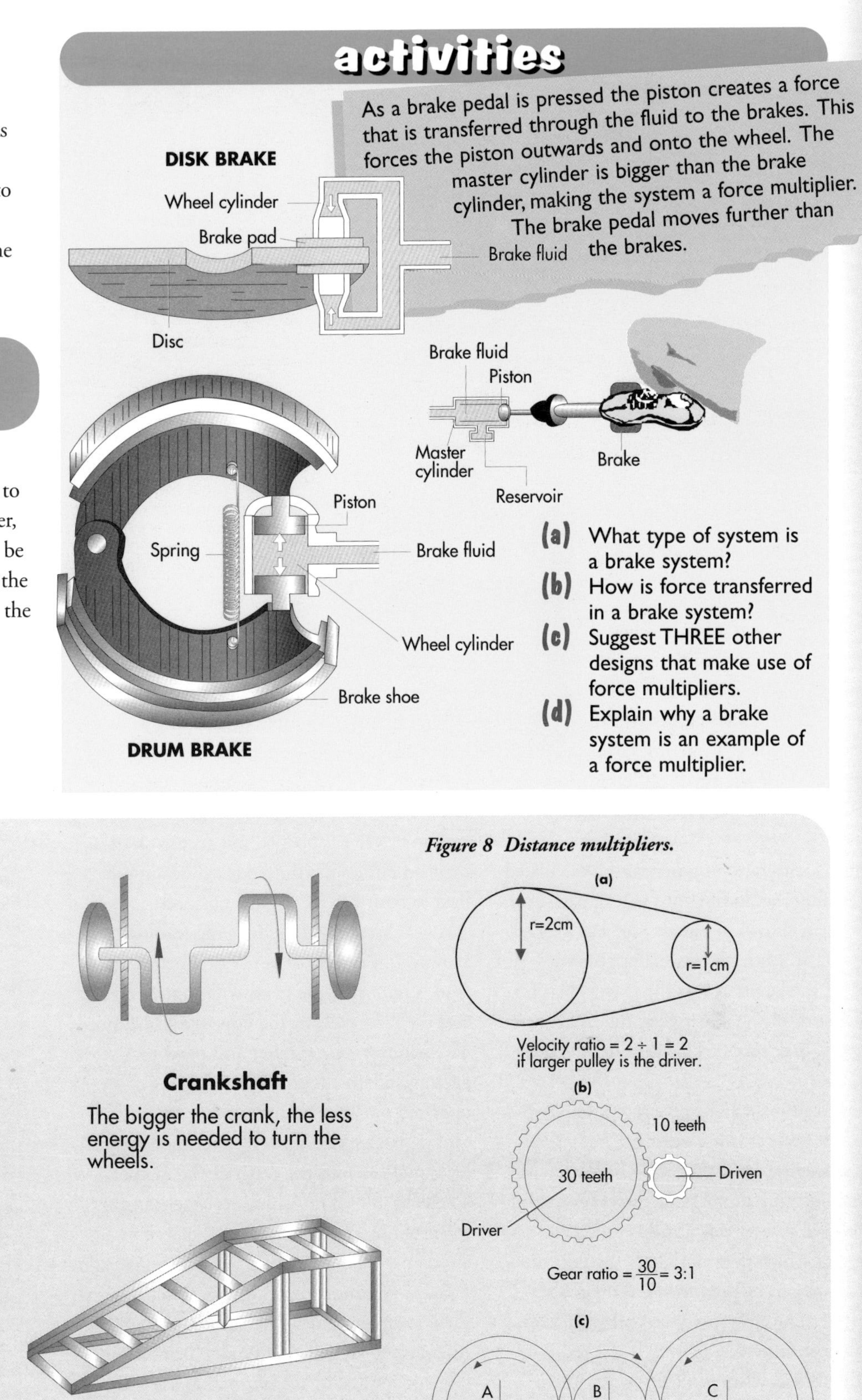

Figure 8 Distance multipliers.

Figure 7 Force multipliers.

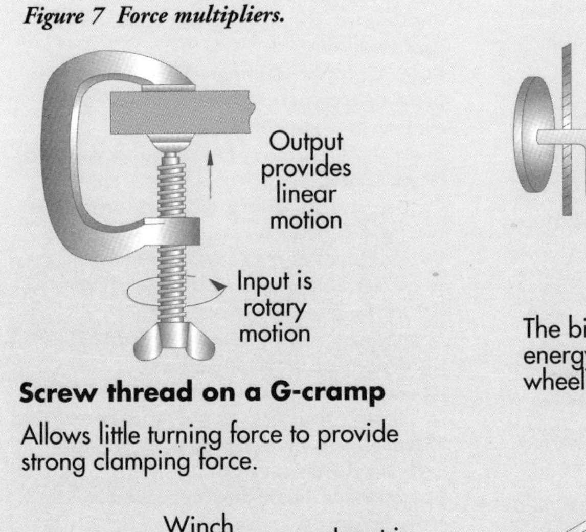

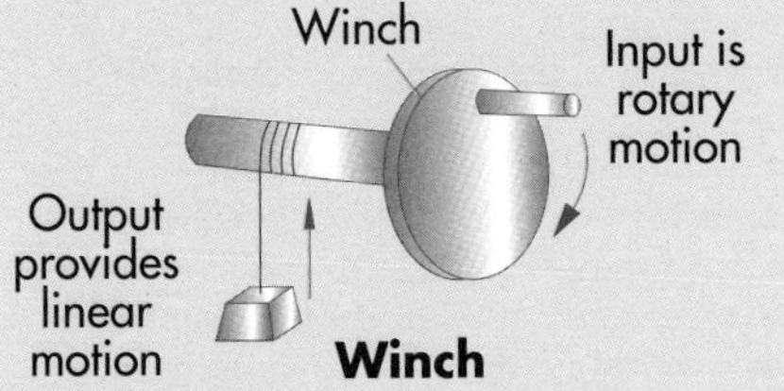

Allows user to wind a heavy weight using a smaller input force. The distance travelled by the weight is less than the distance travelled by the winch handle.

Figure 9 Roller blinds use a ratchet and pawl.

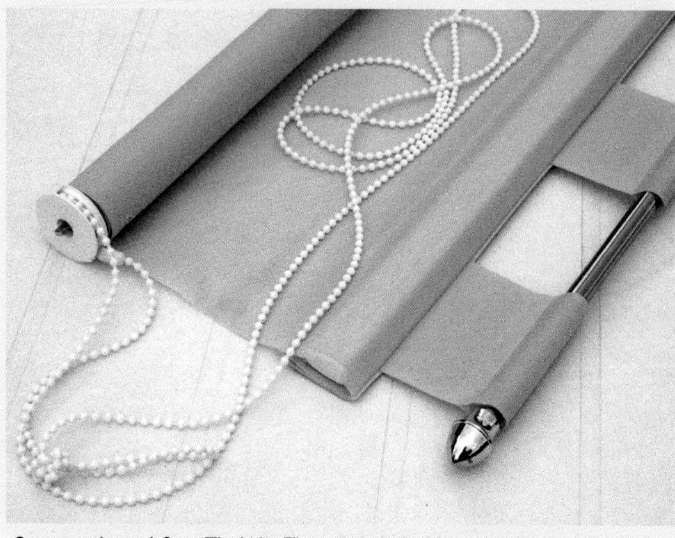

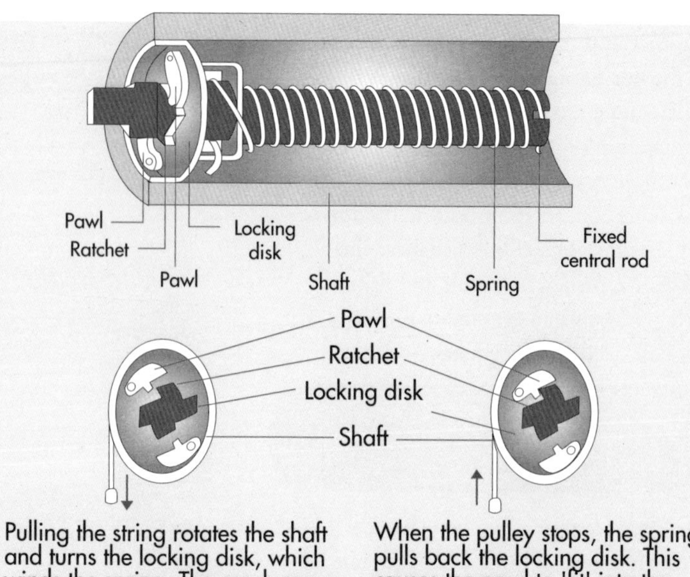

Source: adapted from The Way Things Work, D. Macaulay, Dorling Kindersley.

In Figure 8(a), if a large pulley wheel is attached to a smaller pulley and the larger pulley is the driver, for every full turn of the large pulley the small pulley will turn twice. The smaller pulley is moving faster than the larger pulley. If the small pulley is made the driver then the larger pulley will move more slowly.

The velocity ratio of gears can be calculated by counting the number of teeth of each gear. The system shown in Figure 8(b) has a larger gear with 30 teeth and a smaller gear with 10 teeth. If the larger gear is the driver then for every 1 turn of the larger gear, the small gear will turn three times. This is called the **gear ratio**.

Gear trains usually involve more than two gears in a system with 2 gears meshed. One turns clockwise, the other anti-clockwise. To get both turning in the same direction a third gear is used in between. This is called an 'idler gear which does not affect the gear ratio. Gear trains can be used to speed up or slow down mechanical systems. To calculate the overall gear ratio each pairing is worked out and then they are multiplied together as in Figure 8(c).

Controlling movement

A mechanism will not move unless force is applied. If the force is taken away eventually the mechanism will lose energy and stop.

It may be necessary to prevent a mechanism from returning to its normal position immediately, for example when using a hydraulic lift to raise a vehicle in a garage. In pneumatic and hydraulic systems, taps and valves hold the 'fluid' in the chamber. When the tap or valve is opened the system clears as the load pushes the fluid out , allowing the load to return to its original position.

A gear system will help to move a load. However, if the effort is released before the load is removed, the gears will go into reverse and the load pulls in the opposite direction. The addition of a **ratchet and pawl** to a gearing system allows the system to be operated one way but prevents it from 'sliding back'. The 'pawl' is a toothed shaped lever that fits into the teeth of the ratchet. These are found in fishing reel mechanisms, roller blinds and winding gear, as well as children's toys.

Brake systems can use linkage systems to slow down a rotating wheel (eg a bicycle). Alternatively a hydraulic fluid which operates a piston might be used. Car brakes use this system. Worm gears also have a locking mechanism which only works one way. The worm wheel can turn the pinion, but the pinion cannot be used to turn the worm wheel.

All mechanical systems need **lubrication**. As parts are always in contact with each other they generate heat and cause wear due to friction (see unit 7).

Machines - **mechanical devices that make work more efficient.**
Mechanisms - **moving parts that make up machines.**
Cam - **a special shaped disc or wheel used to convert motion, usually rotary motion to reciprocating motion.**
Pivot or fulcrum - **point around which a lever turns.**
Crank - **a bar with a 'U' or 'L' shape to create a bigger turning force.**
Rack and pinion - **a spur gear with a gear cut along a length to convert rotary to linear motion.**
Spur gears - **wheels with regular notches that mesh together.**
Bevel gears - **gears with teeth at angles to change the direction of rotary motion.**
Worm gears - **a spur gear combined with a cylindrical gear.**
Pneumatics - **using compressed air to transfer force.**
Hydraulics - **using fluid (usually oil) to transfer force.**
Force multipliers - **mechanisms that use a smaller input force to give a larger output force.**
Distance multipliers - **mechanisms that use a smaller input distance to give a larger output distance.**
Mechanical advantage - **comparing input to output forces.**
Torque - **force needed to turn or twist.**
Velocity ratio - **comparison of input to output distances.**

SALAD SPINNER/ WEIGHING SCALES

The diagram shows the parts of a plastic salad spinner used to drain water and wash salads and lettuce. A salad spinner is a mechanical system operated by a handle and a gear system. The large gear is the driver, which drives the smaller gear. One complete turn of the larger gear will mean the smaller gear turns many times.

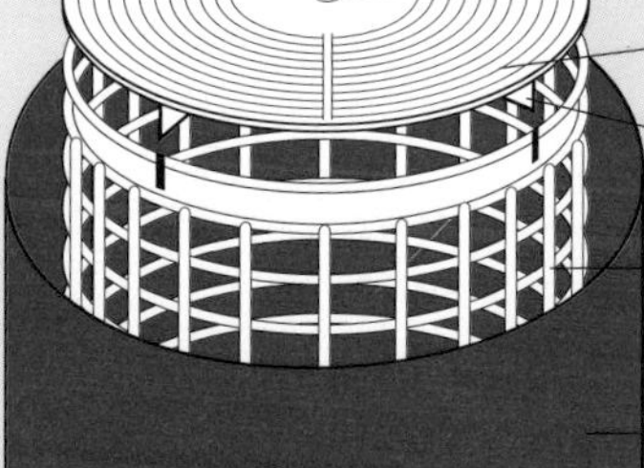

The large gear is spun as the handle is turned. The small gear spins faster as it has fewer teeth. The net spins at the same speed as the small gear and in turn rotates the basket.

Questions

(a) Which gear turns the quickest? Explain your answer.
(b) What type of motion is taking place as the handle turns the gears?
(c) Draw a flow chart to show the steps involved in the operation of the salad spinner.
(d) Suggest TWO other systems where a large gear is used to turn a small gear.
(e) Identify:
  (i) how many teeth are in the large gear;
  (ii) how many teeth are in the small gear;
(f) Use the information in (e) to calculate the gear ratio and explain how the gear ratio could be changed.

Weighing scales are used to measure the weight of food ingredients. The ingredients are placed on a plastic bowl which rests on an inner frame. As the frame moves down under the weight of the ingredients, this causes a plastic rack to which it is attached to move down. This then turns a pinion wheel, which causes a pointer to move. The distance the pointer moves indicates the weight of the ingredients.

Questions

(a) Identify TWO mechanisms which are used in this mechanical system.
(b) Explain how each mechanism operates.
(c) Suggest TWO other pieces of equipment that might use each mechanism.
(d) Use a flow chart to explain how the mechanisms work together to operate the mechanical system.

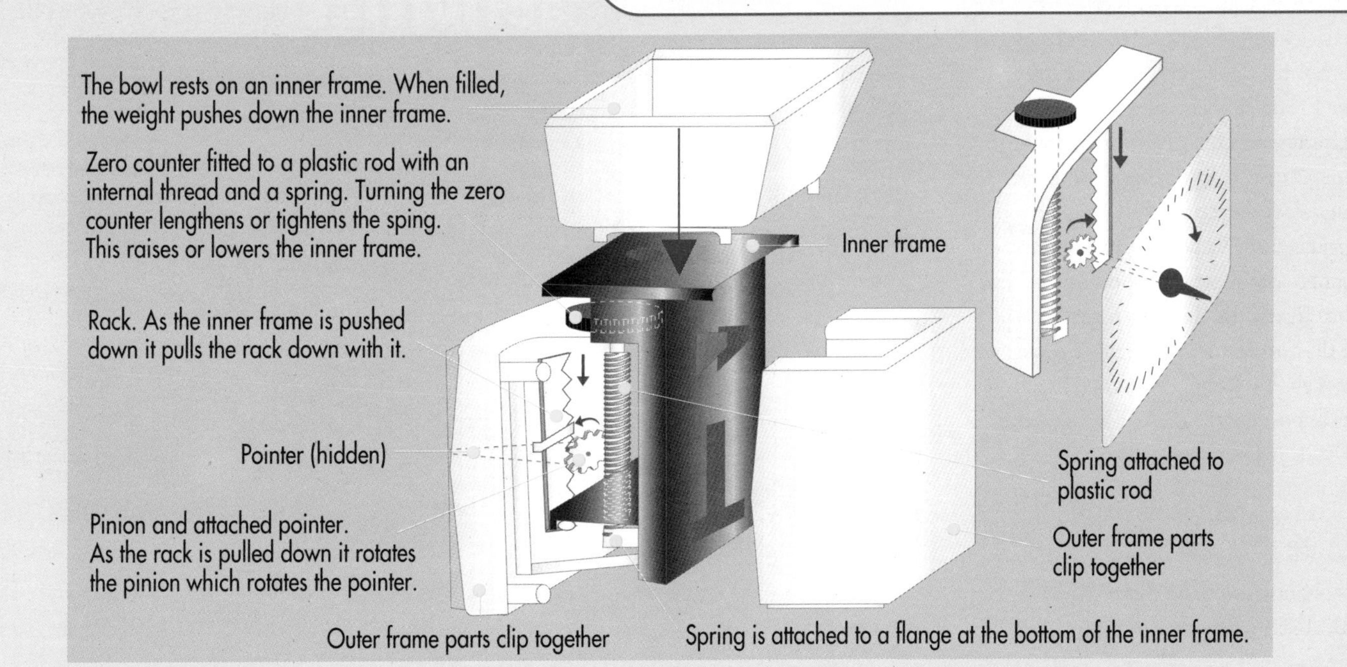

unit 18

Electrical and electronic systems

Types of systems

Electrical and electronic systems need **electrical energy** to work. This can come from mains electricity directly or at a reduced voltage using an adaptor (for safety). Smaller appliances can use energy stored in batteries. When designing electrical systems it is important to match the energy source with the needs of the system. Too much current and the system may be damaged. Too little and the system may not work properly.

Electrical and electronic systems can be divided into three types:

- electrical, such as household lighting, which use a relatively high current;
- electronic, such as personal CD players, which use a low current;
- microelectronic, such as digital watches, which use a very low current.

Electrical circuitry

Electricity will only travel around a circuit if it is complete. There must be no gaps or breaks. Breaks in a circuit may occur when prototyping or making. A continuity tester or multimeter can be used to test for breaks. Not all materials allow electricity to pass through them. Those which do are called electrical **conductors** and those which do not are called electrical **insulators** (see unit 8).

The flow of electricity through any electrical system is a CURRENT (measured in amps). The force pushing the current is called the VOLTAGE (measured in volts). The size of the current in an electrical or electronic system depends on what is in the system. For example, a heater will draw more current than a lamp. This is because they have different resistances. The RESISTANCE of a lamp is much higher.

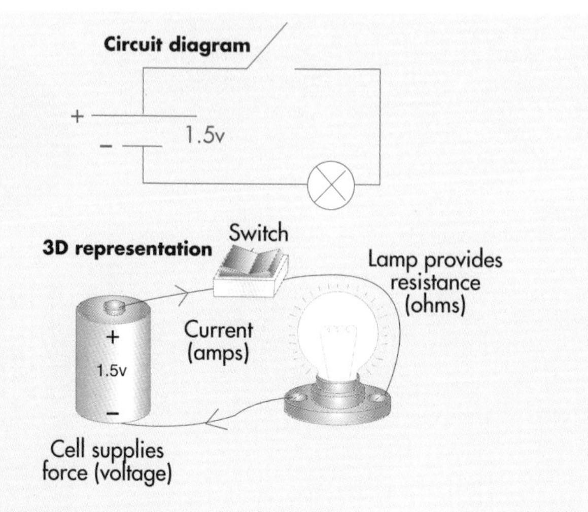

Figure 1 A simple electrical system.

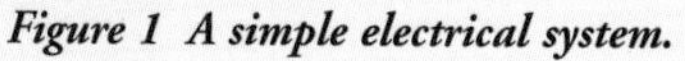

The voltage, current or resistance can be calculated using the equation in Figure 1. When deciding on which components to use, such calculations may be helpful. The maximum power a component can handle and still work correctly is called its **power rating**. The power rating can often be found in a manual. When designing, it is perhaps more useful to use the equation (P=VxI) to decide what voltage supply will get the 'best' from a component. This means rearranging the equation.

Designing electrical circuits

There is a number of stages in designing electrical circuits.

- A flow chart (see unit 3) is sketched out

activities

These products all need electrical energy to operate.

(a) Which of the electrical systems can be: (i) electrical; (ii) electronic; (iii) microelectronic? (Note that they may be more than one.)

(b) Which of the systems can run: (i) on batteries; (ii) from the mains: (iii) on either?

(c) Suggest TWO other systems that might be: (i) electrical; (ii) electronic; (iii) microelectronic; (iv) run on batteries; (v) run from the mains.

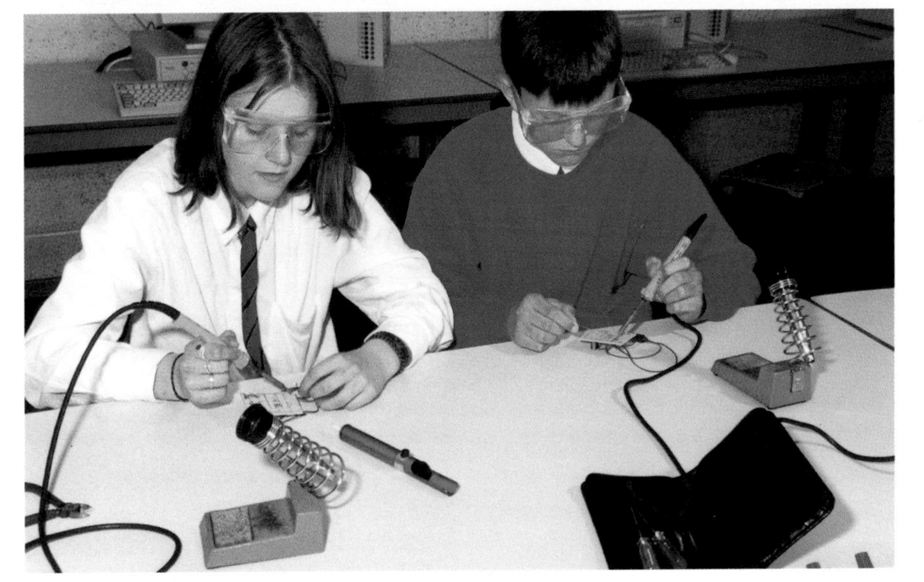

Soldering components onto a printed circuit board.

A stencil, used for manufacturing printed circuit boards, is produced using chemical etch technology.

which shows what is required of the system.

- A circuit diagram is drawn to show likely components.
- The system has to be prototyped (see unit 2). This can initially be done using kits that allow a designer to work in systems blocks.
- Prototyping can be carried out using individual components. This allows the designer to study the details of each part, as many electronic components have their own particular needs.
- A circuit layout will be drawn, showing the positions of each component and its value. If the circuit is drawn for printed circuit board work (see later) then it will have to be drawn as **tracks**. This can be done using black pen, stencil or a computer program. There are computer software programs that will draw the artwork. The tracks must be drawn in a high definition black ink, so that they will photocopy onto acetate, sometimes called a **mask**.

It is important to measure out and mark accurately the distance between **legs** of components and ensure that the circuit will fit into the overall design.

Making an electronic circuit

Electronic circuits can be made in a number of ways. Soldering (see unit 13) is the most popular way of joining components to tracks permanently. Solder is a mixture of tin and lead. It melts easily at 200°C but when cool forms a hard joint. Flux is added to the metals to help them mix while molten.

Components can be soldered to a copper strip board or a printed circuit board (PCB). Copper strip board (veroboard) has an insulated backing. The legs of components are fitted through and soldered onto the copper. When using veroboard it is advisable to abrade the copper lightly to clean it and for better adhesion. It is important to make sure that the solder does not run between the tracks or short circuits may occur.

A printed circuit board is an electrical

activities

Read the information below.

(a) Choose a sensor and say what job it does in the electrical system?

(b) Suggest THREE places in which a sensor might be used to measure:
(i) temperature;
(ii) water levels.

(c) Suggest TWO advantages of using a sensor and a data logger.

Delta-T Devices manufacture sensors and probes. It also produces loggers which record the information taken from sensors. Sensors are used in a variety of situations.

Weather stations can measure:

- air and soil temperature;
- wind speed and direction;
- humidity, rainfall and solar radiation.

Industrial applications include the monitoring of:

- vehicle temperatures in arctic conditions;
- temperatures in fridges;
- corrosion of buried pipes;
- temperatures in kilns used to dry timber;
- durability of paints.

Environmental science uses include the monitoring of:

- water running off a hillside;
- sea and fresh water temperature;
- weight gain by young birds.

Source: Delta-T Devices.

Weather station monitoring.

Monitoring weight gain in young albatross chicks.

A sensor in a security light.

circuit etched onto a copper clad board. PCBs are found in most electrical products and are used to reduce the wiring and space needed for the circuit.

Switches

The simplest form of control (see unit 16) in an electrical system is a SWITCH. This will stop the signal when it is off and allow the signal to move if it is on. The simplest switches are called single pole, single throw (SPST). The **pole** is the contact that moves and the **throw** is the number of ways it makes contact. More complicated switches are SPDT, DPST and DPDT(double pole, double throw). Different types of switches are shown in Figure 2. If a switch is off until switched, it is described as being **normally open** (NO). If it is on until switched it is **normally closed** (NC). When deciding on a switch it is important to consider:

- what job you want the switch to do;
- how it will be activated;
- what working current it will need;
- what size you want the switch to be.

SENSORS are a special type of switch which reacts to changes in conditions. Infra red, temperature and moisture sensors are popular. Light sensors are found in weather monitoring and automatic lighting systems. Temperature sensors are found in oven control systems. Moisture sensors are found in moisture level detectors.

Logic gates

The voltage output from a switch or any other part of an electronic system can be either high (eg + 5V) or low (0V). This is described

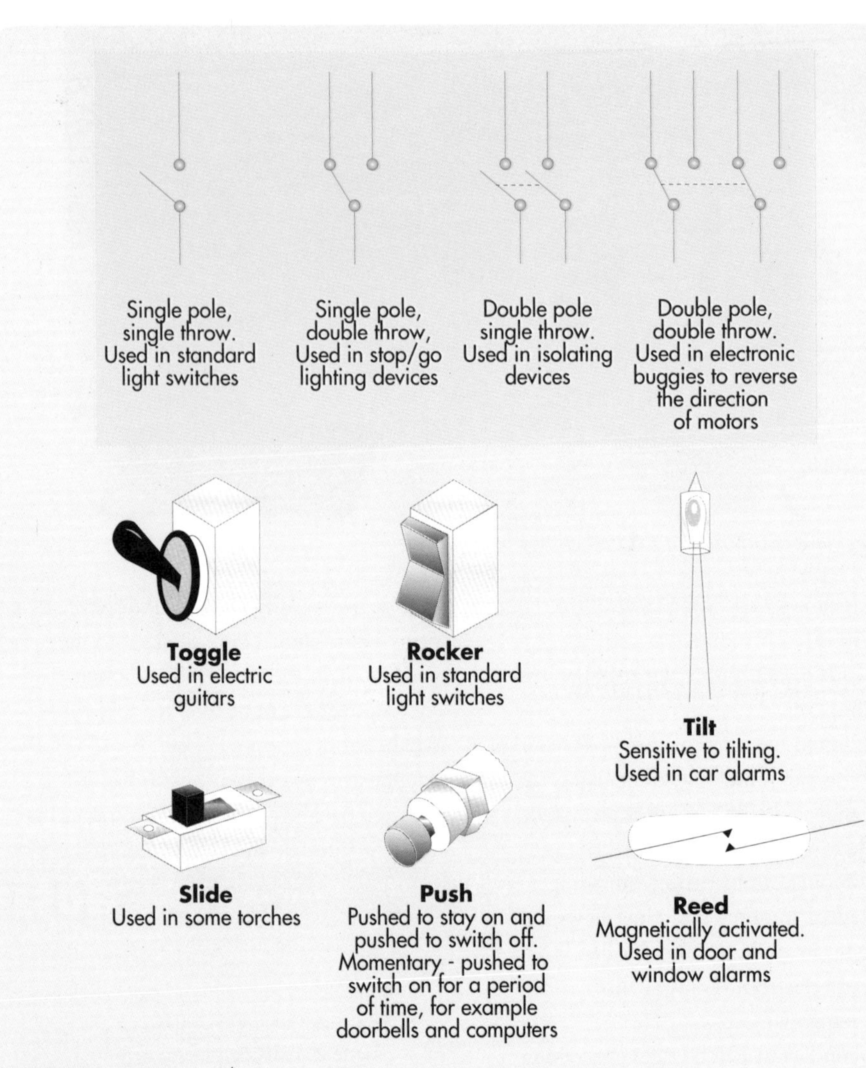

Figure 2 Switches and their uses.

activities

Read the information below.

(a) List THREE electronic devices that use LEDs. In each case say what the LED is used for.

(b) What advantages do LEDs have over ordinary lamps?

(c) Work out the segment combinations to show numbers 1-9 on the segmented display shown here.

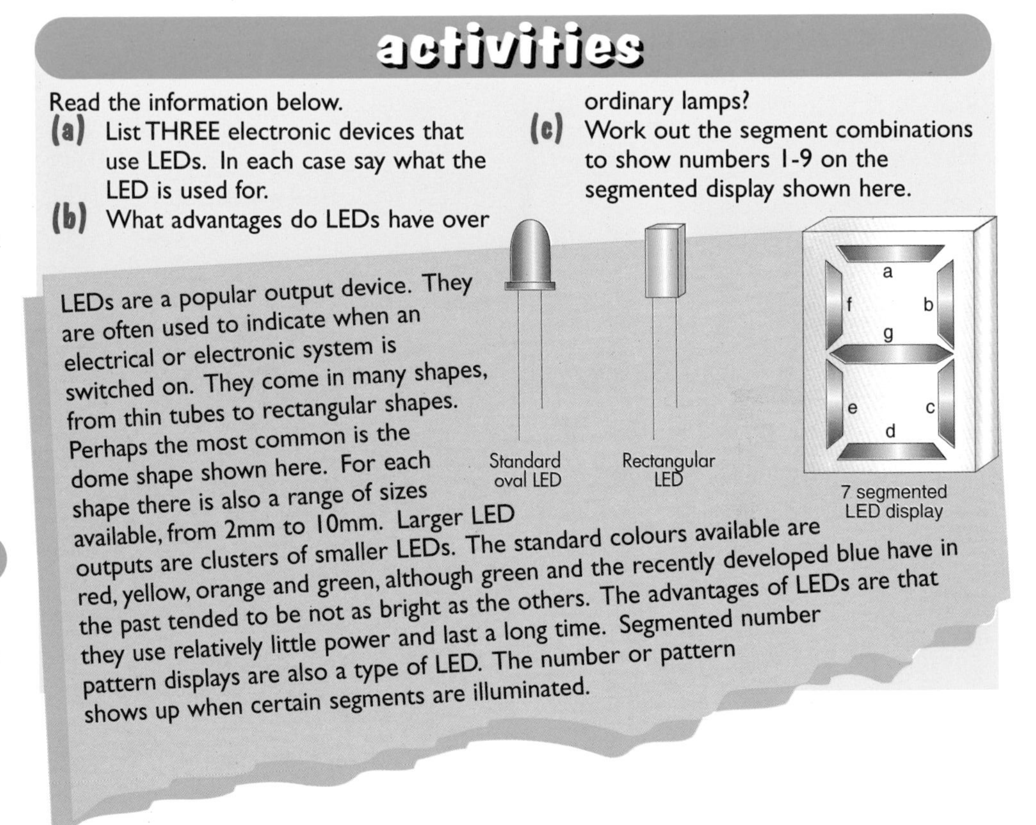

Figure 3 Logic gates and their uses.

NOT GATE

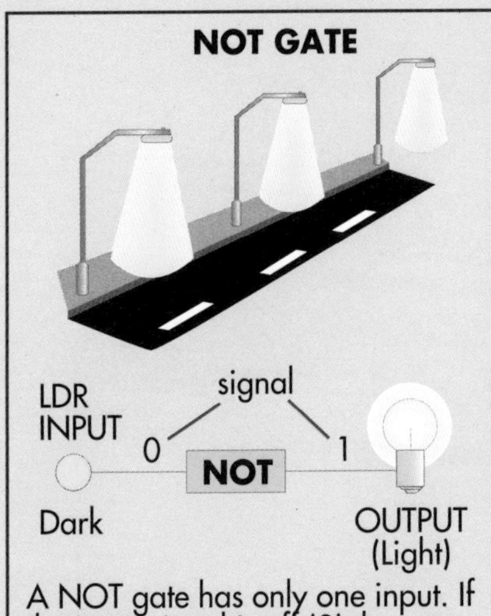

A NOT gate has only one input. If the input signal is off (0) the gate reverses the signal and turns the output on (1). For example, a light dependant resistor (LDR) usually turns a circuit on when light shines on it and off when it is dark. Making it part of a NOT gate system changes this. When it is dark (NOT light) the cicuit is switched on.

Input	Output
0	1
1	0

AND GATE

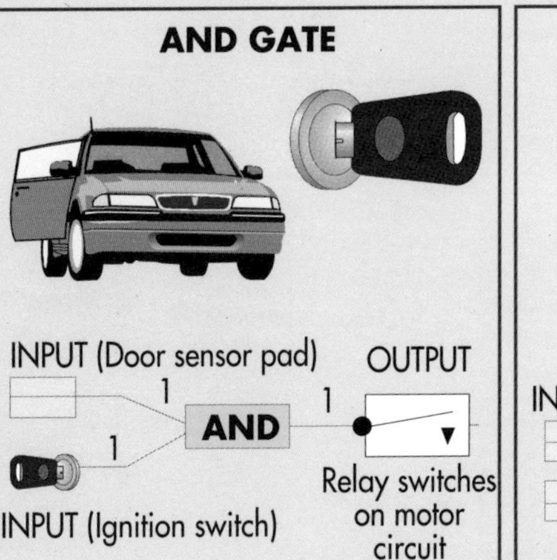

An AND gate usually has two inputs. It needs both input signals to be on (1) for it to work. For example, you might want to close your car door properly AND turn on your ignition before your car will start. The AND gate is a safety device in this case.

Input		Output
A	B	
0	0	0
0	1	0
1	0	0
1	1	1

OR GATE

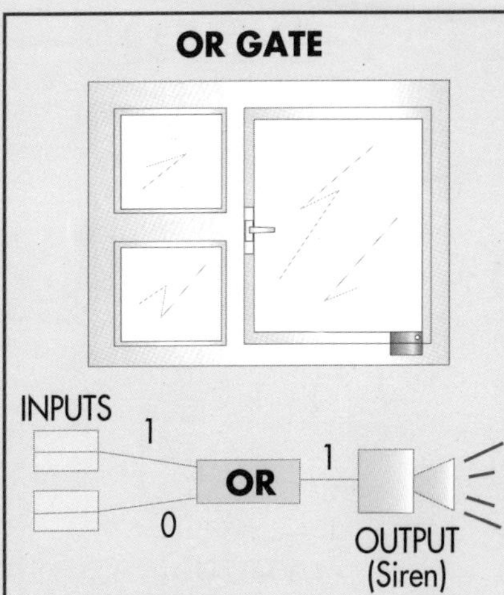

An OR gate has two inputs. Only one OR the other needs to be on to switch on the output. For example, an intruder device to tell you if one window OR another is opened. The inputs might be pads. The output could be a siren.

Input		Output
A	B	
0	0	0
0	1	1
1	0	1
1	1	1

as its logic state or logic level.

A **high** logic state is represented by the number 1. A **low** logic state is given the number 0. Digital electronic systems use high/low (1/0) voltage outputs to switch parts of the system on or off. Basic LOGIC GATES are an an example of systems that use digital electronics. The basic gates can be AND, OR and NOT, as shown in Figure 3. Each gate is activated by a particular high/low voltage combination. These combinations are shown in **truth tables**.

Outputs

Outputs can fall into three categories:

- audio (buzzers, bells etc);
- opto (LEDs, lamps etc);
- mechanical (motors, solenoids, relays).

When choosing an audio output consider what type of sound you want and the level (eg

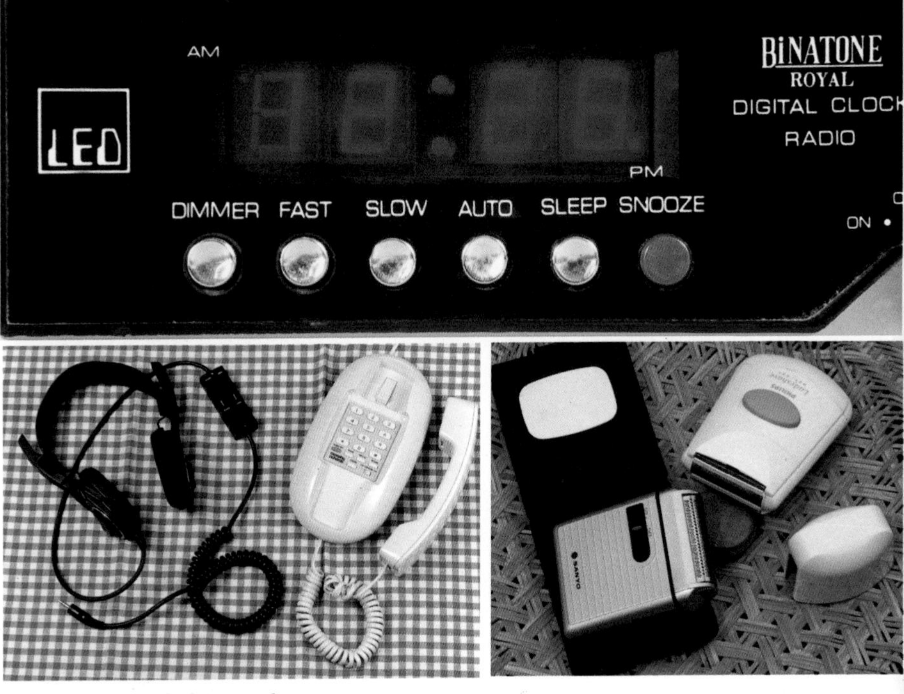

Outputs can be light, sound or motion.

Figure 4 Components.

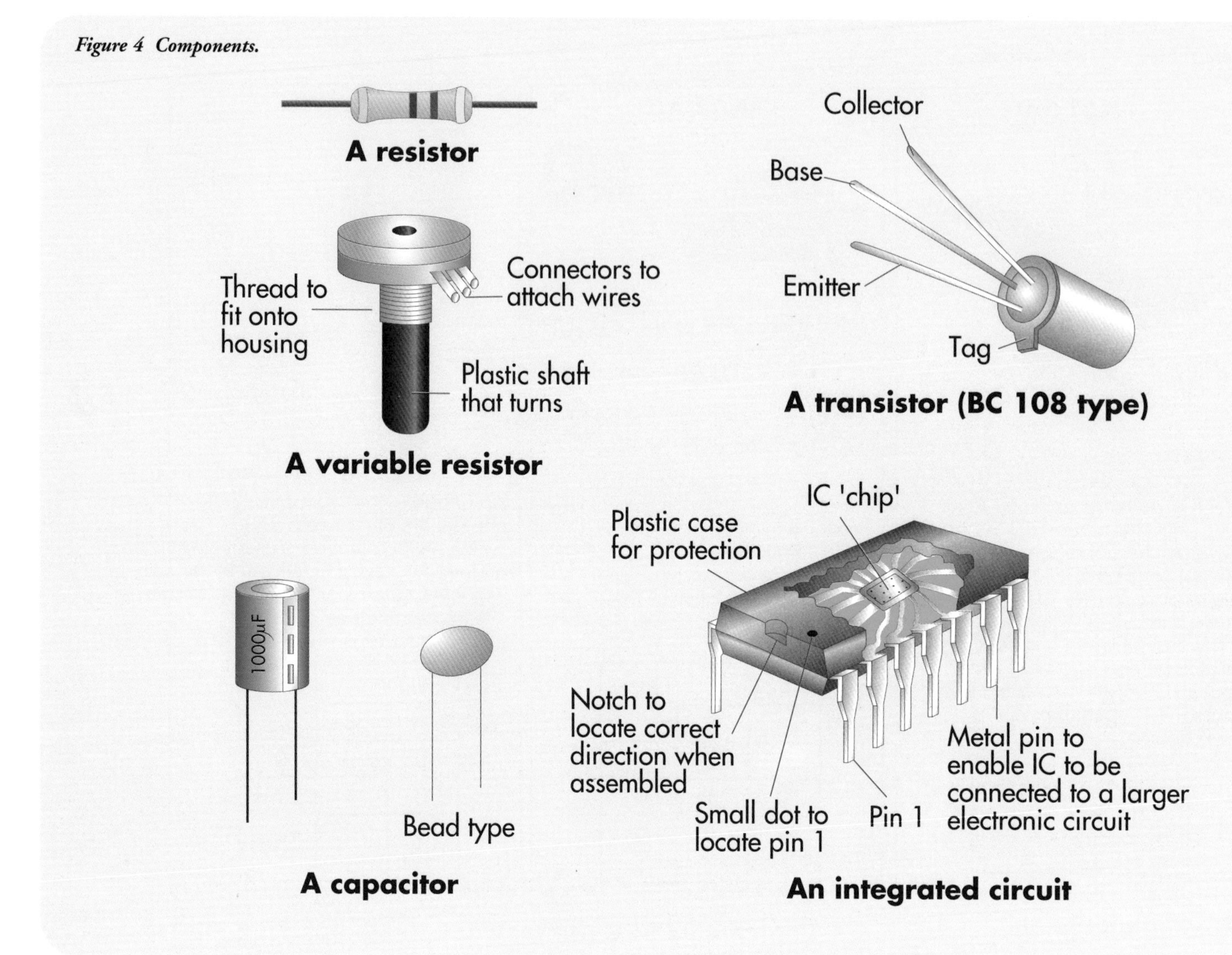

loud, soft). Audio outputs can be simple 'beeps' or rings, two tone 'ding-dongs' or more complex sounds like that from a loudspeaker. The volume of sound required may affect the current needed. Low energy high output audio devices are available.

When choosing an opto device, consider the brightness, colour and other display styles. The brightness of a lamp will depend to an extent on how much current is flowing. Colour can be given by placing a filter over the lamp. LEDs (light emitting diodes) may be used. These are not as bright as ordinary lamps, but last longer and use less electricity. Flashing LEDs can be purchased. LEDs must be placed the correct way in a circuit. They only allow electricity to pass one way. They can be damaged if too much current flows through them. Other visual displays may include LCDs (liquid crystal display) or LED segment displays which are used to give numbers or patterns.

When choosing a mechanical output consider the type of motion needed, the speed required, how often it needs to move and how much work needs to be done. Motors turn in a circle. They can be controlled so that they spin slow or fast (by altering the current) or just turn for part of a circle (using a stepper motor). Solenoids work backwards and forwards (reciprocating). They are controlled by an electromagnet (see unit 8). Relays are

activities

Many businesses require privacy. Doctors need to consult with patients about their health. Bank managers need to talk to customers about financial matters. Business meetings may be discussing confidential information.

The problem opposite is typical of a situation where privacy is needed. An electrical system can let people know that a meeting is taking place.

(a) What type of:
(i) switch;
(ii) output;
might be used for this system?

(b) Suggest TWO other outputs that could be used in the circuit.

(c) Explain how the system could be adapted so that people wishing to enter a room from the outside can indicate that they want to enter.

electronically controlled switches that are used to switch systems with larger values of current.

Other components

RESISTORS limit the flow of electricity in a circuit. They can be used to:

- protect components from electrical damage due to excess current (eg with LEDs);
- set the voltage at a particular point in a circuit (eg in a potential divider sub-system).

Resistors come in many resistance sizes. The most common types are carbon/clay and thin film resistors. These are colour coded to show their value. Each resistor has one fixed value. Variable resistors (**potentiometers**) have a range of values from 0 to the one printed on the body. These are used in control dials (eg volume control on a personal stereo). **Preset potentiometers** are altered using a screwdriver. They are small and 'preset', then left at that value (eg a timed extractor for a shower room).

DIODES only allow electricity to pass in one direction. If placed the wrong way in a circuit, they offer a large resistance. LEDs are specialised diodes that light up when current passes through. Diodes are often used with outputs such as relays and solenoids. They are placed across a component as a **reverse bias** to protect the transistor.

CAPACITORS store electricity. Once fully charged, no further current can flow in that part of the circuit. Electricity **discharges** around the circuit from the capacitor. The discharge can be slowed down by placing a resistor in series with the capacitor. This is how simple electronic time delays work.

Transistors and integrated circuits

TRANSISTORS can operate like electronic switches. A small current in the base allows a current to flow through the collector. Output devices are usually attached to the collector leg. A simple transistor is sufficient to operate a low current output (LED, buzzer). Higher current outputs (eg motors, solenoids) may need a **Darlington pair** or a **field effect transistor** (FET). Thyristors (SCR) can also operate higher current outputs. They can latch. This means that once activated the output will stay on until a reset switch is pressed.

INTEGRATED CIRCUITS are small 'chips' made up from thousands of transistors, capacitors and resistors. They are etched onto a thin piece of silicon. This is sandwiched between two layers of plastic.

Integrated circuits have a number of advantages:

- they usually use very little current;
- they need less space;
- they have fast switching speeds;
- they are cheap to buy.

ICs can be purchased that have a dedicated function. They are designed to carry out a particular range of jobs when combined with other electrical components. For example, resistor and capacitor combinations can be used with a 555IC to produce a time delay system.

Current - **the rate at which electricity flows through a circuit.**
Voltage - **force pushing an electric current.**
Resistance - **limiting of a current.**
Switch - **a component which completes or breaks a system or circuit.**
Sensor - **a type of switch that reacts to changes in conditions.**
Logic gate - **combinations of digital switches that work together to control a circuit.**
Resistors - **components designed to limit current.**
Diodes - **components that only allow electricity to pass through one way.**
Capacitor - **a component that stores and discharges electricity.**
Transistor - **a switching component activated by a small base current**
Integrated circuits - **a miniature circuit etched onto a thin sheet of silicon.**

activities

Portable computers are slower than desk top computers and can run out of power at just the wrong time. Fewer recharges and greater speed usually require bigger batteries, which increase weight. Intel have come up with a new microprocessor (a complex integrated circuit) that can run faster, while using less power. It is already being used in some portable computers made by Toshiba and IBM. The manufacture of the low voltage chip has involved changes to the circuit laid out on the silicon and the size and shape of the transistors.

Source: adapted from The Sunday Times, 2.7.1995.

(a) What is meant by: (i) a transistor; (ii) an integrated circuit?
(b) Suggest THREE advantages of the new Intel chip.

unit 19

Production systems

Automated cellular manufacturing of hi-fi speakers.

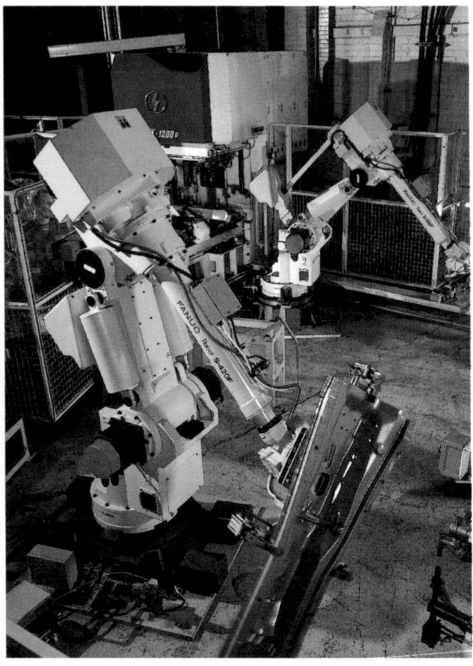
Cellular manufacture of vehicle pressings.

Inputs, processes and outputs

Production systems are the different methods of production which can be used to manufacture designs. Like other systems they have **inputs**, **processes** and **outputs** (see unit 16). One input into a production system is the raw material used for making. This might be sheet metal that has to be pressed and shaped or it might be granules of polythene for injection moulding. Wooden planks or chipboard may be processed before drilling on pre-made jigs. Machinery must be activated for the system to operate. Cutting equipment needs to function, conveyor belts must move and mechanical robots have to rotate and grip.

The processes used in production systems are usually about actual manufacture, for example milling and lathe work (see unit 11) and moulding and extrusion (see unit 12). However, other processes may include computer aided design (see unit 2), automatic storage and retrieval, and quality control. The processes used in production systems fall into three main categories depending on how many products are to be manufactured. These categories are JOB PRODUCTION, BATCH PRODUCTION and FLOW PRODUCTION. The system used to manufacture the product will depend on the:

- quantity of products to be made;
- nature and quality of product required;
- selling price of the product.

The output from a production system will be the product itself. This may be a finished item like a television or a motor car, or it may be a part or component to be used in another product, like a nail, screw, valve, panel or lid.

Another output of a production system could be wastage. This may be left over from cutting and drilling or it may be faulty goods that do not meet the required standard. This wastage might be recycled and fed back into the system or it may be lost and dumped as waste disposal.

Sub-systems and cellular production

More complex production systems have sub-systems. These are usually called CELLS. Each cell in a production system will carry out a particular job or a range of tasks. For example, if a washing machine or a vacuum cleaner was manufactured, one cell may produce the electronics to operate the

activities

Bernie Thurston manufactures brass sundials. Each sundial is made for an exact position in the cosmos. Customers wishing to buy a sundial send details of their longitude and latitude (or just their post code) and mark a paper sundial with a piece of string showing the angle of the sun at midday on a chosen wall. Bernie then sends them a flat pack brass sundial for their location with a name and crest. The sundial won't work anywhere else.

The sundial is engraved using a Haas manufacturing centre. First a drawing is created using a CAD program. The drawing is then fed through another program which changes into a code that drives the drill on the machining centre.

Source: adapted from The Guardian, 17.8.1995.

(a) Do you think that the method of production used to manufacture sundials is job, batch or flow? Explain your answer.

(b) How does a customer benefit from this type of production?

(c) How were computers used in the production of sundials?

A 'one off' wooden design made by turning on a lathe is an example of job production.

product. Another may assemble the mechanisms that allow it to move. A further cell may shape and form the housing to hold the electronics and mechanisms.

Job production

Job production is where **one** item is made. The product is made from start to finish either by one person or by a number of people working on separate parts of the same item. The final product might be unique. It may look similar to other products, perhaps differing slightly in style and shape. Examples of job production might be a brass sign made for a company to be attached to an outside wall or a wooden frame made exactly to fit one picture painted by an artist. Larger designs include bridges built to fit over a span of land and a house or office designed and built to a designer's specifications.

Products made by job production methods are usually of high quality and require a lot of workers' time to complete. This is called being **labour intensive**. The workforce needed is likely to have to be very skilled, perhaps involving years of training. All these features mean that job produced products are likely to be more expensive than those made in batches. For example, hand crafted furniture is dearer to buy than equivalent batch produced DIY or preassembled furniture units.

Batch production

Where relatively small numbers of similar products are made, with tasks being carried out on all products in a 'group', batch production is used. Batch production is useful where the product may have to change, depending on orders coming in. For example, a firm that makes screws may make a batch of a certain shaped screw and then make a batch of different shaped screws for another customer. A joinery firm may manufacture batches of doors and batches of panels, but assemble and finish them (see units 13-14) into furniture only when required.

The manufacture of metal valves in batches using casting techniques.

Batch made products are cheaper than

activities

Magnet Limited manufacture kitchens. The doors for kitchen cabinets are made in batches, with minimum order quantities of 100. The cabinets are also manufactured in batches and then assembled on assembly lines. Increasingly cellular production is being introduced in the production of cabinets.

The steps involved in making the cabinets are:

- MDF panels are cut to size;
- centres are cut using routers. Router programs are built directly from CAD drawing files (CAD/CAM).
- external profiles and panel ends are cut;
- the centre relief is hand sanded;
- painting is done by an automatic panel spray line.

Source: Magnet Limited.

(a) Why might the manufacture of Magnet's doors and cupboards be an example of batch production?

(b) How are CAD and CAM used in the production of panels?

(c) How might production be likely to change if there was a move to cellular production techniques?

equivalent job produced items because production costs are lower. The problem with batch production is that if production is switched from one product to another then time may be lost in resetting the machinery to make a new batch. Increasing the number of products made means that **stock** is often created. This may cause storage problems and wastage if some of the products are left unsold.

Making more than one item means that staff may specialise in one aspect of the work. However, the work may be only repetitive and boring.

Flow production

REPETITIVE FLOW PRODUCTION is where large quantities of the same product are manufactured, for example plastic toy parts or crates, or metal cans. Flow production usually requires very high investment to buy the complicated machinery needed to carry out precise repetitive work. This machinery can sometimes run continuously for 24 hours. Once purchased, the MASS PRODUCTION of items leads to lower unit costs because this initial high cost of machinery is spread over a large output. The unit cost of a product tends to fall as more are produced. If the flow production system is partially or fully automated, then costs can be reduced further because there are fewer workers to pay.

Cars moving along an assembly line are manufactured using continual flow production techniques.

Vehicles made on a moving assembly line is an example of CONTINUAL FLOW PRODUCTION. As the vehicle moves along an assembly line it passes through different stages of production, such as basic body assembly, engine assembly and painting. At each stage employees or robots will carry out a specialised task. When the vehicle passes through all stages it is complete.

Work on an assembly line can be monotonous for workers. If there is a breakdown on one part of the assembly line then the whole production may grind to a halt. Simple manufacturing tasks like spot

activities

1 Read the article.

(a) What TWO types of production are mentioned?

(b) If the company offered the new service, suggest THREE effects that this might have on its production methods, its employees and the company as a whole.

Johnson Frames manufactures picture frames in a variety of sizes and from different timbers. The company is thinking of offering a 'bespoke' service, where customers can give instructions on the type of frame they want and see this designed on a computer screen.

2 The design here is a dog bowl manufactured out of thermoplastic sheet.

(a) Suggest a suitable method that could be used to manufacture a single product.

(b) Explain the stages that would take place when making the product.

(c) How might the process be adapted to manufacture batches of the bowls?

(d) Suggest TWO problems that might arise when adapting the process.

Mass production of injection moulded plastic crates.

Flow production of manufactured boards.

welding or dip coating are used in flow production systems.

Production control

At a basic level, control in production systems may be exercised by holding tools like pneumatic clamps or simple bench vices. Jigs, templates and drill/machine settings (see units 10 and 11) are other examples of controlling a production process. All manufacturing skills from measuring and marking out through cutting and shaping to assembling and finishing can be carried out manually by skilled crafts people or parts of it can be automated.

The design of a product to be manufactured can be carried out by computer aided design (CAD) (see unit 2) whether it is a 'one off' design or a product to be made in batches or mass produced. Computer controlled machines can be used to manufacture these products. They use specially designed computer software which will give instructions to machines to control their operations. The automated making operation is known as COMPUTER AIDED MANUFACTURE (CAM). CNC milling machines and CNC lathes (see unit 11) are examples. CAM can be used for single products such as a pattern or former, for the milling of batches of metal components or for the control of machines used to mass produce items such as vehicles and drinks cans. Large manufacturing or assembly processes may have many machines that are computer controlled, including manufacturing machines and assembly lines.

Advances in computer technology are such that orders can be placed via a telephone. The specification is sent to a different computer which will design the programme to operate the machinery. The instructions will then be sent to another computer which

Figure 1 Computer integrated manufacture.

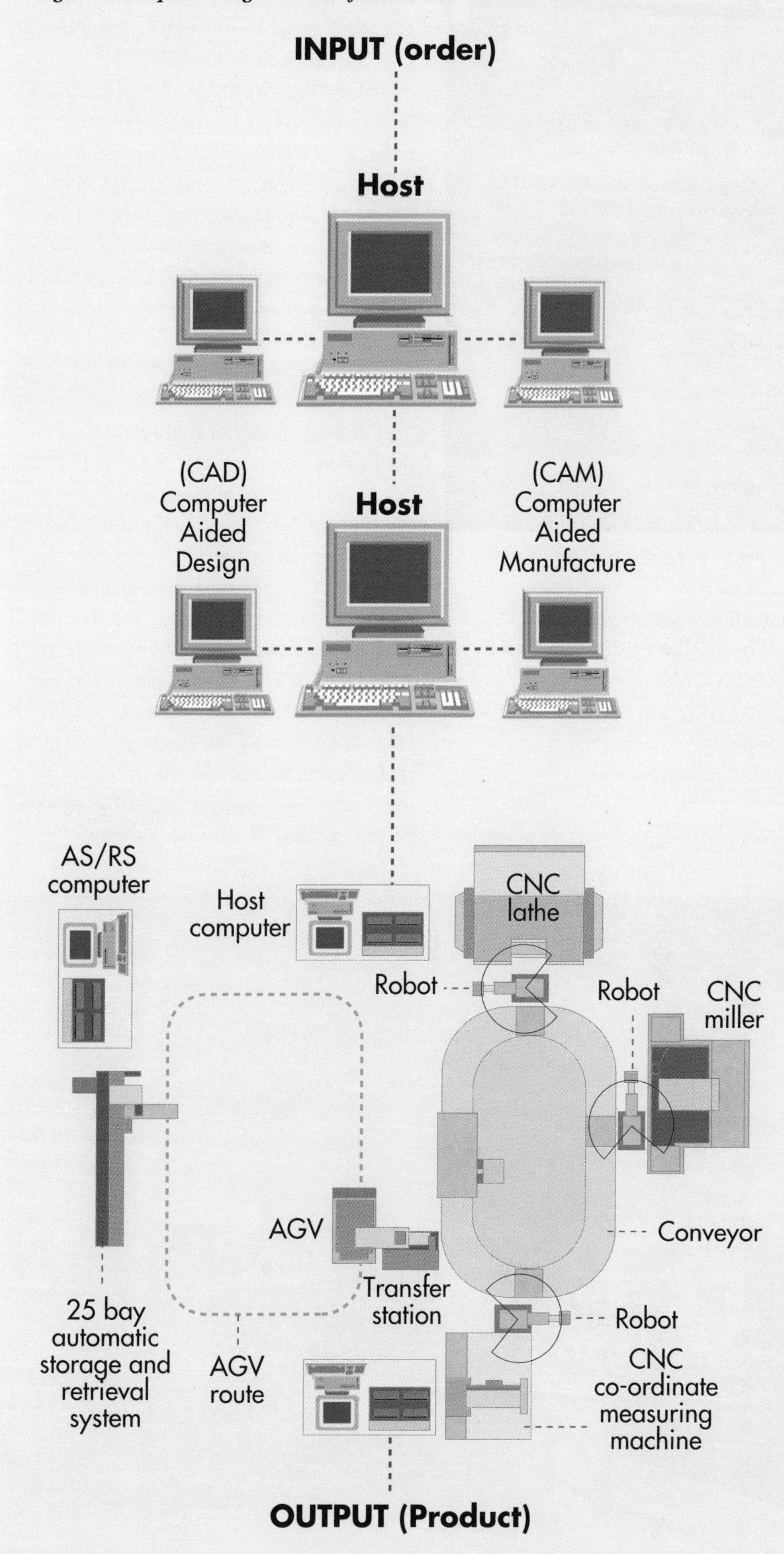

Computer aided manufacture of steel panels.

will operate the machinery and make the product. The finished product can then be checked using a coordinate measuring machine (CMM) system (see unit 10). Once passed, the product can be stored automatically and the bill sent to the customer along with the product. If the product does not meet the specification the information can be fed back to the CNC tools so they readjust their programmes accordingly. The whole process involves few, if any people. This is an example of COMPUTER INTEGRATED MANUFACTURE (CIM). Host controllers act like traffic police, assessing incoming jobs, holding some, sending others on. The advantages of using computers in production are the speed and accuracy of the process and reduced costs. However, the machines must be maintained to avoid failure which can be costly.

Stock control

An important part of controlling a production system is STOCK CONTROL. Stocks are the resistant materials (or components) which are used in the manufacture and assembly of products. It is important to ensure that there are enough materials to make the product and that they are the correct materials to carry out the work. Stocks may be kept in a warehouse and are held in reserve until they are needed. A stock controller will check the stocks in and out so that a flow is maintained. As the stock of items falls, new stocks are ordered so that they do not run out. If stocks do run out production may be halted, which would be very costly for a business.

Some businesses now operate a system known as JUST-IN-TIME production. Stocks held, if at all are very low. Instead, a business asks its suppliers for regular deliveries and these are used straight away in production. This has the advantages that:

- warehouse costs and the cost of stocks being held are reduced;
- a business must insist materials or components are delivered free of faults;
- quality (see unit 23) is improved;
- the system of production is much quicker.

Speed and quality considerations

The speed of production will affect the quality and eventual cost of a product. A one off, hand made product may be 'knocked together' quickly. For example, wooden pallets used for storing and stacking take minutes to make. Compare that with a hand-made oak table that may have taken months to finish.

Quality, accuracy and precision are key

activities

Read the article.

(a) What is meant by mass production of products?
(b) State THREE pieces of evidence which suggest that Sony mass produces electronic equipment.
(c) Explain how mass production affects the unit costs of products.

Sony manufactures a variety of electronic equipment including video and audio equipment and televisions. Sales of televisions amount to over $5000 million a year. Since the launch of Sony's first CD in 1982 total production of optical pickups used in CD players has surpassed 100 million units.

The manufacture of electrical equipment uses production lines. Industrial robots are widely used in assembly lines for precision manufacturing of stereo walkmans and 8mm video products.

In 1996 Sony was aiming to launch a new 25 inch widescreen flat panel television in Japan. Previously the technology had always proved to be too unreliable or expensive for mass production. New technology called Plasma Addressed Liquid Crystal has removed the need for LCD screens which required expensive high grade clean rooms for assembling the screens.

Source: adapted from Sony, Annual Report and Accounts; The Sunday Times, 10.9. 1995.

Assembly lines using industrial robots.

Stock control.

elements in production. To achieve these by hand takes a lot of time and patience. In automated batch and flow systems precision can be set using computers in order to make more items of higher quality, in less time than would be possible than if they were to be hand made. Speed of production is increased, but only for similar products.

For single unique products, automated batch and flow systems would be inappropriate because tools and equipment would have to be reset each time, wasting valuable time and slowing the whole process down. However, some diversity can be achieved by mixing and matching. For example, a furniture company may produce batches of different furniture shapes, which can take a range of different fabrics. This goes some way to increasing choice and providing customers with 'limited' models which appear to be different to the standard range. This idea is used in car manufacture, where special models are made. **Customised** products like motor cycles and guitars might have a basic standard design and then changes are made to colour, shape and materials and functions to suit customers' needs.

activities

MGA Developments specialises in the design and production of model and prototype vehicle bodies, models, aerospace structures and component moulding tools.

The company has invested heavily in computer aided design and computer aided manufacturing (CAD/CAM). This includes CAD/CAM screens and CNC lathes and milling machines. One contract from The Peoples Republic of China to redesign and model the cab and chassis of a truck had a production timescale of just 27 months from concept to production, only achievable by CAD/CAM technology. Studies by the company have found that competitors sometimes operate at six times its cost and timescale.

Very few companies in the aerospace industry can offer its service. Assemblers can give a sketch of the component they want and moulding tools can be then manufactured to make the components.

Source: adapted from The Sunday Times, 26.11.1996; MGA Developments.

(a) What is meant by:
(i) CAD;
(ii) CAM?

(b) What machines indicated in the article might be computer controlled?

(c) Suggest THREE advantages that the company has gained by introducing a CAD/CAM system.

CAM office.

Machining a mould pattern.

Key Terms

Job production - producing a single, often unique, item from start to finish.
Batch production - producing a group of similar products at the same time.
Repetitive flow production - the manufacture of large numbers of the same product in order to reduce unit costs.
Continual flow production - where a product passes through a number of stages during manufacture, often on an assembly line.
Cellular production - using sub systems to carry out particular jobs within a larger production system.
Mass production - manufacturing very large numbers of one type of product.
Computer aided manufacture (CAM) - using computers to control machines that manufacture products.
Computer integrated manufacture (CIM) - using computers to control the designing, making, checking, ordering and distribution of products.
Stock control - the ordering and issuing of materials or components used in production or finished stocks waiting for customers.
Just-in-time techniques - production which needs few, if any, stocks of materials to be held.

case study

BEN TAGGART MODELMAKING AND DESIGN

Ben Taggart is a former specialist effects painter and decorator who has worked on designs for television programmes, as well as television and film advertisements. Having worked for a model maker he set up his own business, designing and making accurate scale models of buildings and property facades. Making the models is a time consuming process, especially where customers want to show minute detail. Every model that Ben makes is different. The cost of each model will vary depending on the detail, but a typical Victorian terraced house facade will cost around £950.

There is a number of steps in the design and production process. Ben first visits a customer to discuss their needs. Then the property is measured up; calculating the size and quantity of bricks allows a calculation of the size of the house to be made. Photographs also help. A plan and elevation are drawn to the customer's required scale and then the model can be made.

The structure for the model is made from MDF because it is versatile and has no grain, which means it can be carved or cut in any direction without splintering or cracking. Plaster is added onto the structure and bricks are cut out individually, which can itself take two days. Each model takes around three to four weeks to complete. The models are built as robustly as possible and are made to last.

Source: Ben Taggart Modelmaking and Design.

Questions

(a) Why might the work of Ben Taggart Modelmaking and Design be an example of job production?

(b) Draw a flow chart to show the stages in the design and production of the models.

(c) Discuss the differences in the production processes of the models produced by Ben Taggart and of a manufacturer producing Victorian model houses of different styles in batches.

(d) Suggest a design that could be made from wood, metal or plastic that is suitable for job production processes. Explain why your design is suited to this production system.

case study LEYLAND TRUCKS LIMITED

Leyland Trucks Limited is Britain's largest independently owned commercial vehicle manufacturing business. It has an advanced automated assembly facility, the Leyland Assembly Plant, with an output capacity of more than 36,000 trucks and buses every year.

The company offers customers a six week lead time to receive orders for most of its product range. This requires component suppliers to be in a position to deliver specific components to Leyland in the right quantity on the right day to support the assembly process. This is a highly refined just-in-time component supply arrangement.

Leyland offers product variety and flexibility to its customers. They can select from many different combinations of features and options.

Source: Martin Hayes and Associates; Leyland Trucks Ltd.

Questions

(a) Suggest FOUR features that a customer might select for trucks they are purchasing.
(b) Describe how production of trucks and vans takes place at Leyland Trucks.
(c) What is meant by just-in-time production?
(d) State TWO advantages of this for a business.

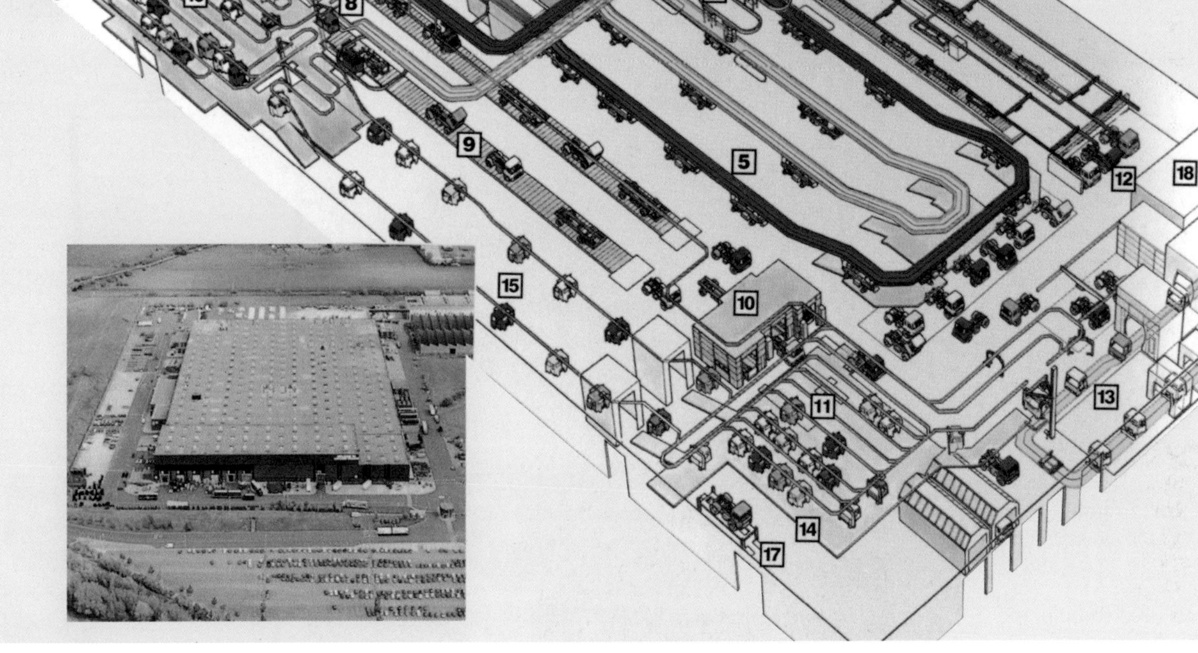

LAP LAYOUT INDEX

1. AUTOMATIC WAREHOUSE - Significant parts are supplied on a just-in-time basis, direct to the assembly line. Other parts are stored in the Automatic Warehouse.
2. FRAME ASSEMBLY - Assembled on a moving floor conveyor in the upside-down position.
3. FRAME TURNOVER - The chassis is turned through 180 degrees and coupled to an overhead conveyor system.
4. ENGINE & GEARBOX FIT - The unit is lifted from its pallet and lowered by the crane carousel into the chassis frame.
5. RADIATOR & FUEL TANK - Radiator, fan cowls, air cleaner, fuel tank, fuel and radiator piping are assembled to the chassis.
6. CHASSIS PAINT - Chassis paint is applied in line with the customer's paint specification.
7. WHEELS & VEHICLE FLUID - The chassis is conveyed onto an upper floor for fitment of wheels and chassis lubrication.
8. CAB DROP SECTION - The cab is issued from the overhead trimmed cab store, and fitted to its scheduled chassis.
9. VEHICLE FINISHING CONVEYOR - The functional systems between cab and chassis are connected, the vehicle is started and then statically tested.
10. ROLLING ROAD TEST - Tests simulate road conditions and put the vehicle through a series of rigorous performance checks.
11. CALIBRATION CHECK - Brake performance checks are conducted to verify conformance.
12. VEHICLE CUSTOMISATION - Special customer requirements are fitted during vehicle assembly or fitted after vehicle completion.
13. CAB PAINTING - Cabs are painted to customer requirements from primer condition.
14. PAINTED CAB STORE - Cabs are automatically called to one of the two trim lines.
15. CAB TRIM ASSEMBLY - All items of cab trim and electrics are fitted.
16. FINISHED CAB STORE - Finished cabs travel from here to be fitted to the appropriate chassis.
17. QUALITY AUDIT - Finished vehicles are selected at random and subjected to a thorough customer quality audit.
18. DESIGN CENTRE - In this area, current vehicles are further developed and new models are designed.

unit 20

Structures

What are structures?

Structures are built to support and protect objects. They are designed and made to resist forces that they will be subjected to. Forces may be **static** (like books on a shelf) or **dynamic** (like rotating machinery) (see unit 7). If the force is large enough or long enough the structure may fail. Structures come in many shapes and sizes and have many uses. Some examples are:

- cranes - structures used for lifting and moving objects, eg fishing rods, pick up tongs for salads;
- bridges - structures used for crossing gaps and for supporting objects that cross over a gap, eg box girders, suspension bridges;
- furniture - structures used for seating, work surfaces and shelving, chairs and tables;
- buildings - structures used for living in, working in or storage, eg houses, offices, shops and warehouses, animal kennels, sheds;
- transport - structures used for carrying objects from one place to another, eg planes, ships, motor vehicles, trolleys, wheelbarrows, cycles;
- luggage - structures used to hold, store and carry objects by hand, eg cases and baskets;
- packaging - structures used to hold and store objects, eg boxes, pallets, bottles, cans and crates.

Most structures are **rigid** like cranes and buildings but some are **flexible**, for example tents, carrier bags and fishing nets.

Frames and shells

Some structures are made entirely as a FRAME. They have interlocking sections called MEMBERS. Horizontal members that are supported at each end are called BEAMS, as used in shelving and joints in a house. If they are only supported at one end they are called CANTILEVERS. Vertical members are called COLUMNS or PILLARS. These are seen supporting bridges, walkways in shopping precincts or overhanging structures like porches. Members that are in tension are called TIES. Those that are in compression are called STRUTS.

SHELL structures are made from sheets of material. They may be joined in sections like washing machines, fridges or video recorders. Many shell structures are fixed to a frame called a **chassis**. Cars are made in this way. So are many buildings. The frame may be made from steel girders, concrete, brick or wood.

Tensile and compression forces

Structures will be subjected to **tensile** or **compressive** forces (see unit 7). A member will have to resist bending or bowing as forces are applied. Pressing down on a vertically held wooden stick will cause it to bow. Placing weights onto a beam will make it

activities

Look at the three designs here.

(a) Explain whether each structure is a shell or a frame.

(b) Suggest forces that might affect each structure.

Plastic storage/stacking trays.

A metal filing cabinet.

A wooden trellis.

bend. Within the beam or strut the material is squashed on the inner curve of the bend (compression) and stretched on the outer curve (tension). If the beam or column is subjected to a continual or great force then eventually the change in shape may be permanent, making it weaker. Cracks may appear and weathering might take place (see unit 9), causing the structure to crumble or split further and eventually fail.

Figure 2 Tensile and compression forces.

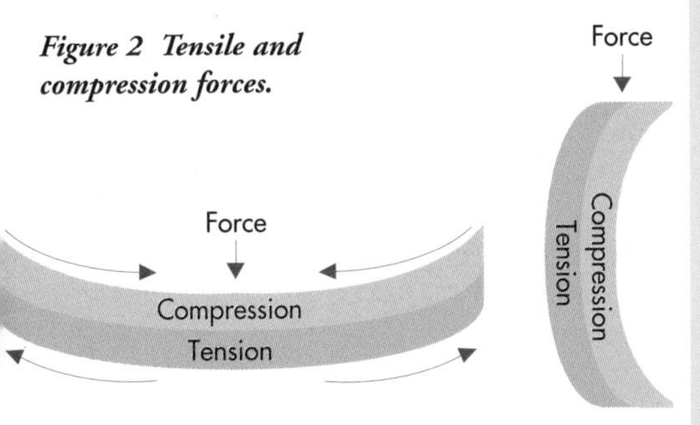

Figure 1 Frames and shells.

Resisting forces

To help prevent bowing, cracking and splitting a member may be made from a material which resists forces better than others. For example, for the same thickness of material GRP has a greater tensile strength than mild steel. Aluminium alloy is better than spruce. For compressive strength rigid PVC is fifteen times stronger than concrete. Members might be made thicker, increasing the 'life' of the beam or strut. But this will also increase the overall weight of the structure as well as the cost because more material is used. Some beams actually begin to sag under their own weight over time. In old houses beams and ceilings droop in the middle, called **creep**.

Composite materials can be used to strengthen structures. For example, concrete is quite brittle when in tension. If concrete is set around steel rod (reinforced concrete) the concrete becomes stronger as the steel withstands most of the tension. Recently glass fibre has been used to reinforce plastic (GRP) in boats. Carbon fibres are used with plastics in some car bodies. The fibres form a framework to create a shell structure. Laminated wood also resists tensile forces because of the cross grains of each layer. Laminated board like plywood (see unit 4) can be made in large sheets unlike ordinary

Figure 3 Resisting forces.

timber. It is available in thin sections, reducing cost whilst improving strength.

To help prevent bowing of a beam it might be supported underneath by a column or strut. This may remove the problem for short beams. Longer beams need support across the whole length of the beam. This can be done by using cable ties, as in suspension type structures such as suspension bridges and sails on a yacht. The cables are attached to raised pillars and placed at equal points along the beam. The weight of the beam pulls the cables tight (tension) which in turn keep the beam in compression by pulling it upwards. Another method of keeping a beam in compression is to place an arch or curve underneath it. The weight of the beam is spread along the curve forcing it outwards and keeping it in tension. Most arches have a wedge shaped keystone as in doorways. As the arch is forced down the **keystone** is held tightly in place, holding the whole structure together.

TRUSSES are also used to distribute the force about a structure. The trusses keep sections of the beam in tension, preventing bowing. Corrugated cardboard is designed in this way, as are box girder bridges and car ramps.

Figure 4 Triangle shapes are used to keep structures rigid.

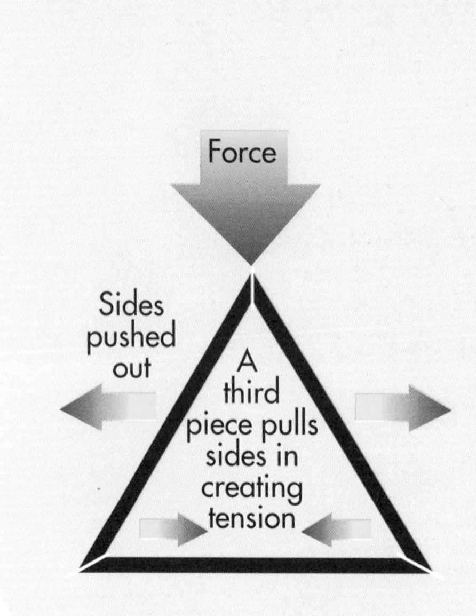

Honeycomb frames

Honeycomb shapes are seen in many structures. Plastic dip coated steel fencing is often hexagonal in shape as are some storage systems. The shape is taken from the natural structure found in bee hives. The regular hexagonal pattern has excellent compressive and shear strength (see unit 7). It provides a lightweight structure with rigidity. Honeycomb frames are found in aircraft bodies. Aluminium alloy foil is made into hexagonal cells and aluminium sheet is fixed to the frame using adhesive film. Other vehicles using a honeycomb shaped structure include saloon cars and boats.

Triangulation

If a frame is made in the shape of a rectangle, it will lose its shape when a force is applied. However, if a member is placed across the frame, the frame will keep its shape and will be quite rigid. This is called **cross bracing** and is seen in garden gates and electric cable pylons. The total number of members needed can be found by calculating:

(number of joints x 2) - 3

The cross bracing creates **triangles**. Triangulation is used a lot in frame structures. It is the strongest of the 'polygon' shapes. When the triangle is put under stress each member reacts to resist the force. If the force is applied at a corner of the triangle the two adjacent members stretch the third member, putting it in tension. This locks the structure and makes it rigid.

Triangulation is seen in a wide variety of structures, including tents. Many corners of frames have triangular pieces attached to reduce the amount of material used or to reduce the need for cross bracing which may interfere with the workings of the frame. Goal posts would be of little use with a cross braced member. Instead, corner braces are used to keep the posts upright. Corner bracing is seen on shelving and wall brackets. Corner plates are found on picture and photograph frames.

activities

A play tent is constructed using tubular HDPE members which slot into moulded HDPE corners. The shell of the tent is made from PVC sheeting which is folded at the edges and glued to allow the members to slide through.

(a) What TWO types of structure are used in a play tent?
(b) The tent is most stable when it is completely assembled. Explain why.
(c) How might the tent be made more rigid?

Shape and strength

When a beam is subjected to a force it is the outer edges that are under the greatest stress. In the centre the stress will be very little. There is an imaginary area running through the middle that separates the compressed area from the tensed area called the neutral axis. If material is removed from around the neutral axis the beam will not be weakened. In fact it will make the member stronger because it will become lighter itself, reducing the stress given by its own weight.

If a beam is turned on its edge it resists compression and tension better than when it is flat. If these two ideas are combined then a structure is created that is very strong yet light compared with a solid beam or a hollowed beam or tube. This is the 'I' shaped girder. Other hollowed out beams are made to suit different needs. Girders are made by rolling the metal while it is still hot, hence they are called rolled steel joists (RSJ). Timber joists are not made this way because they are difficult to shape. They tend to be solid beams or rectangular sections.

A flat sheet of any material is likely to buckle and bend easily. Changing the shape of the material improves its rigidity. This can be done by folding the edges. The corners of a cardboard box are stronger than the faces. The lid may be folded over at the edges to increase the rigidity. Plastic containers are also folded, but the fold shape is different and doubles as a seal to attach the lid. Sheet material can be pressed to form shapes across the whole of the sheet. These include corrugating, fluting and ribboning. Corrugations may be triangular, castle shaped or curves. These shapes act like miniature arches, making the structure more rigid.

Folds and changes in the shape of sheet materials make the shell stronger. If folds are deep enough or if there is a lot of space behind the sheet structure, this creates 'crumple zones', which protect the contents of shell structures from damage. For example, the front and rear of a car has folded sheets of metal which crumple to absorb the force of impact in an accident. Passengers are further protected by a strong chassis frame. Many large sheet structures are

Figure 5 Beam shapes and uses.

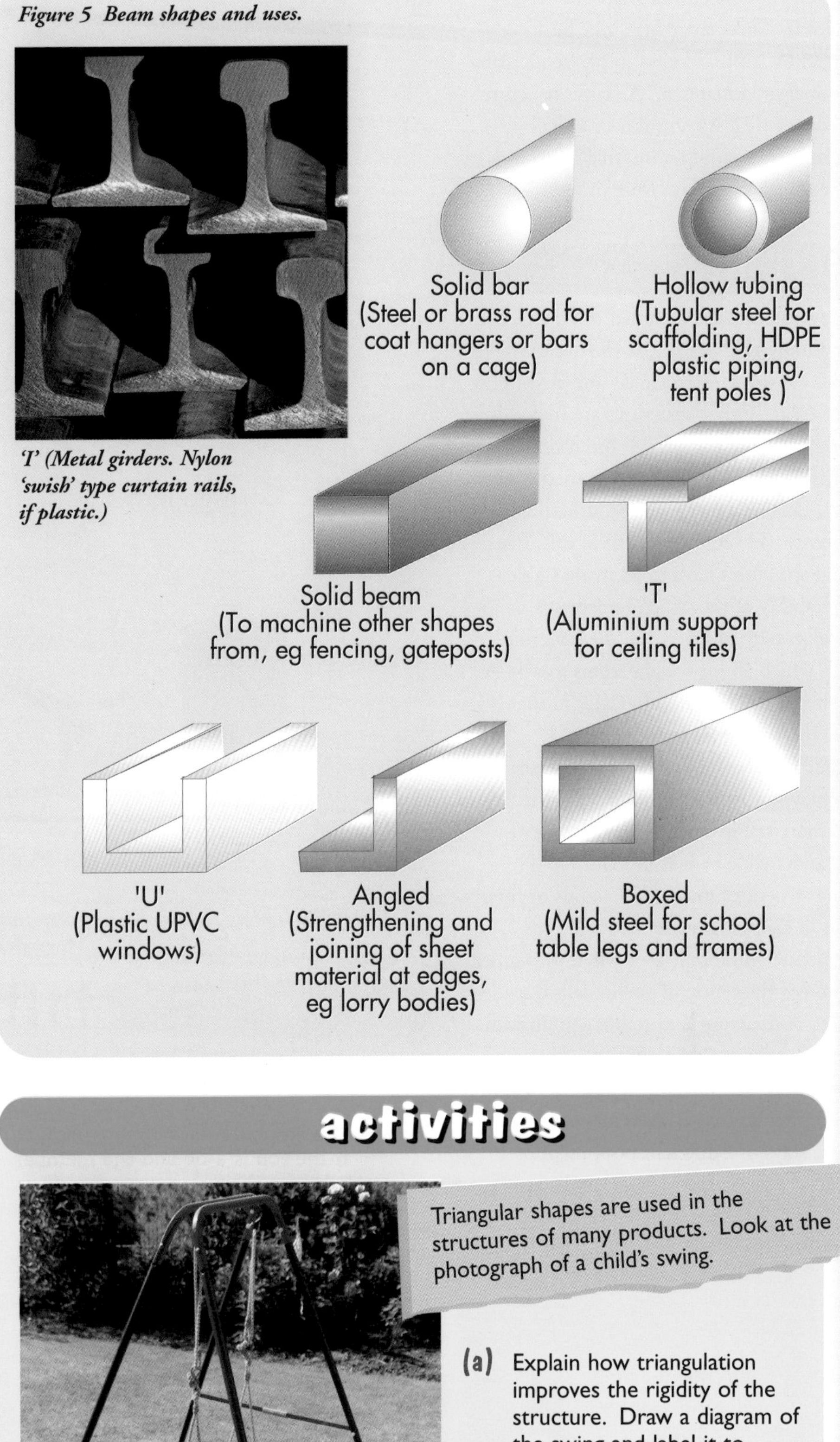

activities

Triangular shapes are used in the structures of many products. Look at the photograph of a child's swing.

(a) Explain how triangulation improves the rigidity of the structure. Draw a diagram of the swing and label it to illustrate your answer.

(b) Suggest THREE other structures that may make use of triangulation and explain why it improves the rigidity of the structures.

made using 'double curves' (hyperbolic paraboloid). Sheet structures may be reinforced by laminating, as in plywood, or by using corrugated material. A frame structure attached to a shell is common or a shell structure built around an internal mesh or frame, eg GRP or carbon fibre, if used for Formula 1 car bodies.

Stability

Some structures are designed to be attached to something more stable. A shelf is attached to a wall. A car wing mirror is attached to the body of a car. Other structures are free standing such as a cabinet. If too much weight is placed on it or if it is pushed it may tip over, causing damage to the structure and its contents. To reduce the risk of this, free standing structures have to be made stable.

The stability of the structure depends on its **centre of gravity**, the point in the structure through which all the weight seems to act. A simple beam has a centre of gravity in the middle, the point at which the beam is balanced. The centre of gravity of irregular shapes may not be in the middle. A structure will be more stable if it has a low centre of gravity and a wide base as in Figure 7. Free standing structures such as TV stands or rotary displays in shops are made with wide bases.

A structure will topple over when the vertical line through the centre of gravity falls outside the base. A structure is in **stable equilibrium** if it returns to its original position after being tilted a bit. It is in **unstable equilibrium** if it falls over after any slight movement. If the structure stays in a different position after being tilted it is said to be in neutral equilibrium. Structures can be tested for stability by finding out the angle of tilt needed before they topple over.

If a structure is top heavy and unbalanced it will be unstable and fall in the direction the force pulls it. This will be in an arc. In other words, the structure will turn about a point in a circle. The **moment** of a force is a measure of its turning effect. A way of stopping this is to oppose the moment by counter balancing - by placing a weight

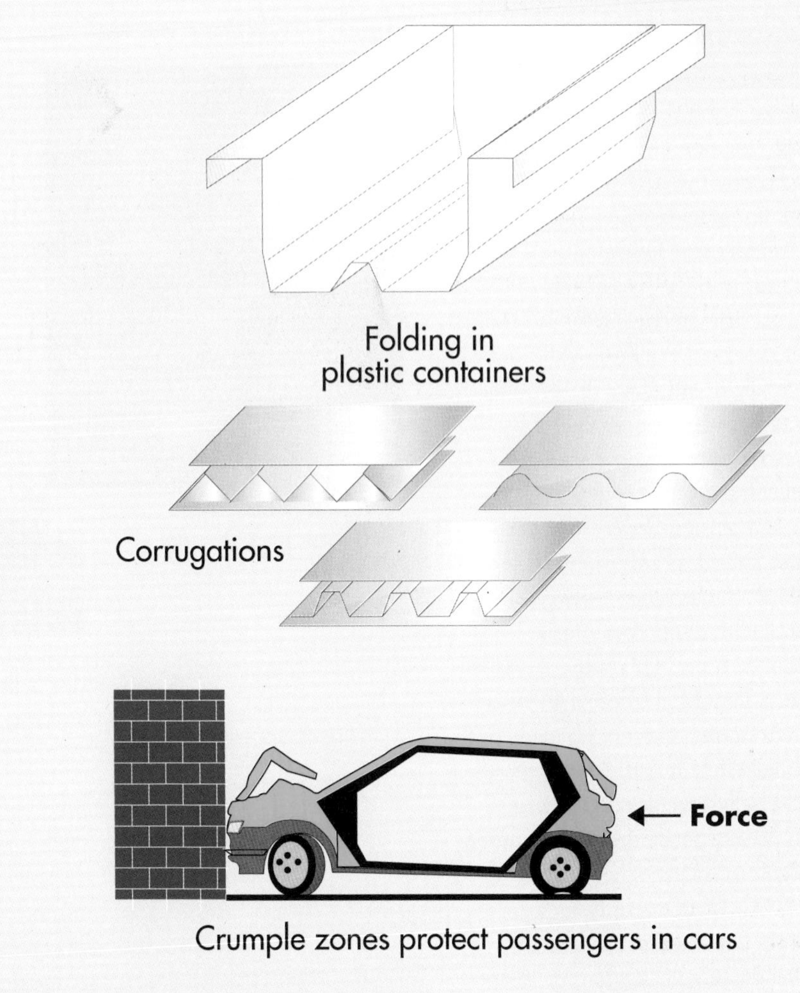

Figure 6 Improving rigidity in sheet materials.

activities

(a) The diagram below shows a structure used to fix a satellite dish to a wall. Explain why the member at the top is a tie and the member below is a strut.

(b) It is possible to calculate the force the strut has to withstand by drawing a scale diagram of the structure on graph paper.

* Assume that the scale of the diagram is 10 mm to represent 10 Newtons of force.
* Assume the force in the tie is 90 Newtons, shown by drawing a tie with a length of 90mm on the diagram.
* Assume that the force of the dish is 50 Newtons, shown by drawing the distance between the two brackets as 50mm.

Draw the diagram on graph paper and use it to calculate to the nearest 'N' the force the strut has to withstand.

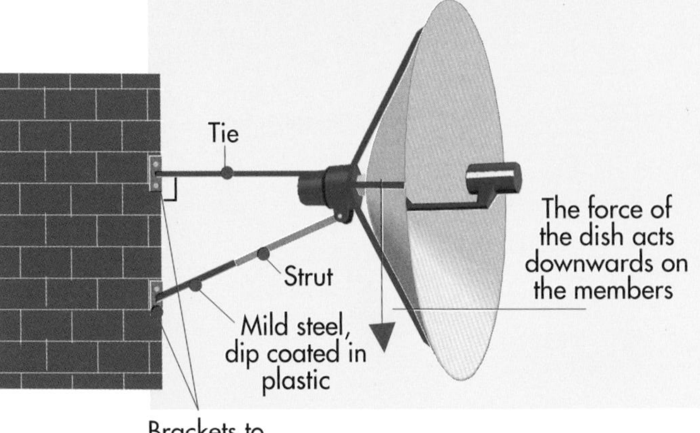

on the other side. This is used in car park barriers.

When designing any structure it is important to take into account the forces it will be subjected to. Crumple zones in packaging is one way. So are force calculations when working with triangulated structures, along with calculations of how many members are required. These all contribute to safety factors associated with structural design.

However, none of this takes into account the material that is used. Material will be subjected to stress and strain. If enough force is applied the material will eventually fail - the point of ultimate stress. Before this point the material will be subjected to various working stresses when carrying out the job it was designed to do. A factor of safety is calculated. This is the ratio between the ultimate stress and the working stress. A factor of safety of four is used a lot and means that it would take four times the allowable force before the material will fail. It is found by:

$$\text{factor of safety} = \frac{\text{ultimate stress}}{\text{working stress}}$$

Frames - structures built from members.
Members - interlocking sections in a frame structure.
Beams - horizontal members.
Cantilevers - beams held at one end only.
Columns or pillars - vertical members.
Ties - members that are in tension.
Struts - members that are in compression.
Shells - structures built from sheet material.
Trusses - used to distribute force about a structure.

Centre of gravity

CG

CG

A tumbler

A champagne glass

A red wine glass

As the centre of gravity of a glass gets higher, its stability gets less

Widening the base of a plastic plant holder will improve its stability

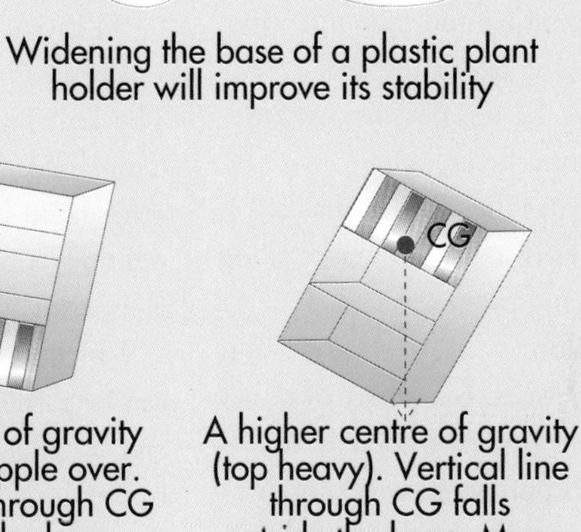

A low centre of gravity Difficult to topple over. Vertical line through CG falls inside the base.

A higher centre of gravity (top heavy). Vertical line through CG falls outside the base. More likely to topple over.

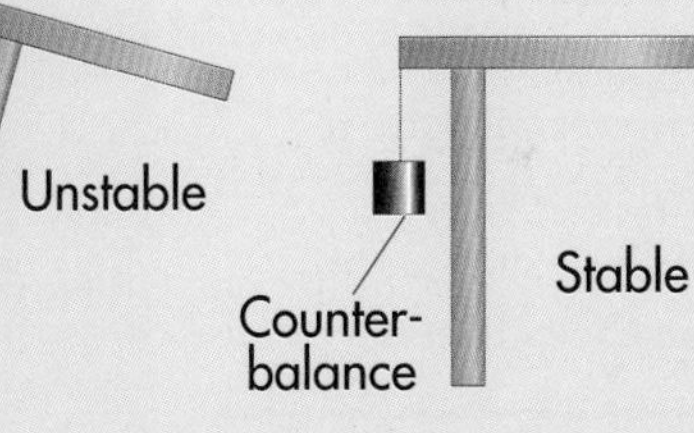

A counterbalance will prevent a structure from toppling, eg a crane

Figure 7 Stability.

activities

Read the information.

(a) Why is it important for speaker stands and candle holders to be stable?

(b) Suggest FOUR ways in which speaker stands or candle holders could be made stable. Explain in each case how your suggestion would improve stability.

- Apollo manufactures a variety of metal hi-fi equipment stands and speaker stands. The stand here is 20cm high and has a base measuring 10 x 8cm.The structures are free standing but include 'screws' which are attached to the base and grip the carpet.
- Candle holders can be made by turning on a lathe and hand carving.

unit

21 Evaluation methods

Evaluation

EVALUATION is a process used by manufacturers to make sure their products meet certain targets. Products are evaluated at every stage of designing and making. To be effective this is done by testing and trialling. It may also be less obvious, where people may make superficial `value judgments' about what they like or dislike. Evaluation that takes place at key stages along the design and making process is called **continuous evaluation**.

Evaluation may be **selective**, where one aspect of a product is studied in detail. It may also may be **comprehensive**, taking in the whole product or a much wider range of aspects. Comprehensive evaluation is likely to throw up conflicts. Decisions will have to be made about which aspects are most important. The manufacturer will have to **prioritise** each aspect.

Value judgment guidelines, such as basic opinions or whether somebody likes or dislikes a product, may not provide enough detail for evaluation purposes. For a more thorough and accurate set of targets, standards have to be set by which products can be evaluated. These standards are called CRITERIA. Each criterion needs a gauge or scale by which a product can be measured. The scale might be physical, such as a template or a scientific investigation. On the other hand it might be a way of gauging opinion, such as market research or comparing and contrasting.

Whichever scale or criterion is used, data can be gathered, analysed (looked at in detail) and conclusions can be drawn. The more information that is gathered, the more reliable the information is likely to be.

Table 1 Evaluation criteria.

- Cost - raw materials and production.
- Environmental effects - resources, waste.
- Aesthetics - colour, shape and form, taste, smell.
- Function - does it work properly?
- Ergonomics - is it the right size for handling or the place it is going to fit?
- Anthropometrics - to fit human measurements and sizes.
- Health and safety - strength, flexibility, smoothness, grip.
- Needs of different cultures.
- Suitability for age range, social group, special needs.
- Suitable material for purpose.
- Fitness for purpose.
- Quality of product - accuracy, how well it has been made.
- Process - how well the product has been made.

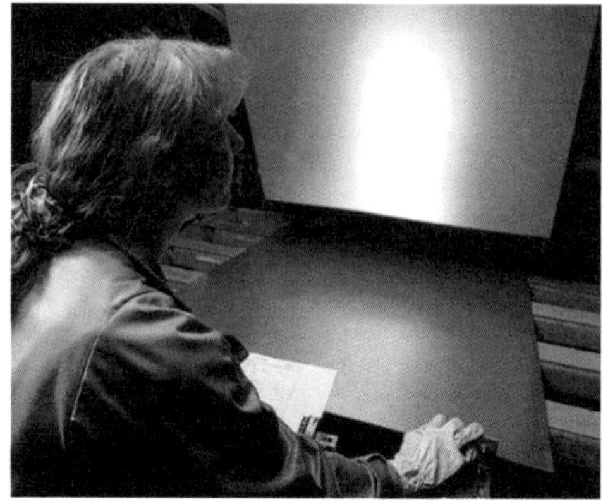

A quality check on material used for printed circuit boards to check that tolerances are met.

Meeting original needs

Perhaps the main criterion of any product manufactured is whether it meets the needs of

activities

(a) Suggest FOUR criteria that might be used to compare televisions.

(b) Explain how a manufacturer might:
(i) test the products;
(ii) gauge consumer reaction to the products.

(c) Explain why the production of a prototype might be important before manufacturing electrical equipment.

the people it was designed for. The starting point for evaluating any finished product or its prototype has to be the product's **specification** (see unit 1). This will lay down the guidelines and details required by the consumer. It will also set the TOLERANCES that the manufacturer will have to work towards. To check a prototype or finished product against a specification it will be necessary to convert each criterion into a question. An affirmative answer indicates that the criterion has been met.

Product specifications and tolerances are examples of CONSTRAINTS. Constraints are limitations placed on a design. These might be measurable limits like tolerances. They could also be other specific criteria such as colour, the type of material to be used or some physical property like being waterproof.

Comparing and contrasting

A manufactured product may be **compared** with or **contrasted** to other similar products on the market. This type of evaluation is often carried out as part of information gathering before a specification is written. However, it can also be used to judge a completed piece, or perhaps a prototype. For example, a handle for a new golf club may be made from styrofoam as a prototype then compared with existing handles with respect to what it is like to grip. The criteria used for comparison could be any of those in Table 1. For example:

- suitability for age groups - one bath may be more suitable than another for older people as its handles are designed with this group's needs in mind;
- safety - one toy may be more suitable than another for very young children as it is more flexible or has no detachable parts;
- value for money - one camera may be more expensive than another, but may be better value for money because it can be used in many different ways;
- function - a seat made from wood may be more suitable for a conservatory than one made from metal because changes in temperature can cause discomfort if metal heats quickly.

Testing and trialling

A product or prototype might be tested scientifically. This is usually to test the

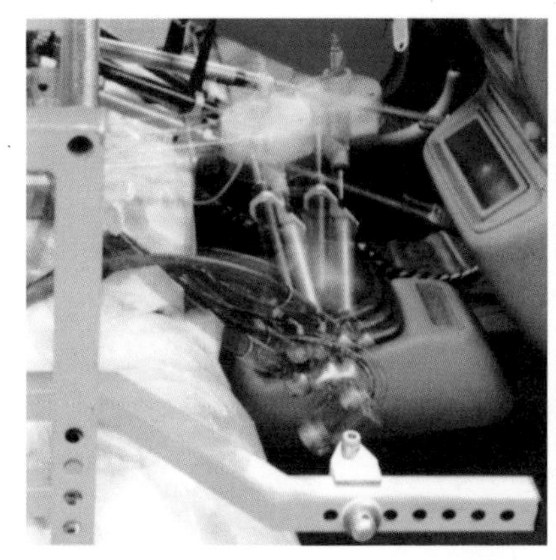

Testing clutches on cars. Over 1 million gear changes take place to test reliability.

Using a drop test to measure the impact resistance of steel toe caps.

working properties of materials it is made from. TESTING can be **destructive**, where the material or product is tested till it breaks or **non-destructive**. TRIALLING is a form of non-destructive testing.

Scientific testing is about generating reliable information. This is done by fair-testing. In any scientific investigation there is a number of factors that might affect materials. These factors are called **variables.** Each of the possible variables has to be identified. All of the variables are then kept the same except for the variable that is to be tested. These may be compared against a 'control'.

For example, different types of timber might be tested to assess their strength for use in the arm of a piece of furniture. It is not just the type of timber that will affect the strength, but the thickness, length, width and

activities

Table 2 Tests of tensile strength of materials.

Material	Tensile strength MNm^{-2}	Average MNm^{-2}
Oak	72 70 68	70
Pine	48 50 53	
Cast aluminium	105 80 96	
Cast steel	459 521 532	
Polyethylene	24 32 28	
Nylon	65 80 70	

Sources: adapted from Tables of Physical and Chemical Contents, GWC Kaye and TH Laby, Longman.

Different materials have been tested to see which is the strongest as a strut, for example for shelving or seating. The materials were tested using variations in their length, width and thickness. Some of the results are shown in Table 2.

(a) Calculate the average tensile strength of each. Which has the greatest tensile strength?
(b) Is it likely that tests would be carried out to destruction? Explain your answer.
(c) Suggest ONE way in which the strength of materials could be tested. In your answer discuss how accurate results can best be achieved.

A new toy may be tested for accuracy or for the opinions of children.

other factors. In order to test types of timber for strength, their width, length and thickness will all have to be kept the same. This will help the designer get a more accurate evaluation of which type of timber is the best. To improve accuracy even further the same test might be repeated many times and an average strength calculated for each type of timber. This depends on how much timber is available.

Trialling involves `trying-out' a design or product in the same or a similar environment to that in which it will be used. Prototyping (see unit 2) is a type of trialling. A circuit might be set up on a prototype board to check how accurately it works. Perhaps a timing circuit is tried out to see how many seconds it is accurate to. A mechanical system may be trialled using a kit to assess mechanical advantage (see unit 17) or to gauge space needed to house the components.

If a product has been made with a person or other people in mind it can be trialled by inviting the person or the people to actually use it. For example, if a piece of furniture is designed for use by children in a library, it might be placed in the library for a short while to see how well it is received. The designer may have designed it to be attractive for young children but young children may think otherwise. They may not like the shapes painted on its sides. Perhaps the seat is too big for them or the parents do not like it because the wooden edge catches on their children's legs. It is not until the furniture is trialled that these problems can be identified.

Market research

Information, observations and comments about a product can be gathered and assessed. This is called MARKET RESEARCH. A set of questions can be answered by the people asked to test out the product, perhaps using a **questionnaire** or **interview**. If a lot of people are questioned, to get a cross-section of

Market research can be used to evaluate consumers' reactions to designs.

activities

Graham Powell, designer, has designed a prototype alarm clock with a difference - it sends people to sleep. Standard alarm clocks wake you suddenly. The Concept Snoozer plays 'musak' for 15 minutes before you wake up tuned into frequencies of the brain. Gradually they change from deep sleep, to light sleep, to waking up frequencies. At night the process is reversed. You program in the time you want to sleep and it plays music for 15 minutes, gradually more serenely.

It also shines coloured lights on the ceiling. These can lull you to sleep or tell you to wake up or if you are late. The casing is made out of steel mesh that can be covered and coloured. The lights cannot be changed. Neither can it make tea. But the tape can be changed every day so you can play what you want.

Source: *adapted from The Guardian, 7.9.1995.*

(a) What is meant by a prototype?

(b) What benefits do a prototype give to a designer prior to manufacturing the product?

(c) Suggest TWO changes that you might make to the Concept Snoozer and explain how they might improve the design.

(d) Make TWO concept drawings for a prototype of either:
(i) a portable tray for the elderly;
(ii) a security wheel clamp for a cycle;
(iii) a portable carrier for compact discs.
Annotate the drawings to show the differences between your designs and how they would affect its use.

opinion, then it is likely the results will be more reliable than if only one or two people are questioned. The information can be collated and analysed using a **database** and **spreadsheet**.

Reviewing

It is not just the product that might be evaluated. The process of designing and making may also be evaluated in order to highlight problems or to emphasise good working practice. This type of evaluation is usually called REVIEWING.

Before a manufacturer makes a product, a schedule or plan for making will have been designed (see unit 3). It might be a single person working out an order for making. This might be carried out as a paper exercise. Alternatively, it may be done on computer software for use in computer aided manufacture.

The product will be made on a `dry-run'. This will highlight any problems in the process. A number of these may have to be carried out to test different parts of the process. For example, a new machine for milling timber might be checked out and the speed of manufacture might be altered. It is only by actually trying out the process that a manufacturer will find out how reliable it is.

On the evidence gathered, problem areas can be highlighted and adjustments made in order to improve the process. This is called REFINING. For example, CAM batch production (see unit 19) of a children's toy might be speeded up to see if more can be made in less time. Alternatively the process might be slowed down in order to reduce wastage caused by damage to the products during production. The aim of many reviews of industrial manufacturing processes is to improve the efficiency of the system. If a system is not working as expected then alternative ways of making might be suggested. This may involve changing all or parts of the process.

Large companies may have whole departments dedicated to product modification. Practical work in class, by necessity, is usually limited to prototyping work, with little opportunity to refine or start again. However, valuable suggestions could be made as to how the process of making can be improved if the work was to be carried out again. This is called **process evaluation** and can be carried out as follows.

- Identify all stages in manufacturing (including design work).
- Highlight problem areas (eg accuracy of making, available equipment, drying times).
- Explore how problems were resolved.
- Suggest possible future improvements to the process.
- Propose alternative ways of making the product with respect to certain criteria:
  - batch production/flow production;
  - reducing cost;
  - improving quality;
- improving health and safety.

Evaluation - a process used to make sure products match the targets set.
Criteria - value judgments by which products are evaluated.
Tolerances - maximum and minimum levels for each criterion set.
Constraints - limits placed on a design.
Testing - investigations to discover the working properties of the materials shown.
Trialling - trying out possible designs before making.
Market research - gathering information about products from people's opinions.
Reviewing - evaluating the designing and making process.
Refining - making adjustments based on evaluation evidence.

activities

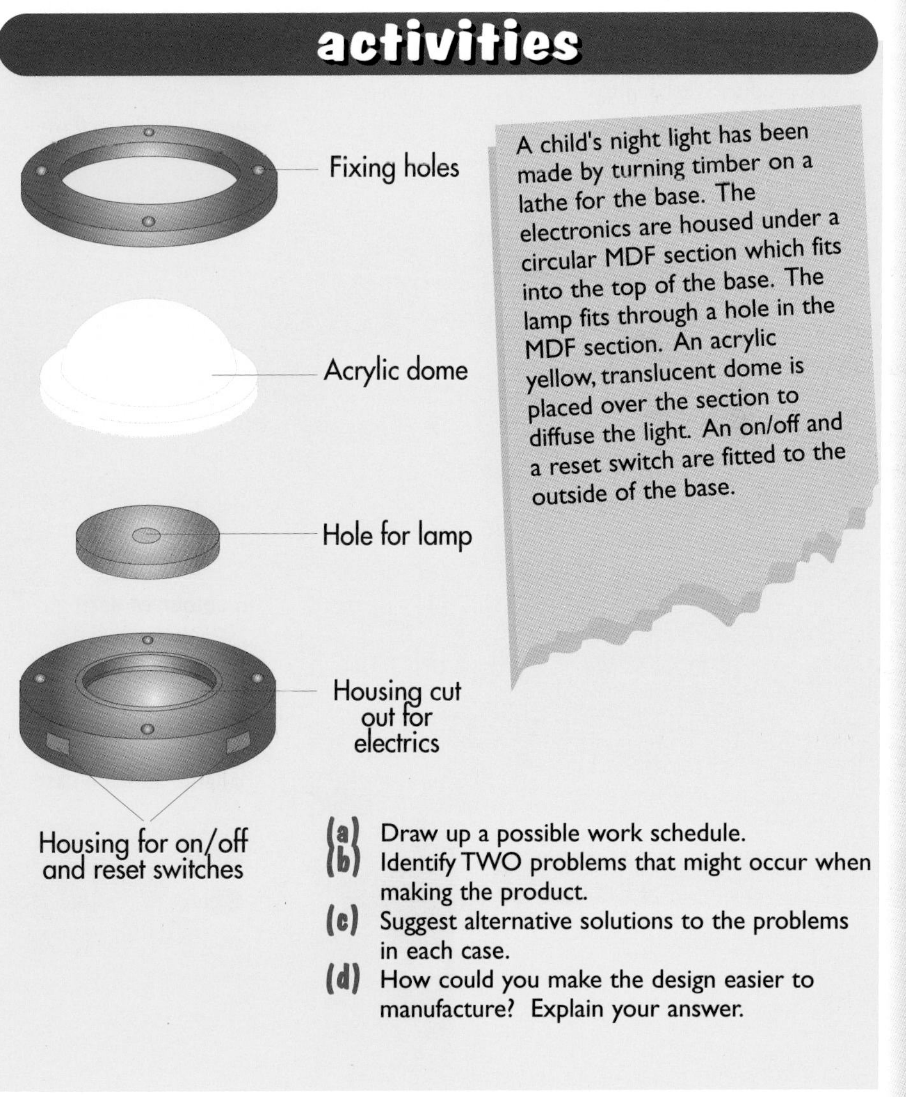

A child's night light has been made by turning timber on a lathe for the base. The electronics are housed under a circular MDF section which fits into the top of the base. The lamp fits through a hole in the MDF section. An acrylic yellow, translucent dome is placed over the section to diffuse the light. An on/off and a reset switch are fitted to the outside of the base.

(a) Draw up a possible work schedule.
(b) Identify TWO problems that might occur when making the product.
(c) Suggest alternative solutions to the problems in each case.
(d) How could you make the design easier to manufacture? Explain your answer.

unit

22 Aesthetics

What are aesthetics?

What often first attracts people to a product is its appearance. It might be the shape of a 'futuristic' vehicle or the bright colours of a cycle helmet. It may be a new and different design, moving away from the 'normal' appearance of a product, for example, 'flat screen televisions', lap top computers and transparent watches stand out from the way these products are normally made.

What a person likes or dislikes about the appearance of a product is related to a product's AESTHETICS. What attracts them may be one or more of the following:

- colour;
- form (shape, style or proportion);
- texture;
- finish.

These can be used to evaluate if a product is aesthetically pleasing. They may also be used as a starting point to help design an aesthetically pleasing product.

Aesthetics is not just about the visual. It is also about how it stimulates the other senses creating a feel or 'ambience' about a product. For example, a product made from timber like pine will release a natural fragrance that is found in the sap of the timber. It may also give a feeling of warmth and comfort. Metals and plastics do not have such a distinctive odour. Metals are sometimes used to give a feeling of efficiency, perhaps in a working environment.

Colour and form in cameras and pencil cases.

Colour

Colour can improve a product's aethetic appearance. Vehicles come in a wide range of colours. So do telephones and furniture. Other products tend to have only one colour. Many hi-fi units are black or grey. Refrigerators and washing machines are mainly white.

Objects around us are seen because they reflect light which is detected by our eyes. In a blackened room, it is likely that we would not be able to see anything. We see colours for similar reasons. Natural light is called white light and is made up from seven distinct colours. These are collectively called the SPECTRUM. Natural light also contains colours that humans cannot see (eg infra-red, ultra-violet) but other animals can. When white light hits the surface of a material, pigments on the surface absorb some of the colours in the spectrum and reflect others. Coloured filters work in a similar way.

activities

Look at the guitars.

(a) What does the colour of each guitar suggest?

(b) What might affect the shape of a guitar body?

(c) Suggest THREE parts of the guitar other than the head that may have their design changed. In each case suggest ONE change that could be made.

(d) Suggest TWO ways in which the guitar head at the end of the neck could be designed to make it more ornate. Select one idea and draw your design.

Colours are grouped as **primary**, **secondary** or **tertiary**. Primary colours cannot be made by mixing other colours. The primary pigment colours are red, blue and yellow. Secondary pigment colours are made from mixing pairs of primary colours. They are magenta, cyan and green. Tertiary colours are made by mixing primary and secondary colours. Colours mixed with white are called **shades**. Colours mixed with black are called **tints**. Colours themselves are called **hues**.

Pigments made from primary colours absorb all other hues except the primary colour they contain. Pigments made from secondary colours, absorb any hues that are not used to make the secondary colour they contain. They reflect these to produce the colour.

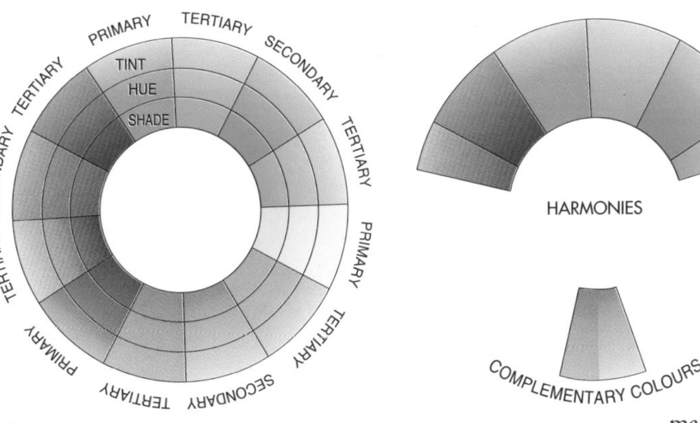

Figure 1 A colour wheel.

Colour mixing and matching

Mixing pigments to obtain a colour is different to mixing different coloured light. When light of different colours is mixed the colours add together to give a new colour. This is called **additive colour mixing**. When pigments in paints and dyes are mixed they absorb light of different colours. This is called **subtractive colour mixing**. For example, red, blue and yellow light give white light. Red, blue and yellow paints absorb all the light, so the surface will look grey.

Matching colours is about placing colours next to each other on a surface. This might be painting different wooden surfaces or using different coloured plastics for a child's toy. The colour wheel in Figure 1 is used by designers to match colours in products. Colours which are opposite each other across the wheel are called COMPLEMENTARY COLOURS. Because they are 'opposites' they stimulate the eye, making the colours seem brighter. Colours which are adjacent are called HARMONIES. These may clash making each other look dull.

A 'walkman' used during sports activity has a yellow rather than a black body.

Colours can carry different meanings. There is a colour psychology that designers use to influence opinions or feelings. For example, red is used in signs to mean 'danger'. Designs may be made from green plastic or painted green to look environmentally friendly. Grey metal designs often give the impression of being 'technically superior'. Some plastics designs are also produced in grey to give this idea.

'White goods', such as fridges, give the impression of cleanliness. Different timbers and wood finishes (see unit 14) can be used to create certain effects. Mahogany can give the impression of something antique or expensive. Pine is light and gives a 'rustic' impression.

Colours are sometimes described as warm or cold. Reds, yellows and browns are warm, eg 'firey red'. Blues and greens are cold, eg 'ice blue'.

Metal products can convey a clinical impression or give an image of hygiene as metal is associated with hospitals and professional kitchens where stainless steel has a functional use.

activities

Read the article.

(a) Suggest TWO aesthetic qualities that a hi-fi might have.

(b Why are many hi-fis likely to be black or grey?

(c) State THREE ways in which the hi-fis mentioned have been changed and explain how the changes were designed to improve their appearance.

(d) Choose ONE of the themes suggested in the article. Make an annotated drawing of an amplifier that would suit the theme.

Hi-fis often look like 'black boxes with electronics'. Unusual designs, such as speakers that look like plant pots, often substitute style for substance.

Some good hi-fi designs are conservative and adventurous with good sound. The Meridian hi-fi range has a dark translucent front with controls picked out by inset strips. Quad's hi-fis are made in two tone grey and blue. Moth's modular amplifiers contain wood on the front. Audio Innovation's amplifier in the Alto range is a sleek, cigar like creation tapered at each end to a point.

There will always be those who want unusual shaped and coloured systems. What would a 'Victorian' styled hi-fi, a psychedelic hi-fi or an environmentally friendly hi-fi look like?

Source: adapted from The Times, 3.6.1995.

Shapes, forms and patterns

Shapes are made by joining lines together. They are two dimensional and flat. A circle,

Metal products can convey a image of hygiene.

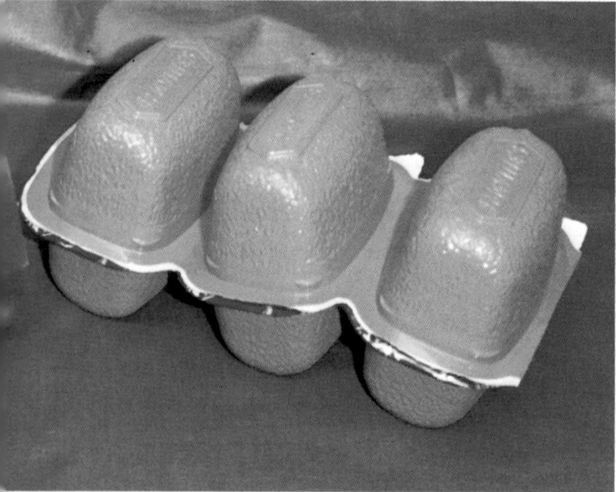

Patterns used in packaging.

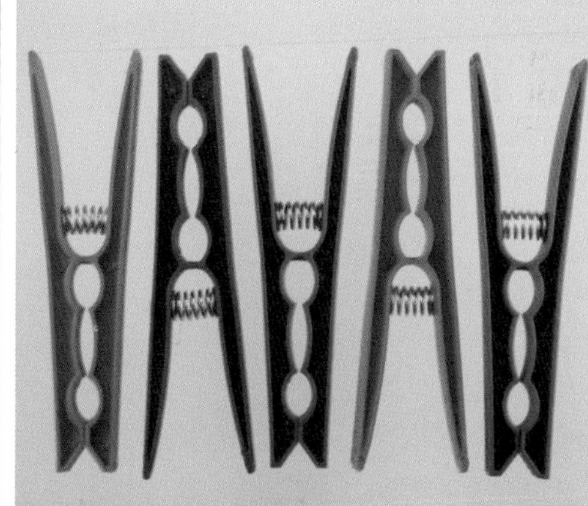

Symmetrical designs.

Asymmetrical designs.

oval or rectangle are examples of flat 'shapes'. Manufactured products are usually 3 dimensional (see unit 2). They have **form**. The ties and struts of a chair have shape when they are assembled to make the chair. The chair has form. The outline of a product or the edges of parts of a product are called contours. People often admire the curved contours of a sports car or the comfortable look and feel of a new type of tennis racket.

Patterns are groups of shapes or forms. Patterns can be regular and repetitive. They can also be irregular, for example, the grain on a piece of timber. Timber also contains knots which can be used as a design feature. Regular patterns have a sequence. These can be adapted for production purposes using a template, former or jig. Once a template has been made it can be used again and again to create a regular pattern. This is useful for batch production (see unit 19) of designs because the same product can be made many times. Tessellations are interesting patterns. These are shapes that lock together, for example, 'L' shaped blocks. Sheet material may have a tessellated pattern used to cut it. This is a way of maximising material used and reducing wastage.

The shape or form of a product may not be purely aesthetic. A sports car may look good. However, it is also functional. Improving the aerodynamics will make the car move easily through air. This reduces friction and energy costs in relation to fuel consumption and wear. The skill of the designer is in improving performance yet keeping the product attractive.

Regular shapes have SYMMETRY. Imagine an invisible line through a design. The design would look the same on each side. Some guitars are symmetrical. So are some table lamps and plastic bottles. Some irregular shapes are asymmetrical. For example, from the side, a golf club and a kettle are asymmetrical.

The shape or form of a product will usually have its parts constructed in PROPORTION to each other. This means that each part is compared with another. Parts of a product do not end up in proportion by chance. Natural laws like gravity and evolution dictate how large or long something will be. For example, a wooden beam cannot extend beyond 3.5-4.5 metres without being supported or else it will snap. Timber must have a certain thickness in relation to its length or else it will bend or snap. A spout of a kettle has only a limited range of length. Too short and it will not pour properly. Too long and it may topple over (see unit 20).

Quite often it is easy to see if a part of a product is out of proportion or not just by looking. However, there is a mathematical way of calculating proportion called the **golden ratio**. Compare two sections, with (m) being the smaller section and (M) being the larger section. If the size of the smaller section is divided by the number 0.618, the size of the larger section can be calculated to fit the ratio. Designs which have shapes that conform to the golden ratio are said to be **aesthetically pleasing**.

activities

The design here shows a plastic watering can. The measurements of two sections are shown on the diagram.

(a) What is meant by the golden ratio and what does it show?

(b) Calculate the golden ratio and suggest a suitable length for the longer section (M) if the watering can is to meet the golden ratio.

(c) Suggest how the watering can design can be changed to meet the golden ratio.

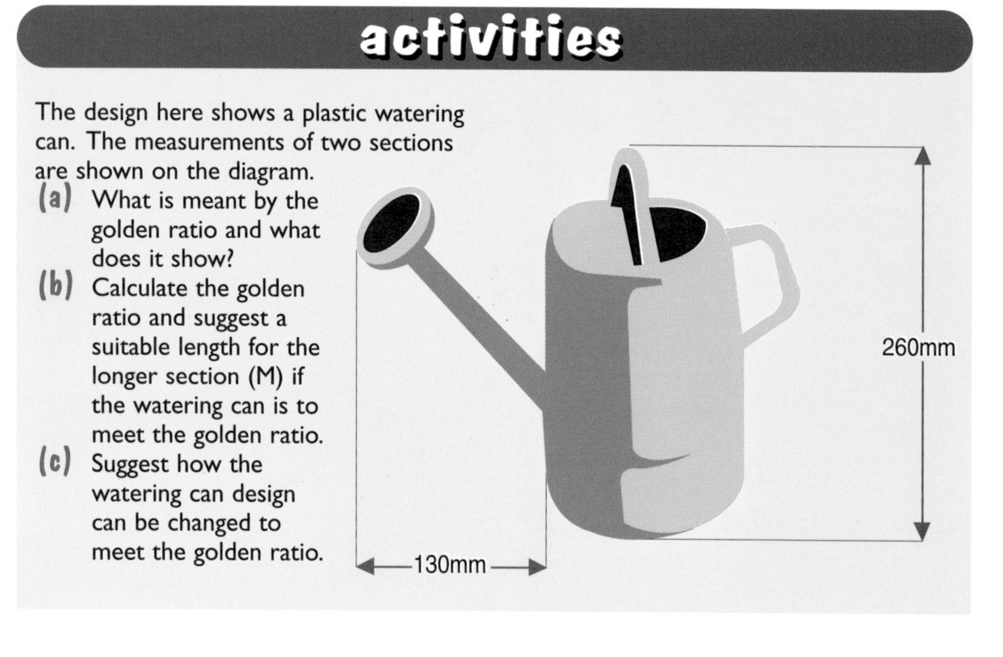

Fashion and style

Designs which are very popular at a particular time are said to be **fashionable**. Fashions do not last forever. People's opinions change and new designs take the place of

m	PA/0.618	M (approx.)
1	1/0.618	2
2	2/0.618	3
3	3/0.618	5
5	5/0.618	8
10	10/0.618	16

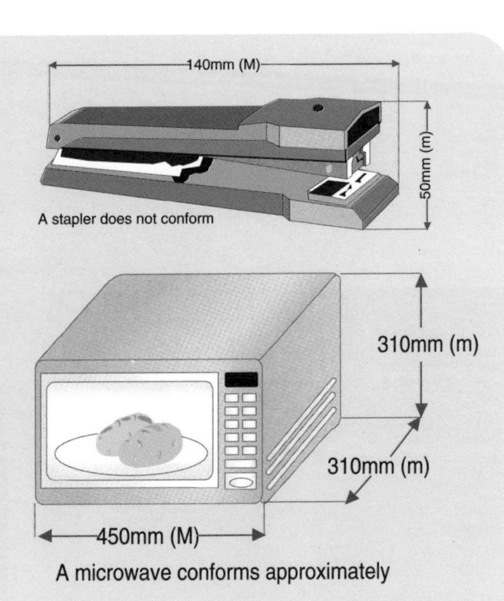

Figure 2 Designs which have proportions that conform to the golden ratio are said to be aesthetically pleasing.

older ones. Within fashions there are many different **styles**. Fashions can be tied to a time peiod. Architecture may be called 'Victorian' or 'Georgian' as this is the period when many houses in this style were made. Some styles come back into fashion after a number of years. Examples include leaded windows, window shutters, lanterns outside front doors and shapes of spectacles.

Fashions can be very short-lived. Many popular designs only stay in fashion for a few weeks or months. These are called **fads**. Examples of short lived fads include some children's toys such as hula hoops.

Texture and finish

It is not just the colour of material that appears on its surface. It may also have a TEXTURE and a finish (see unit 14).

Texture is usually gauged by touch. A surface may range from rough to smooth. An unplaned piece of wood has a rough texture. After planing and sanding its texture will be much smoother. Plastics have a naturally smooth surface, even if the surface is marked it may still feel smooth. Metals are usually worked to give a very smooth texture. A rough texture may create edges that catch on other materials.

Texture can also be visual as well as tactile. The texture of timber is related to the size of the cells in the wood. Timbers with a coarse texture like oak and red cedar have relatively large cells. Beech and maple are fine textured timbers. The cells are seen as short lines like scratches in the timber. Manufactured timbers like particle board and fibreboard have a textured appearance. Metals and plastics do not. Manufactured boards can have their colour and texture changed by the addition of **veneers**. These are thin sheets or laminates which are glued onto particle and fibreboards making them look like wood, making them smoother or adding a different type of texture. Self assembly furniture uses a number of different veneered materials (or surfaces) which can be altered to suit customers' tastes.

'Fads' are short lived fashions.

The finish on a material might be textured, ranging from rough to smooth. Sanding, varnishing and painting will give a smooth finish. The finish may also be coloured with paints or dyes or stains. This type of finish might be matt or gloss. A matt finish disperses the light that falls on the surface giving it a dull appearance. A gloss finish is designed to reflect a lot of light, giving the surface a shiny appearance.

activities

The two photographs show office furniture made of wood.

(a) Describe the patterns on the wood in each picture.

(b) Explain how the patterns could have been created.

(c) Suggest THREE reasons why wood might be aesthetically pleasing for use in office furniture.

Aesthetics - what people like or dislike about a product.
Spectrum - the range of colours in the visible range.
Complementary colours - colours which are opposites and stimulate the eye.
Harmonies - colours which are similar.
Symmetry - shapes which are identical on either side of an imaginary line placed down the middle.
Proportion - the relation of one part to another so that they are in harmony or balance.
Texture - how rough or smooth the surface of a product is.

unit 23

Quality

Identifying quality

A product may be said to have QUALITY if it has achieved a degree of excellence or a 'high grade'. Manufacturers try to produce quality products. Whether a product has quality depends on the opinion of the customer. To be of quality, a product (or service) must meet customers' expectations and specifications.

Customers often judge a product by its shortcomings. A plastic toy which breaks easily, a metal key which is not the right size for a lock or a wooden bowl which is an incorrect shape may be thought of as poor quality. Some products are made up from many parts. To customers it does not matter how many parts of a computer work. If any fail to function they may judge the computer as 'faulty'.

So far we have dealt with the quality of **products**, but it is also possible to identify:

- the quality of a design - the ideas, drawings and plans for the product;
- the quality of a production process - the methods used to manufacture and assemble a product.

Paying attention to quality is very important when manufacturing. It can reduce production costs, for example by reducing waste and lost time, improving efficiency and producing fewer faulty goods. It can also improve profits, for example by improving efficiency and improving a company's reputation, including sales of a product.

Measuring quality

When setting criteria (see unit 21) to measure quality it is important to set a realistic standard. If a company sets a standard that it can not achieve, this could be counter-productive, producing more defects and taking up more time. The standard set should be the **optimum** (the best possible) for the skills of the workforce, the equipment and the materials available.

Some small defects may not affect the smooth running of a product. These minor faults can be taken into account by setting **maximum and minimum tolerance limits** (see unit 21) for a product or its component parts. Tolerance limits are best established after testing and trialling of an item. The more data available, the more reliable the limits will be.

A product that achieves the stated requirements, specifications and set tolerances in areas such as:

- reliability;
- durability;

Quality products achieve the set requirements, specifications and tolerances.

activities

Two companies manufacturing model racing cars and aluminium cans have used attribute analysis and have found that a number of their products are exhibiting the same faults. Examples of these are shown below.

(a) State which of the items 1, 2 and 3 each company would accept or reject. Give reasons for the items rejected.

(b) Explain what is meant by attribute analysis and what it would tell a company about quality.

(c) Suggest TWO problems that may result from faulty products for a business.

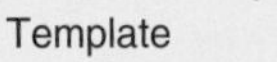

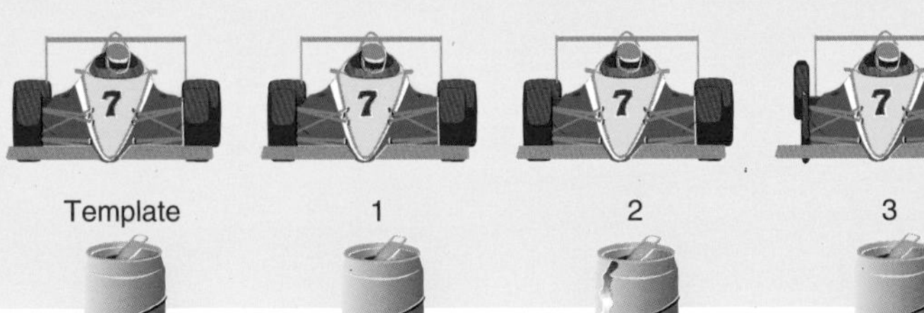

- safety;
- strength;
- size and shape;
- appearance;
- function;
- cost ;

could be said to be a quality product. A quality product will be 'fit for the purpose' for which it is intended. When comparing two similar products, one may be said to be of higher 'quality' if, for example, it lasts longer, has a better finish, has more exact components or has more functions.

Methods used to evaluate quality might include quality control, attribute analysis and quality assurance.

Quality control

QUALITY CONTROL is about inspecting and/or testing parts of a product or the production system. For example, a piece of wooden dowel may be passed through a template to ensure it is the correct diameter for the job. Light may be shone through a clear polystyrene beaker to measure its clarity. A micrometer gauge may be used to measure the diameter of mild steel tubing. A mechanism for a child's toy or an electric circuit for an alarm system may be tested out at various stages to make sure it works correctly.

Checking products are within tolerances.

Many businesses have a **quality control department** that carries out these jobs or they may be done by employees with responsibility for this part of the manufacture of a product. CAM (see unit 19) can set tolerances by adjusting the software program which controls the process. The specifications will be set and used by the **quality controller** to make sure that the product is within the required tolerances. If a component is not within these limits extra work may be necessary or it might be discarded and replaced. Both of these cost a business time and money.

Attribute analysis

Evaluation of quality need not be measured using quality control inspection or testing. It can be judged simply by the presence or absence of defects. This is called ATTRIBUTE ANALYSIS. For example, during manufacture:

- parts may be left off by accident or damaged;
- parts may be assembled incorrectly;
- features may look 'bad' (perhaps glue runs, or paint is smudged).

In batch or large volume manufacture the quality of production can be calculated by working out the percentage of faulty goods. This is not possible with one-off items because unique goods are produced.

Quality assurance

In the past companies have designed and made products without talking to potential customers, or using design briefs which lack detail. They have relied mainly on their own experience to produce products they think people want. Designers have drawn up their own specification and the production team has made the product to that specification. The sales force have 'presented' the product to the customer. What happens if the product is not what the customer wants? The product will not sell and the business will have wasted time and money.

QUALITY ASSURANCE is a way of working that involves a customer either directly or indirectly in the manufacturing process. Before a product is designed a detailed specification is carried out using information from market research (see unit 21). During the designing stage and sometimes during manufacture the customer might be involved directly.

For many products that are sold to millions

activities

Read the article below.

(a) Identify the countries or areas that have quality standards.
(b) What is meant by a Kitemark?
(c) Suggest FIVE features that are important in sunglasses.
(d) How might the use of shade numbers in glasses with a BS 2724 standard help a customer when deciding which glasses to buy?

Sunglasses are designed to protect eyes from harmful ultra-violet light (UVB and UVA). Sunglasses with a BS 2724 Kitemark are recommended. The BSI sets performance levels for quality, strength, stability, design and manufacture as well as the amount of ultra-violet light let through. Sunglasses with a BS 2724 Kitemark have a shade number which tells customers about the amount of UV light that is let through. Some products with a Kitemark let 8-29% light through and are suitable for driving. Those that let in only 3-8 % are not, and are recommended for skiers, mountaineers and sailors. Products that carry the European standard CE 89696 are also recommended.

Source: adapted from The Guardian, 13.6.1995.

of people every year, like cars, plastic buckets or DIY furniture, it is not realistic to 'invite' everybody to check that the work is being carried out to their satisfaction. To solve this problem quality assurance CODES OF PRACTICE have been established. These tell a customer that work has been carried out to a certain standard and to the required specification. Many countries have their own codes of practice and there are European and International codes as well. Each can be recognised by its own initials. The number that follows identifies what particular code of practice is being followed. A common example is the ISO 9001 1994 (formerly BS 5750) which relates to the quality of a company's management system. Many organisations in the UK are able to offer ISO 9000 registration, eg BSI, Lloyds.

Evidence that people are working as they should be comes from auditing (checking) agreed working procedures and job instructions. The audit might be carried out internally (first party), by a second party or independently by an accredited body (third party). Companies that carry a code of practice standard are checked regularly by external assessors. If procedures and instructions are not being followed then the company will risk losing its code of practice.

Table 1 Codes of practice for different countries.

BS - British
ISO - International
CEN - European
AS - Australian
CAN - Canadian
ANSI - USA

Table 2 Product standards.

Product	*Quality sign*	*Quality features*
Electrical equipment, eg PCs, CD players	CE mark	Companies must ensure that their products do not radiate electromagnetic energy at a level that prevents other radio and telephone equipment operating 'as intended'. It removes 'crackle' on radios from this type of interference.
Kitchen units, child car seats, door locks, safety goggles	BSI Kitemark	The product has been independently tested to a specified standard and meets its requirements.
Inflatable arm bands	CE mark	Used when arm bands have less than 2 air bags and are designated an aquatic 'toy'. Must have valves that do not deflate during use and carry a safety warning about supervision.
'Open championship' cricket helmet	BSI Kitemark	Passed the BSI repetitive impact test.

Total quality management

Quality assurance is not just about inspection and testing. It is a way of working

Products with a CE mark and a Kitemark.

A Lion Mark.

activities

Read the article below.

(a) Explain how the approach to quality changed at Black and Decker using the terms quality control and quality assurance.

(b) What is meant by Total Quality Management? Suggest ONE way in which this is shown at Black and Decker.

(c) Suggest TWO benefits to the company of the new approach to quality.

Black and Decker manufactures a variety of work tools, such as drills. In the early 1980s quality meant conforming to a specification which would state what the drill should be capable of doing. In the late 1980s the company began rethinking its approach, aiming to put the customer first. Its Total Customer Service initiative was geared at not just providing high quality products, but also those that customers wanted.

Customer feedback showed people wanted quieter drills. This was tackled by a self-managing project group of workers with an interest in the problem, along with expert help. The noise was caused by the shaft and gear teeth not being aligned concentrically as a result of hardening after machining, which led to distortions. Their solution was to harden before machining. This would mean buying more expensive machines. However, large cost savings could be made by reducing scrap, reworking and other inefficiencies caused as a result of noisy tools.

Source: Black and Decker.

that requires everybody in a business to take responsibility for ensuring quality work. This is known as TOTAL QUALITY MANAGEMENT. Rather than wait for someone else to inspect or test that a job is being done correctly the person doing the job carries out his or her own inspection. This leads to a more efficient business operation because people take a pride in what they do and so defects and wastage are reduced.

Quality symbols

There is a number of signs and symbols that are used by manufacturers to tell customers about **product** standards.

The British Standards Institution (BSI) is an independent organisation which operates in the fields of standards, standardisation and quality assurance. The Kitemark that accompanies some BSI codes tells the customer that the product has been tested to destruction, to ensure that it meets with a certain safety standards. The first kitemark was used on tram rails in 1903 and has been used as the official mark since 1926.

The CE mark is a European Community standard. Products with the mark have to have a technical file which tells how productive standards have been maintained. This file can be checked at any time. Products with the CE mark are allowed to pass freely within the European Community. It is not, however, a measure of quality, safety or environmental protection.

Testing that it is impossible to pull a child's toy apart.

The Lion Mark is a symbol of toy safety and quality displayed on toy packaging. It was developed by the British Toy and Hobby Association (BTHA) as a badge of 'membership' for toy manufacturers who must take out a licence with the BTHA. A manufacturer has to have signed a strict code of practice which includes toy safety matters, advertising standards and other matters such as counterfeiting and marking on toy guns. Displaying the Lion Mark shows customers that products conform to British Standard BSEN 71.

Product safety

One of the criteria used when evaluating the quality of the product is whether it achieves safety requirements. It is important that every product is safe to use. Safety is particularly important for products used by young children, the very old, pregnant women and people with injuries. Ensuring that products are safe can be achieved in a number of ways.

- Making sure that products do not contain toxic paints or other dangerous chemicals or materials.
- Creating a design which does not contain unnecessary sharp edges or spikes. Where these are needed for function, protection should be given.
- Finishing (see unit 14) so that edges and faces are clean and smooth.
- Testing designs so they are durable. A product that breaks easily can be dangerous.
- Ensuring the size and shape of a design is safe, for example, making sure a toy does not fit into a child's mouth or that a handle is not so large that it causes strain.
- Designing products with safety features, such as child proof locks or child proof caps on bottles.

Quality - **a level of excellence or a grade.**
Quality control - **the inspecting or testing of parts of a product or a production system to ensure that standards are met.**
Attribute analysis - **a method used to evaluate quality which looks at the presence or absence of defects as a percentage of the total products manufactured.**
Quality assurance - **a way of working that involves customers' wishes when setting standards for quality.**
Codes of practice - **standards which indicate that the quality of production processes is being maintained at a certain level and specification.**
Total Quality Management - **a method that attempts to ensure quality by making it the responsibility of everyone in the business.**

activities

APPROVED LION MARK RETAILER

TOY SAFETY FIRST

BRITISH ASSOCIATION OF TOY RETAILERS

The BATR joined with BTHA in adapting the Lion Mark for use by retailers ...The symbol displayed in the shop, in catalogues and in retailer advertising, indicates that the retailer has agreed to the Code of Practice and, as such, is prepared to make strenuous efforts not only to offer safe toys for sale, but to ensure management and staff are briefed on toy safety matters such as age warnings. Some, though not all, toys will carry the Lion Mark.

Safety regulations demand that the parts used in toys for children under 3 years must pass the Choke Hazard Test. The dimensions of the test tube are critical, having been specifically designed to reflect the size of the gullet in a child of 3 years and under. This test has dramatically reduced the incidence of choking on small items. The Choke Hazard test does not apply to toys for the over-threes.

Source: Toy Safety Information Booklet for BATR Lion Mark Approved Retailers and their staff, British Association of Toy Retailers.

Pass

Fail

(a) What is meant by a Lion Mark?
(b) What does the British Association of Toy Retailers BATR sign tell a customer about a shop selling toys?
(c) Why are tests likely to be very important for young children's toys?
(d) The BS 5665 standard relates to safety standards for toys. Suggest THREE aspects of safety that toys would need to take into account.

unit

24 Ergonomics and function

Ergonomics

ERGONOMICS is the study of the interaction of people with the equipment they operate and the environment in which they work. Studying ergonomics should help to improve an environment, so that people can operate in comfort, using the smallest amount of energy. For example, unsuitable machinery and poor conditions in a workplace may result in inaccurate work and an unsatisfactory product being produced by an employee. A badly designed kitchen may cause accidents or lead to wasted time and effort when cooking.

Two important aspects of ergonomics are **anthropometrics** (the study of body sizes) and **anatomy and movement**. Taking these into account when designing should help to produce products that are:

- easy to use;
- difficult to operate incorrectly;
- able to be operated correctly every time;
- EFFICIENT, so that operations are carried out competently, in the least possible time and with minimum waste.

Collectively these help to define the FUNCTION of a product (see later). A light switch is easy to use, will turn a light on every time, unless faulty, and the operation is quick and requires little effort.

Anthropometrics

ANTHROPOMETRICS is the scientific study of body sizes. It can be used to produce a range of approximate sizes, identifying maximum and minimum limits, that a product can be designed for.

Any part of the human anatomy can be studied to produce anthropometric data. For example, the hand might be studied to obtain data for the manufacture of hand grips for sports equipment, computer game consols or cooking utensils. To be efficient, a range of people need to be able to grip a handle in comfort without straining. This may be for long periods, such as a whole tennis match, or simply to maintain a strong grip to improve a sudden 'hit', as in golf or hockey.

Height measurements might be studied for library shelving or kitchen construction.

Situations where anthropometric data is important.
- ***The width of hand held electronic games.***
- ***The width and height of a desk.***
- ***Space in the work area.***

Library shelving is set at various heights. The highest shelf needs to be reachable by people under a certain height without stretching. If they stretch too far they may overbalance or fail to hold an object safely. Low shelving should be able to be accessible without bending the back too much. This may cause discomfort and injury, particularly if loads are heavy.

Data can be found by measuring different

activities

Look at the diagram showing guidelines for seating and posture for a typical office task. Choose THREE areas where measurements are important.

(a) Explain whether you would be measuring for distance or movement.
(b) Suggest what part of the body is likely to be measured.
(c) Explain what ergonomic problems might occur if the guidelines are not met.

Source: Health and Safety Executive, Display Screen Equipment at Work, HMSO.

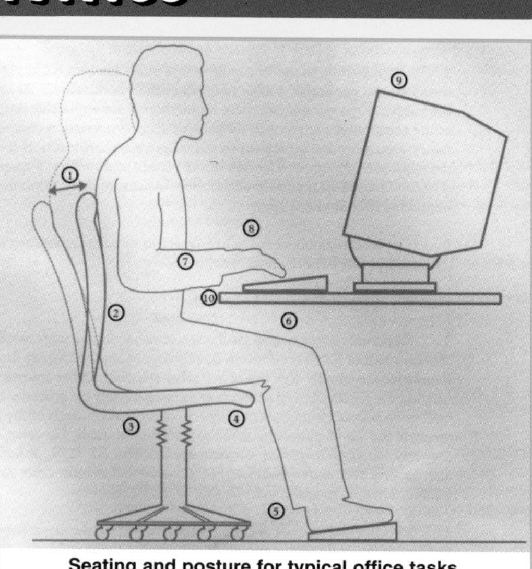

Seating and posture for typical office tasks

1. Seat back adjustability
2. Good lumbar support
3. Seat height adjustability
4. No excess pressure on underside of thighs and backs of knees
5. Foot support if needed
6. Space for postural change. No obstacles under desk
7. Forearms approximately horizontal
8. Minimal extension, flexion or deviation of wrists
9. Screen height and angle should allow comfortable position
10. Space in front of keyboard to support hands/wrists during pauses in keying

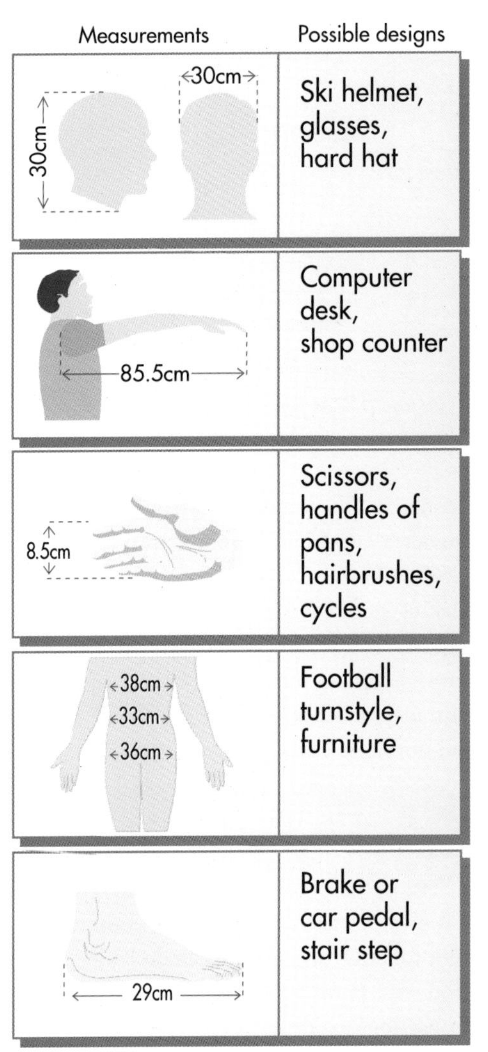

Figure 1 Anthropometric measurements of an average male adult and designs for which they could be used.

people, taking averages and setting maximum and minimum limits.

Anthropometrics have to be given special attention for arthritis sufferers, wheelchair users and children.

Anatomy and movement

There are many situations where frequent movement is required. This means that space is needed for safe and comfortable operation. Designs must take this into account.

For example, when continuously pedalling a bicycle or moving a wheelchair, limbs need to move to give maximum force to operate the machine without being cramped or overstretched. It is not commercially viable (see unit 25) to make a product to suit each person's individual anthropometric needs. An adjustable setting, such as on a seat on a bicycle, solves this problem to an extent. The seat can be raised or lowered to suit different needs. The front seats in a car move backwards and forwards on a track to give leg room. The backs of office furniture chairs have adjustable back rests to allow angled movement of the spine. The heights, lengths and angles required to design these products can be found by gathering anthropometric data.

Building layouts, involving the positions of windows, doors and furniture, are important aspects of ergonomics. A narrow street can cause problems. So can incorrect spacing of seating in a cinema or theatre. This is especially true if a person has to use a wheelchair, a walking frame or crutches to get around. Designing for public places has to take into account the safe and comfortable movement of 'traffic'. This, in turn, may affect the design of a product.

Where a lot of space is available, allowing for movement is fairly easy. Where there is little room the design becomes a lot more challenging. **Space saving designs** is the term used for making the best use of the available space. For example, wall units in a small kitchen allow easier movement around the floor of a kitchen. Stackable storage jars, tins and boxes conserve space by using up the body of a cupboard. When camping, cooking equipment that fits inside one another that is not in use allows more items to be packed, making better use of what little space is available.

An exercise bike has an adjustable seat.

activities

The diagrams show different handles that could be used on a drawer.

(a) In each case, suggest what measurements would be taken; (i) from the handle; and (ii) from the drawer; to gather anthropometric data.

(b) Suggest which handles might be a problem for:
(i) a person with large hands;
(ii) a child;
(iii) a person who was weak with illness and had problems gripping.

(c) Choose ONE design and suggest how you might make it easier for an elderly person to grip.

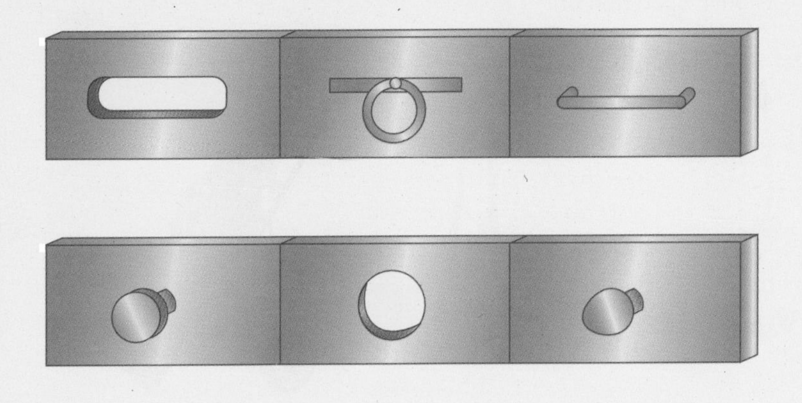

A fold away bed is a space saving design.

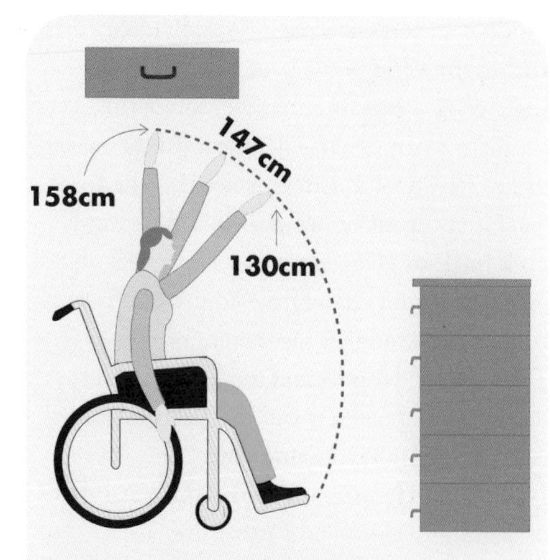

Figure 2 The reach of a person in a wheelchair can influence the height of shelves, worktops, cupboards and drawers. The diagram shows measurements for an average adult female.

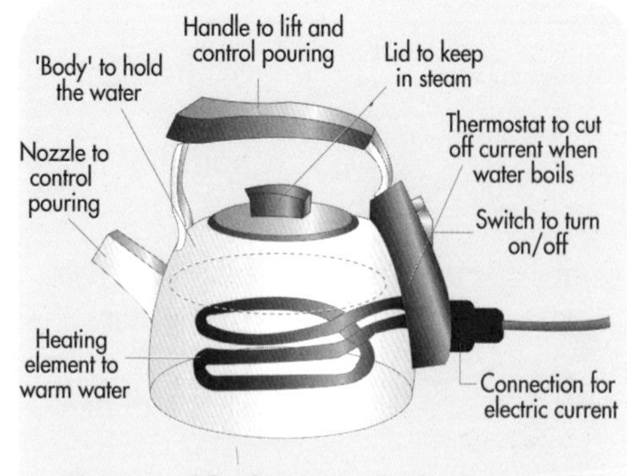

Figure 3 The function of a kettle and its parts.

Function

The function of a product is the action which is characteristic of a product (or put more simply, what a product does). For example, a light switch turns a light on and off. A door handle allows a door to be opened and closed. Chairs support your weight. Sunglasses shield and protect your eyes from sunlight.

Component parts of more complex products have their own functions and their combined actions lead to a 'greater' action taking place, for example in an kettle, as shown in Figure 3. All these actions lead to water being boiled.

The function that a product has will determine the APPLICATIONS for which it can be used. For example, the function of a seat is to support a person for a period of time so that they do not have the strain of standing. Seating is found in a variety of situations including living rooms, offices, waiting rooms, gardens and parks and cinemas. The function of a handle is to provide a safe grip on a product. It can be used on doors, spades and toothbrushes. Making sure that the function of a design is suitable for a particular application often means **adapting** the design. For example, a bath may be adapted so the elderly can get in and out more easily.

activities

(a) Explain the function of the golf trolley.

(b) Suggest TWO other possible uses for a product that carries in this way.

(c) Explain FOUR pieces of anthropometric data that may be useful when designing this product.

(d) Explain how it would improve the ergonomic operation of golf practice.

Golf trolleys are designed to hold a golf bag containing clubs when playing golf. It can be pulled, pushed or moved around a golf course, removing the need to carry heavy clubs. The Hill Billy Powered Golf Trolley is a lightweight trolley made from zinc plated mild steel. It comes in two wheel or three wheel versions. The two wheel version weighs just 7.6kg. It is powered by a small, compact rechargeable battery. The speed of the trolley is controlled by a switch in the handle. It is designed to suit all normal sized golf bags.

Source: *Hill Billy.*

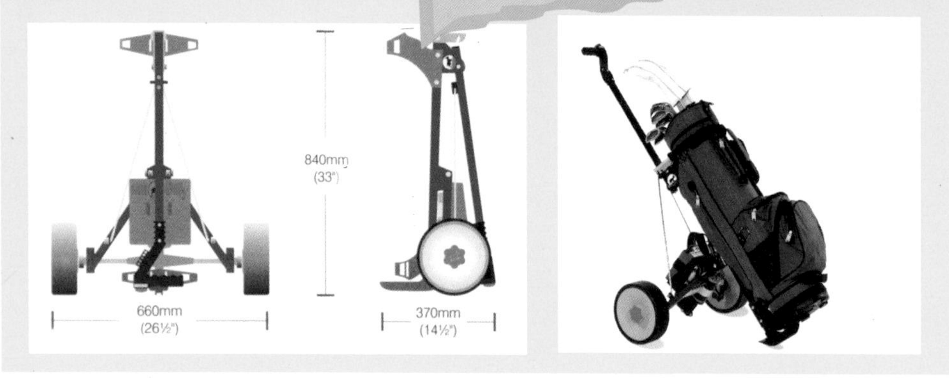

Function and form

It is important for designers to consider both **function** and **form** when designing products. Form is the shape, style or proportion of a design. There may be a **conflict** between function and form which successful designs will solve. For example, a square wheel will not function on a road and so wheels are made round. A surf board may look interesting if it is shaped like a guitar, but this will be difficult for the surfer to stand on and will not cut through the water as well as standard designs. A triangular shaped bed may cause problems when sleeping. In most cases when designing, form follows function.

Age, gender and special needs

We have already seen that it is important for designers to take into account body sizes and space for movement when designing products. The designs of products and their functions are likely to be different if aimed at different groups of people.

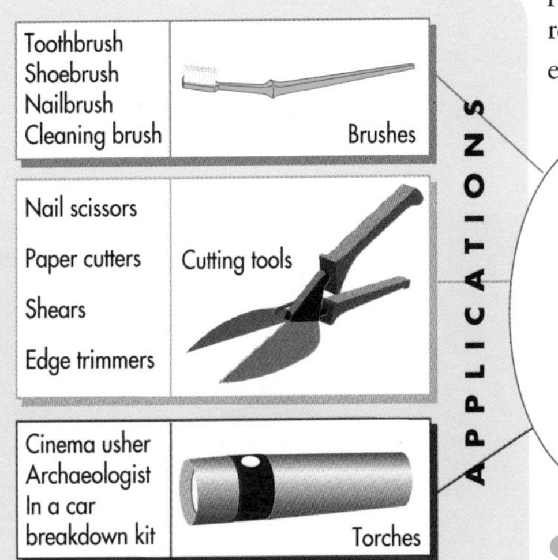

Figure 4 Applications of a handle.

Age differences The design of a product will depend to some extent on whether a young, adult or old person is using it. Products may therefore differ in size, shape and function depending on which age range they are made for. Sports equipment designed for children, such as tennis racquets, is often smaller than equipment designed for adults. Furniture and beds for use by children tend to be smaller. Handles used by older people may need to be wider so they can grip more easily. Even if products are designed for adults they may be manufactured in different sizes, such as small, medium, large or extra large.

Gender differences The anatomy of men and women is different and this can sometimes influence a design. Increasingly products are being designed without a gender bias. Some products are still manufactured in smaller sizes for women than men, such as golf clubs, although adjustable parts can get around the problem for other designs. Most products require no changes in design at all for ergonomic reasons for male or female use.

Special needs Designs may be adapted to take into account the special needs of different groups, such as:

- people who are handicapped (blind, deaf, wheelchair bound);
- people who are injured in a way which restricts movement;
- people who are temporarily unable to carry out a task (a pregnant woman lifting a heavy item, an infirm person who is unable to bend down or use both hands);
- groups with special work conditions (people working long hours on a computer or people working in extreme temperatures).

Equipment for children is often manufactured at different sizes to adult equipment.

Ergonomics - the interaction of people with their environment.
Efficiency - operations carried out with minimum waste and cost.
Function - the 'job' a design is intended to do.
Anthropometrics - the science of body sizes.
Applications - varieties of uses for a product.

activities

The Neptune is a portable battery powered bath lift designed specially for the elderly to be raised and lowered into a bath without the need for help. The lift fits easily into the bath and is held in place by four strong suckers. The lift is operated by a safe waterproof hand control. When raised, the flaps on the seat fold out to give a stable surface for transfer, to a seat at the side of the bath. It is designed ergonomically to give a comfortable sitting position, the maximum possible legroom and a low position in the water to enjoy most of the bath water. It comes with a choice of seat shapes and also has a cushion available with some shapes.

Source: Mountway Limited.

435MM (17")
70MM (2¾")
470MM (18½")

(a) What group of people is the bath lift designed for?
(b) Suggest TWO reasons why this group might need a bath lift.
(c) Suggest FOUR ergonomic features of the bath seat and explain the anthropometric measurements that would need to be taken before designing these features.

unit

25 Production considerations

Units 22-24 show that aesthetics, quality and ergonomics are factors that a manufacturer of products made from resistant materials must take into account. There is a whole range of other factors that a manufacturer might also consider.

Environmental effects

The processes used to produce a design can affect the environment. It is possible to assess how environmentally friendly a product is by carrying out a 'cradle to the grave' analysis. This examines the effects of the extraction of raw materials, the production process itself, and the disposal of the product when its useful life comes to an end.

Raw materials

It is not possible to extract raw materials without causing some damage to the environment. Careful management can limit the damage, however.

In the past much of Britain was covered in hardwood forests of oak, beech and ash. These forests were cut down to make timber for ships, houses and fuel. In many temperate regions hardwood forests have been lost completely due to the high demand for timber (see unit 4). Because of the temperate climate the land regenerated and became moorlands. In tropical rainforests, without the cover protection of trees, the land has become desert. This is called **deforestation**. A further environmental problem is that rainforests are needed for the production of oxygen and to help remove carbon dioxide from the atmosphere. SUSTAINABLE FORESTRY is one solution to these problems. Trees are grown from saplings, allowed to mature and then cut down. New trees are planted to replace the ones felled. Another solution is selective felling, where trees are only cut when required. These methods, as well as recycling, can preserve forests without causing permanent damage to the environment.

Metals are extracted from ores which are either mined or quarried from rocks. Mining can cause subsidence at the surface and quarrying leaves large holes. Both dump waste on the surface, which creates 'spoil heaps' as the waste piles up. All these features make the environment look ugly. The wastes may also contain chemicals that are poisonous to flora and fauna. Noise caused by heavy machinery and dust are added pollutants. Some of the problems with ore extraction can be reduced by landscaping. Recycling of metals can reduce the need to mine. Alternatively, new

activities

Plysu is a manufacturer of lightweight plastic containers for the British Dairy industry using blow moulding techniques. Containers produced by the company contain liquids such as milk and juice, lubricating oils, chemicals and detergents. The company believes that 'it has a responsibility to minimise the environmental impact of its products'. Some of the methods it uses to do this are shown below.

Source: Plysu.

(a) Suggest TWO environmental problems that Plysu's environmental policy is minimising.

(b) Explain TWO methods used by Plysu to minimise environmental problems.

(c) Draw a 'cradle to the grave' flow chart showing the 'life' of a plastic container.

Recycled Packaging

Reprocessed plastic is used by Plysu in the manufacture of a wide range of products. The reprocessed plastic is known as PCR (post consumer recycled) material to distinguish it from bottles made simply from factory scrap. Plysu uses PCR to make numerous containers from its standard range as well as custom bottles designed for individual customers. The external appearance and performance of PCR bottles is indistinguishable from those made with virgin plastic.

Reusable Containers

Some customers use Plysu's products to package hazardous chemicals. Even when empty these bottles are too dangerous to be considered for recycling. In such cases Plysu can provide an alternative environmental solution in the form of reusable containers. These specially reinforced containers, in conjunction with a sophisticated valve system, can be refilled and reused time and again, thus keeping hazardous, empty bottles out of the waste stream.

materials that could cause fewer problems may be used. Copper has replaced lead piping and is itself being replaced by recyclable plastics. Fibre optics are replacing copper wiring in telecommunications.

Plastics are obtained from oil or coal. Damage from coal mining can be reduced by landscaping. Pollution caused by oil spillages can be limited by regular maintenance of machinery and the use of modern, up to date equipment. Recycling can reduce the pressure for new raw materials.

Production problems

Raw materials have to be taken to factories where they are used to manufacture products. They may be carried by road, rail or ship. These methods of transport use fuel, which adds to global pollution as exhaust fumes are emitted. Transportation can be kept to a minimum by producing goods near to raw material sites. Modern vehicles with efficient and clean burning engines will also reduce pollution. Recycling may reduce the need for transportation, although recycled products themselves may have to be transported.

Once at the factory, production needs energy. It also produces waste energy, usually heat. Both may lead to global warming, making the temperature of the planet 'heat up'. Efficient production processes that use as little energy as possible are most environmentally friendly. Hand made products might use no machinery at all, relying on 'human' energy, which should reduce energy waste to a minimum. However, this will affect levels of production and costs. Buildings can be insulated to reduce heating costs and microelectronic circuitry and operations can lower electrical energy demands.

The life of a product

Some products are `built to last' whilst others are designed to survive for a short period. For example, a polythene shopping bag may only be used only a few times before it is disposed of. A wicker shopping basket may last for years before it is replaced.

Products manufactured with planned obsolescence in mind.

The longer a product lasts the fewer new products have to be made to replace it. This could reduce the amount of environmental damage caused by repeated production.

When a product is designed deliberately to wear out or be used up over time this is known as PLANNED OBSOLESCENCE. A disposable camera, for example, is designed to last for a specified period of time after which it does not work. Some razors are designed to last for only one or two shaves. Other examples might be a crisp bag, an 'ice lolly' stick or a fast food container.

Disposal

Products wear out over time. Many products are discarded as refuse and left to rot away naturally (see unit 9). The recycling of product materials is becoming increasingly important. Recycling might involve the melting down of materials such as plastic or

activities

The Kodak Fun Gold Camera contains 27 exposures of Kodak Gold film. Users are told that after taking the pictures, they should take the whole camera to a dealer to process. Kodak then recycles the single use camera. Instructions on how to use the camera are given on the packaging.

The product is available in a variety of forms. These include the flash camera, the gold flash camera, the panoramic camera, the mini camera and the aquatic sports camera. Drawings of these are also included on the packaging.

(a) Suggest TWO reasons why this camera is an example of planned obsolescence.

(b) Suggest THREE differences between this type of camera and one which is not disposable.

(c) What might be an advantage of this type of camera for:
(i) the customer;
(ii) the business that produces it;
(iii) the environment?

(d) Suggest FIVE pieces of information that may be contained on the packaging.

(e) Explain TWO legal requirements that would affect what was included on the packaging.

metal to use in another product, the use of 'waste' timber in MDF or the reuse of timber to make new products (see units 4-6).

Legal factors

As a product is designed and made there is a number of legal considerations that must be taken into account. These protect both the manufacturer and the customer.

Patents A manufacturer may find that the product it is producing is a totally new invention (see unit 1). To prevent this being copied it is possible to obtain a PATENT from the patent office in the UK. This prevents other businesses copying the invention for a period from the date of application. International patents can be applied for which cover all countries. A patent will only be granted if the product is completely new and if the invention does exactly what the manufacturer says it will.

Logos Many businesses have their own logos. These are 'emblems' which may contain letters or the company name. They allow customers to distinguish one business and its products from those of another business. Many companies register their logos as **trademarks**. This means patenting the logo so that others cannot copy it.

Company logos can be found on products.

Labelling Labels on products or packaging will state the features of a product, such as its dimensions and weight or whether it is made from recyclable plastic or timber. It may also contain special features which are indicated, such as battery operated, longer life. Other labelling might be company logos, bar codes, contents lists, assembly details, photographs, company details or methods of production. Labelling is restricted by law.

Consumer legislation There is a number of pieces of legislation designed to protect customers buying products.

- The Trade Descriptions Act makes it illegal to make false or misleading claims about products. It covers statements, adverts and labels that make false claims.
- The Weights and Measures Act makes it illegal to sell goods which are underweight or short measured.
- The Consumer Protection Act aims to prevent the sale of harmful or defective goods. Injured people can sue the supplier.
- The Consumer Safety Act gives the government the power to ban or regulate the sale of dangerous goods, eg place controls on electrical equipment.
- The Sale of Goods Act and The Supply of Goods and Services Act state that goods when sold must be of satisfactory quality, fit for the purpose as described.

Social, cultural and moral factors

A designer and manufacturer of a product must take into account that different people have different needs to create a successful product.

Different cultures have different values. For example, furniture based on the Japanese culture may be designed for people to sit cross legged on the floor at a low level table while eating and drinking. Different cultures may go about their daily lives in different ways. They may eat or pray at different times. Many different cultures have festivals. Christians celebrate Christmas and Easter. Muslims celebrate Ramadan. Some religions like Jehovah's Witness do not celebrate any festivals, including birthdays. It is important to evaluate whether and to what extent a product will be accepted by different cultures.

Product designed for athletes may also be used for leisure exercise.

Different social groupings or age ranges may also have different needs and values. For example, walking aids may be designed for older people. 'Learning' games may be designed for young children. Many products are designed with a particular age range in mind. Products like furniture often show variations in design to suit the likes of different age ranges.

Other groupings might include male and female, able bodied and disabled. Specialist social groups might include athletes, slimmers or smokers. There is a wide variety of 'minority groups' who have their own needs. Some products are produced with these groups in mind, although they may be used by other groups. For example, 'pick up sticks' designed for the disabled are now used as labour saving devices.

Sometimes it may be necessary to consider whether it is moral or ethical to produce a certain product. For example, knives produced for young children might be considered unethical.

Economic considerations

Businesses want to be successful. They want to provide people with the things they need. They want people to buy the products they are manufacturing. They want to earn enough money to 'stay in business'. How can they do this?

Satisfying people's needs profitably is called MARKETING. Marketing is not just about selling. It involves finding out what people want (see market research, unit 21), producing products that people want, charging a suitable price, promoting products and selling them in a convenient place. This is shown in Figure 1.

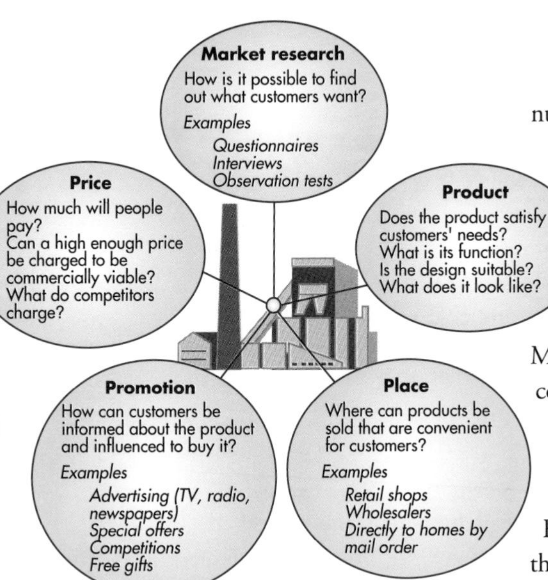

Figure 1 Marketing.

To be COMMERCIALLY VIABLE over a period of time the costs of production need to be lower than the price charged for the product. The likely costs of production might include:

- the cost of raw materials or components used to make products;
- the cost of factories, offices, machinery and equipment;
- the salaries and pay of workers and management;
- energy and transport costs.

A business can reduce costs in a number of ways. It could try to reduce the amount of waste material in production. It can organise production more efficiently. Some businesses have found that cell production or just-in-time production (see unit 19) lead to time and cost savings.

It is possible to reduce the **unit cost** or AVERAGE COST of a product by increasing output. For example, a business might buy an injection moulding machine. If it then produced only one product, the cost of making that product is likely to be higher than the unit cost of making many. This is because the cost of the machinery can be 'spread' over a greater output (see activity for a numerical example). This is one reason why one-off products tend to be more expensive to produce than products made in batches. Products in batches may also be made to simpler, standard designs, so each product can be made more quickly, perhaps with cheaper materials. Mass producers (see unit 19) have very high costs of equipment, but can spread these over enormous production runs.

There may be a conflict between economic considerations and other factors. For example, it may be possible to reduce the cost of production by using cheaper or fewer materials, but this might affect the quality of a product. Production may be cheaper if a business can 'dump' its waste products and energy into rivers and the air, but this can cause environmental problems. It may be cheaper to manufacture a single standard product, but this may not take into account the needs of other cultures or certain social groups.

activities

Intzar Hussain and Gurrinder Nijjer manufacture picture frames. Their business manufactures specialist and unique frames designed and built to fit in with the appearance of the room in which they will be hung. It can take up to a day to design and build a frame exactly to a customer's requirements. The cost of equipment, wages, premises and energy over this period is estimated at £100 and the materials used to produce the frame cost £20 per frame. The average cost of each frame is calculated by:

$$\frac{\text{Total cost (£100+£20)}}{\text{Quantity (1 frame)}} = \frac{£120}{1} = £120$$

Recently an order has come in for 5 frames made in a standard design for a hallway of a house. Gurrinder and Intzar estimate that these frames will be easier to make, so that all five frames will take only a day to manufacture. The average cost for each frame is calculated by:

$$\frac{\text{Total cost (£100 + [5 × £20])}}{\text{5 frames}} = \frac{£100 + £100}{5} = \frac{£200}{5} = £40$$

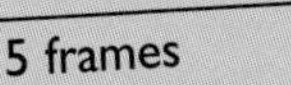

(a) Suggest FIVE costs that the business might face when producing frames.

(b) Suggest TWO reasons why the cost of producing a frame has fallen.

(c) Explain:
(i) why the production of specialist frames might be an example of job production; and
(ii) why the new order might be an example of batch production.

(d) How might the falling cost affect the price charged when the frames are sold?

Key Terms

Sustainable forestry - continuous replacement of trees cut down for timber.
Planned obsolescence - designing products that will wear out over time.
Patent - a licence which prevents an invention being copied.
Marketing - finding out and satisfying consumers' wants and needs.
Commercially viable - where revenue from sales is greater than cost over a period of time so that a profit is made.
Average cost - total production costs divided by the number of products made.

TOOTHBRUSH COMPARISON

Toothbrushes come in a variety of shapes and colours, with a variety of features to attract the customer. Some examples are shown here. Other ideas include brushes which tell the user when they need replacing.

A Colgate Total Precision
Manufactured by Colgate Palmolive. Bristles on the outer edges are splayed outwards with traditional straight ones in between. This should mean that whatever brushing method is used - up and down, left or right - the brush works equally well. To develop the design, tests were done on volunteers wired up with electrodes on their heads and hands. Computers recorded how they brushed.

B Superbrush
Manufactured by Dent-O-Care. It has three heads which 'hug' the teeth so all sides are brushed at once. It means that even people who brush for a short time are getting 3 times the 'brushing'.

C Reach Wondergrip
Manufactured by Johnson & Johnson. Colours and the unusual shape of the brush are designed to attract children and encourage them to brush their teeth more regularly. Some ideas in the development of the brush worked, but others such as black bristles were found not to.

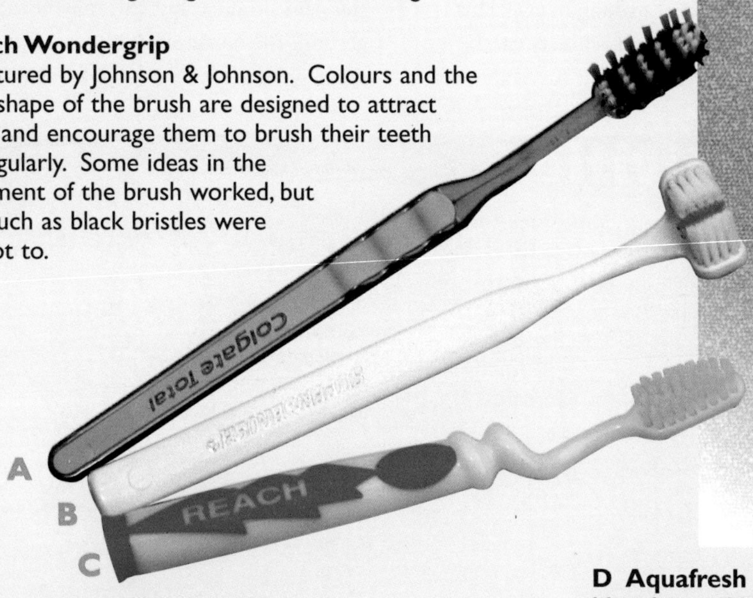

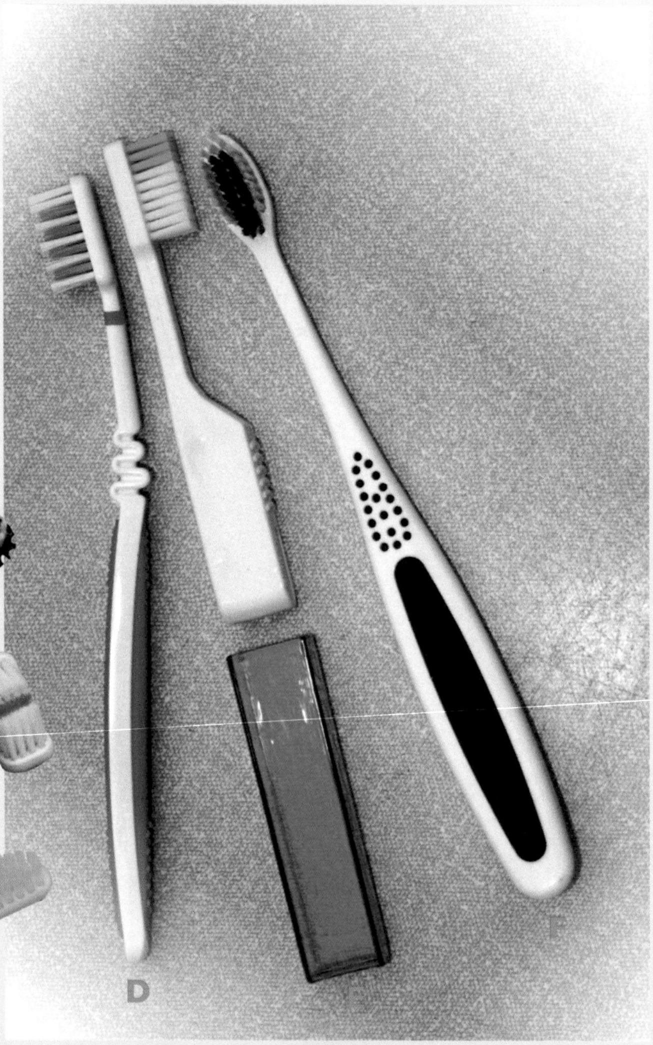

D Aquafresh Flex'N'Direct Interdental
Manufactured by Smith Kline Beecham. Has a neck which bends backwards when brushing to reduce the effect of brushing too hard. Also has long filaments to clean the gaps in between teeth. A directable head is designed to reach areas of the mouth which are difficult to brush. Ideas developed from brainstorming sessions and lateral thinking.

E Sensodyne Travel Brush
Manufactured by Stafford-Miller Ltd. The head folds away into the handle to save space when travelling. Replacement heads can be bought when a brush is worn for the Sensodyne Switch Brush, which is also made by the company.

F Wisdom Contour
Manufactured by Wisdom. A large handle makes it easy to grip and control when brushing. The head is an oval shape.

Source: adapted from The Mail On Sunday.

Questions

(a) Draw up a list of criteria that could be used to evaluate toothbrushes.
(b) Suggest THREE items that may appear in a specification for a toothbrush.
(c) Explain how you might: (i) test and (ii) trial a toothbrush.
(d) Suggest TWO parts of a toothbrush that might need refining after testing and trialling. Explain why they might need to be refined.
(e) Draw concept sketches for a design that may help an older person or ill person to grip a toothbrush.

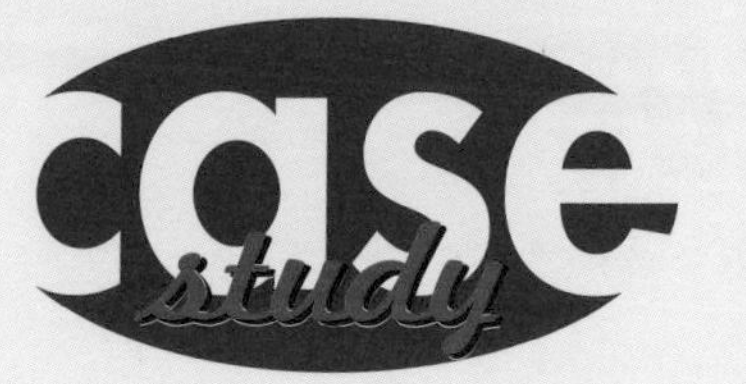

STREET CRANE

BS 5750 PART 1, ISO 9001, EN 29001

Street Crane is a manufacturer of industrial cranes. These are mainly used inside factories to move components from one part of the factory to another, or to lift components so work can be done on them. The company is a BSI registered firm, with BS 5750 Part 1, ISO 9001 and EN 29001 accreditations for quality assurance. They aim to provide customers with 'all round excellence, safety, operational reliability and lasting value'. Street Crane is independently assessed for its quality assurance standards. Crane components are subject to round the clock lifetime testing. There is also a comprehensive after sales service, which includes testing, inspection and spares.

Source: Street Crane Co Ltd.

Lifetime testing of working loads.

ISO 9000

The standard known as ISO 9001, 9002 or 9003 (depending on the product or service) is a measure against which a company's quality system can be compared. There are a number of steps to obtain ISO 9000 registration.

A business must prepare a quality system that meets the standard's requirements, use the system, check its effectiveness and modify if necessary.

Next it should apply for registration to an accredited body and arrange for the system to be assessed by the accredited body. An auditor visits the company for an in-depth appraisal against requirements. Procedures that do not comply must be corrected. Registration will follow if non-compliances are minor. If they are major it may be deferred until corrections are made.

Continual monitoring takes place to ensure standards are maintained. Once registered, the logo may be used on stationery, but not on the product.

Advantages of having ISO 9000 include:

* the integrity of independent auditing;
* customer recognition - a benchmark against which customers can measure potential suppliers;
* it raises the company's marketing profile;
* it is a recognised quality standard in over 200 countries;
* by working to set procedures, data can be gained from which improvements can be made.

Source: Jim Eaton, Quality Inspector.

ISO 9001:1994 requirements

Procedures are required for the following.

* Management responsibility, eg for creating a quality policy and quality systems, and appointing quality representatives.
* To review incoming orders.
* To control design planning, inputs, outputs, changes etc.
* To control documents and data, eg drawings, specifications.
* To control purchasing, eg lists and performance of suppliers.
* To control customer-supplied products, eg verify, store, handle.
* To identify and trace products.
* Controlling and planning of production, eg use of equipment, work instructions, monitoring and control of processes.
* Inspection and testing of a product at all stages of production.
* The control of inspection, measuring and test equipment.
* To check a product has or has not been tested.
* To identify products that do not meet standards.
* To take corrective or preventative action.
* Handling, storage, packaging, preservation and delivery.
* Control of quality records.
* Internal quality audits.
* Training.
* Servicing, eg site regulations.
* The use of statistical techniques, eg for sampling or testing.

Questions

(a) Identify the quality assurance accreditations that Street Crane has.
(b) What do they tell a customer about a business?
(c) Draw a flowchart to show the steps involved in obtaining ISO 9000.
(d) Select THREE requirements of obtaining ISO 9001 and explain what the company would be required to do.
(e) Suggest TWO advantages to:
(i) a potential customer;
(ii) the company;
of obtaining ISO 9000 registration.

case study: BRITISH AIRWAYS' CLUB WORLD SEATS

British Airways had been developing new seats for a new aircraft, the Boeing 777, to begin delivery in Autumn 1995. This type of aircraft had to meet tighter legislative and safety requirements. Each seat had to be stronger and designed to withstand a dynamic test. Lighter materials were needed. There was also greater competition and demands by customers for increased comfort and features. This led to a new seat for BA's business class Club World.

The seat was developed with a design company, Jones Garrard, working with the (then) ergonomic consultancy ICE (Institute of Consumer Ergonomics). A method of tilting the seat was found by lowering the 'H' point, where the seat pivots, and linking the seat base with the seat back so the two moved in unison. This 'cradled' a passenger, reducing the pressure points put on the lower legs as a conventional seat reclines.

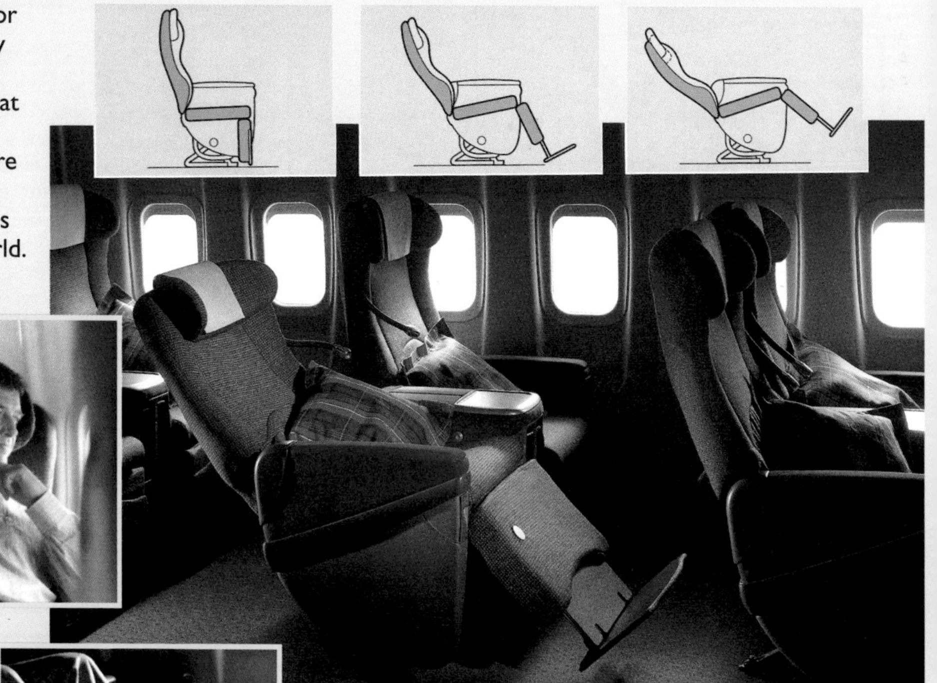

Other design features included in the new seats were:

- a fully adjustable leg rest;
- an inflatable headrest ;
- adjustable ears that fold toward the head to provide more lateral support;
- 50 inches of legroom compared to 40 inches previously;
- an inflatable air bag to support the lower back.

The 'cradle seat', as it became known, was fitted to all longhaul aircraft after successful passenger research trials.

Source: British Airways.

'Ears' support and relax the head.

Fully supporting, totally adjustable, extendable leg rests.

Questions

(a) Suggest THREE reasons why British Airways felt there was a need for a new type of seat.

(b) Explain what is meant by 'successful passenger research trials'.

(c) How did the new 'cradle action' improve the seat ergonomically?

(d) Suggest THREE adjustable features on the seats and how they might improve comfort.

(e) Suggest THREE anthropometric measurements that might have been considered when designing the new seats and why they are important.

(f) Explain how the features of the new seats might be used in TWO other types of seating.

Index

Terms which are defined in the 'Key Terms sections' of each unit have their references shown in colour. Terms which appear in activities and case studies have references in bold.

In memory of Agnes Lever

Cover and page design by Caroline Waring Collins
Cover illustration provided by The Image Bank
Graphics by Elaine Marie Sumner
Drawings by Alan Fraser
Photography by Ian McAnulty, Andrew Allen
Technology/education consultants - Tony Martin,Maxine Griffiths, Steve Blockley
Industrial consultants - Maurice Hamer, Jim Eaton, David Alcorn
Edited by Dave Gray, proof reading by Mike Kidson
Special thanks to technology staff at Thamesmead School, Shepperton

British Library Cataloguing in Publication Data
A catalogue record of this book is available from the British Library

ISBN 1-873929-61-7

Causeway Press Limited
PO Box 13, 129 New Court Way, Ormskirk, Lancs, L39 5HP

1st impression 1996, Reprinted 1998, 2000, 2004
Page origination and production by John A. Collins (Waring-Collins Partnership), Ormskirk, Lancs
Printed and bound by Scotprint, Haddington, Scotland

Acknowledgements
The publisher and the author would like to thank the large number of businesses and outside contributors that have helped to produce this book.

Acknowledgement for their work is given next to their contributions throughout the book. In addition, the following have provided photographs and artwork: Adwest Group p 97, Asea Brown Boveri p 123, BBA Group p 129, Ben Taggart p 120, BI Group p 72, Blackline p 10, BLP Group p 90, British Airways p 150, Bullough plc p 140, Canning Group p 88, Cape Worldwide p 117, Centurion Safety Products p 30, Charles Baynes p 11, Cookson Group pp 75,109,128, Corel Stock Photo Library pp 4,16,123,134,136,141,144,146, Delta -T Devices p 109, Digital Stock pp 54,96,135, Electrolux pp 32,33, Euroquipment p 39, Fairline Boats p 93, First Technology p 41, Flymo p 92, Ford Motor Company p 116, Hall Engineering pp 98,114,118, Hepworth plc p 136, Heywood Williams Group pp 24,28,72,97, Hill Billy p 142, ICI p 29, IMI p 56, Lego Group pp 27,77,130,146, Leyland Trucks p 121, Made of Waste p 53, Magnet pp 14,115, Mailbox International pp 11,31,43,71,116, 122, Manganese Bronze Holdings pp 13,96, Martin Hayes and Associates p121, Medite of Europe pp 19,23, Metalrax Group pp 97,98, MGA Developments pp 9,15, 119, Mountway Ltd p 143, NJ Barber p 22, Photodisc Inc. © 1995 pp 19,27,40,42, 45,89,125,133,135,143, Plysu pp 10, 69,144, Precoat International pp 43,55, Renishaw pp 2,56,64, Senior Engineering Group p 35, Sony pp 118,133,136, Street Crane pp 11,149, Syltone p 96, Telegraph Colour Library pp 50,51, TGI plc 114, Tomkins plc pp 113,129, Topham Picture Point pp 2,44,49,52, Twinbridge Precision and General Engineers p 67, UPF Group p 80, Victorian Pine p 21, Wassall plc p 43, Wolseley p 119, 123